U. Schmid, J. F. Krems, F. Wysotzki (Eds.)

Mind Modelling:
A Cognitive Science Approach to Reasoning,
Learning and Discovery

PABST SCIENCE PUBLISHERS
Lengerich, Berlin, Düsseldorf, Leipzig,
Riga, Scottsdale (USA), Wien, Zagreb

Library of Congress Cataloging-in-Publication Data

Mind Modelling: A Cognitive Science Approach to Reasoning, Learning and Discovery / Ute Schmid ... (Eds.). - Lengerich ; Berlin ; Düsseldorf ; Leipzig ; Riga ; Scottsdale (USA) ; Wien ; Zagreb : Pabst Science Publ., 1998
ISBN 3-933151-25-2

© 1998 Pabst Science Publishers, D-49525 Lengerich

Printing: KM Druck, D-64823 Groß Umstadt
ISBN 3-933151-25-2

Contents

List of Contributors

Alpay, Laurence
The Open University Milton Keynes,
Great Britain

Bachmann, Thomas
Humboldt University of Berlin, Germany

Berendt, Bettina
University of Hamburg, Germany

Baxter, Gordon D.
University of Nottingham, Great Britain

Cardoso, Amilcar
University of Coimbra, Portugal

Cooper, Richard
Birkbeck College, London, Great Britain

Dieng, Rose
The Open University Milton Keynes,
Great Britain

Fox, John
Birkbeck College, London, Great Britain

Giboin, Alain
The Open University Milton Keynes,
Great Britain

Gobet, Fernand
University of Nottingham, Great Britain

Johnson, Todd R.
The Ohio State University USA

Jones, Randolph M.
University of Nottingham, Great Britain

Klix, Friedhart
Humboldt University of Berlin, Germany

Krems, Josef F.
Technology of University Chemnitz

Macedo, Luis
University of Coimbra, Portugal

Miles, Gareth
University of Wales, Cardiff,
Great Britain

Pereira, Francisco C.
University of Coimbra, Portugal

Read, Tim
Universidad de Granada, Spain

Ritter, Frank E.
University of Nottingham, Great Britain

Scanlon, Eileen
The Open University Milton Keynes,
Great Britain

Schlieder, Christoph
University of München, Germany

Schmid, Ute
Technical University of Berlin

Strube, Gerhard
Centre of Cognitive Science (IIG)
University of Freiburg, Germany

Sutton, David
Birkbeck College, London, Great Britain

Taatgen, Niels
University of Groningen, The Netherlands

Wysotzki, Fritz
Technical University of Berlin

Yule, Peter
Birkbeck College, London, Great Britain

Mind Modelling: A brief introduction

Josef F. Krems, Ute Schmid & Fritz Wysotzki

This book focuses on the role and impact of computational models as research tools in major areas of cognitive science. In particular, it deals with the development, implementation and evaluation of computational models in the fields of reasoning, learning and discovery. The book addresses the discussion of formalization and computation with respect to different cognitive architectures as well. Furthermore, major architectures will be compared with regard to their impact on theories of information processing in different domains (e.g., natural-language understanding, problem-solving, knowledge representation).

In addition to empirical studies of cognitive processes the development of formal computational models of cognitive phenomena is the central method for gaining insight in human cognition. While there has been outstanding and well recognized work in this area by some researchers since the 60's (such as Newell & Simon and J.R. Anderson), the cognitive modelling approach is still not as well established a methodology as the strictly experimental approach.
Although the understanding and modelling of cognitive processes was a main goal of early AI-research, it has been rapidly dominated by efforts to develop efficient and innovative methods in data processing (knowledge processing), and has received more attention only in the last decade. In the following we will give a short outline of the history of cognitive modelling and will then provide some examples of how AI and cognitive psychology might profit from this approach.

A presupposition for the use of cognitive modelling in AI is the claim that evolution has yielded optimal strategies of information processing which are worthwhile studying to obtain hints for how to develop and apply new (optimal) computer systems and intelligent robots. There have been two lines of research on cognitive models which could be identified as starting points of the cognitive modelling approach: First there is the early work in symbolic artificial intelligence, tightly connected with experimental psychology. Well-known systems of this kind are the General Problem Solver (GPS) by Newell and

Simon (1963), the concept learning system (CLS) by Hunt, Marin and Stone (1966) which was based on experiments conducted by Bruner, Goodnow and Austin (1956), the EPAM system for the recognition of syllables of Feigenbaum (1963), and the checkers program of Samuel (1963). The second line includes models of distributed memory based on neurophysiological research. The most prominent approach was the perceptron of Rosenblatt (1958), originally based on the "law of mass action" by Lashley (1950), and its variants like Adaline and Madaline (Widrow, 1962; Nilsson, 1965). This line has been somewhat interrupted by the book by Minsky and Papert (1969) who showed the limitations of the original perceptron model. However models of distributed memory had their comeback in the eighties trough the work of Rumelhart and McClelland (1986) and others.

Today, cognitive modelling is established as a central methodology in cognitive science. Main impacts on research in cognitive science come from cognitive psychology (searching for more and more concise models of cognitive processes), from AI (trying to apply insights about cognitive phenomena towards resolution of yet unresolved problems), from the neurosciences (providing understanding of the realization of cognitive processes in the brain and on the neural microlevel), from robotics (embedding cognitive systems in an environment by sensor and motor processing), from computer linguistics (modelling human language understanding and production on the basis of analytical and empirical theories), and from critical philosophy (pointing out problems underlying the methodology of cognitive modelling).

While cognitive science and the methodology of cognitive modelling has long been established in the USA, the importance of this kind of research has been recognized in Europe only during recent years (with the exception of Great Britain and the Netherlands, where there is already an established tradition in cognitive science). In Germany for example there is now support for both basic research (i.e. the joint project "spatial cognition" supported by the German Research Community, including research in cognitive psychology, AI, neuropsychology, robotics and computer-linguistics) as well as applied research (i.e. projects on intelligent robots, learning and action planning with artificial neural networks and on sensory/motor coordination, supported by the German Ministry of Education and Research). Cognitive science is also gradually becoming part of regular

regular university education: Graduate colleges and first curriula for studies in cognitive science have recently been established. Cognitive science is not only of interest for fundamental research, but also has potential industrial applications. This is shown by the growing interest of industry. For example the "First European Conference on Cognitive Science in Industry" took place in 1994 in Luxembourg. The European project COMAPS (Cognitive Management for Anthropocentric Production Systems) deals with human operators optimal control actions to get optimal rules for quality control of some industrial processes.

Before we provide a review of the chapters of this book, we will outline some current questions of fundamental research in cognitive science. One question is how to relate and integrate symbolic and sub-symbolic processing. That is, overcoming the gap between symbolic AI and (sub-symbolic) systems theory. Symbolic processing can be regarded as "being on the top" of sub-symbolic processes of the brain, the very nature of which is analog computing. Gaining more insight into these processes might overcome the current limitations of computer simulations based on the paradigms of symbolic computation and complexity evaluations using complexity theory and the concept of the Turing machine. Furthermore, investigating special optimal coding and reduction techniques used by the brain might result in new algorithms for dealing with problems of very high complexity.

A second area of current research which is not included in this book is the understanding and modelling of distributed processing in the visual system. How are computations of different features like form, color, motion, position and orientation taking place in different parts of the occipital and parietal lobe, and how are they respectively integrated to cause the subjective sensation we have when we "see objects"? Models for long range interactions of neural sub-systems are necessary and may also lead to deeper insight into the mechanisms of higher level knowledge processing.

A third problem is the very nature and modelling of causality and the representation of time. Current approaches of "causal networks" and the usage of simple rules do not suffice to model this phenomenon. Another domain of interest is the understanding of metaphors and of analogical reasoning. Purely symbolic approaches like structure mapping are not sufficient since "analogical" reasoning might be understood - at least on a deeper, sub-symbolic level - by models of analogical computation (as opposed to digital computers)

11

only. Insight in the processes of analogical reasoning is also an important basis for understanding creativity.

A fourth area of research deals with the role and status of general architectures of cognition. Architectures of cognition provide a set of mechanims that allow a system to acquire and use content (information about the environment and the system itself) for achieving goals (Newell, 1990). They define a fixed structure, changing comparatively slowly if at all, that realizes a symbol processing system. Differences in behavior arise mainly from changes in goals and knowledge and not from properties of the architecture. Pylyshyn (1991) added two further ways of looking at architectures: as counterparts to algorithms and as theories of cognitive capacity.

Further research questions (connected with human learning) are the formation of higher order concepts (i.e. "equal" or "causal") and the acquisition of behavioral skills, which could both provide new ideas for research in machine learning. Finally, the crucial methodological question of cognitive modelling is how to integrate the detailed results of psychological experiments into large scale AI models.

This book gives an overview of several different domains where the application of cognitive modelling may may be a fruitful supplement to the experimental approach. Additionally -- especially the first part of the book -- deals with methodological questions of cognitive modelling. Therefore, the book also demonstrates a variety of different types of model development, such as using architectures, production systems, and special purpose algorithms. The book is divided into four parts. The first part deals with "Architectures, Modelling Environments and Their Applications". In five papers different architectures and approaches towards building cognitive models are discussed. A major focus is on ACT-R and Soar. The second section deals with "Reasoning and Discovery". Spatial reasoning, diagnostic reasoning, planning and analogy detection are addressed in four papers. The third section contains another set of four papers dealing in particular with learning.

Acknowledgement

The book contains papers that were originally presented at the First European Workshop on Cognitive Modelling, held at the Berlin Institute of Technology (Technische Universität Berlin), November 14th-16th, 1996. We have to thank the Department of Computer Science and the DFG (German Research Funding Foundation) for technical and financial support.

References

Bruner, J. S., Goodnow, J. J. & Austin, G.A. (1956) *A Study of Thinking*. New York: Wiley

Feigenbaum, E. (1963). The simulation of verbal learning behavior.In E. Feigenbaum and J. Feldman (Eds.). *Computers and Thought* (297-309).New York: McGraw-Hill

Hunt, E., Marin, J. & Stone, P.J.(1966). *Experiments in Induction*. New York: Academic Press

Lashley, K. (1950). In search of the engram. In Society of Experimental Biology Symposium: Psychological Mechanisms in Animal Behavior (vol. 4, 478-505). London: Cambridge University Press

Minsky, M. & Papert, S. (1969). *Perceptrons, An Introduction to Computational Geometry*. Cambridge, MA: MIT Press

Newell, A. (1990). Unified Theories of Cognition. Cambridge, MA: Harvard University Press

Newell, A. & Simon, H. (1963). GPS, a program that simulates human thought. In E. Feigenbaum and J. Feldman (Eds.), *Computers and Thought* (279-293). New York: McGraw-Hill

Nilsson, N. (1965). *Learning Machines. Foundations of Trainable Pattern-Classifying Systems*. New York: McGraw-Hill

Pylyshyn, Z. W. (1991). The Role of Cognitive Architectures in Theories of Cognition. In K. VanLehn (Ed.), *Architectures for Intelligence* (189-224). Hillsdale, New Yersey: Erlbaum

Rosenblatt, F. (1958). The perceptron: a probabilistic model of information storage and organization in the brain. *Psychological Review, 65*, 386-408

Rumelhart, D. & McClelland, J. (Eds.) (1986). *PDP - Parallel Distributed Processing* (Vol. 1). Cambridge, MA: MIT Press

Samuel, A. (1963). Some studies in machine learning using the game of checkers. In E.Feigenbaum and J. Feldman, *Computers and Thought* (71-105). New York: McGraw-Hill

Widrow, B. (1962). Generalization and information storage in networks of ADALINE "neurons". In *Self-organizing Systems* (435-461). Washington, DC: Spartan Books

Section I

Architectures, Modelling Environments and their Applications

1.1 A comparison of ACT-R and Soar

Todd R. Johnson

Abstract:

This paper compares the Act-R and Soar cognitive architectures, focusing on their theories of control. Act-R treats control (conflict resolution) as an automatic process, whereas Soar treats it as a potentially deliberate, knowledge-based process. The comparison reveals that Soar can model extremely flexible control, but has difficulty accounting for probabilistic operator selection and the independent effects of history and distance to goal on the likelihood of selecting an operator. In contrast, Act-R's control is well supported by empirical data, but has difficulty modeling task-switching, multiple interleaved tasks, and dynamic abandoning of subgoals. The comparison also reveals that many of the justifications for each architecture's control structure, such as some forms of flexible control and satisficing, are just as easily handled by both.

Introduction

The last decade has seen the emergence of a variety of cognitive architectures. This is good for cognitive modeling, because architectures provide a ready-made set of tools and theoretical constraints that can assist the cognitive modeling enterprise by constraining the possible models of a set of phenomena or even making the "right" model an obvious consequence of the architectural constraints (Newell, 1990). However, these architectures make many different theoretical distinctions, which can of course have a major influence on the nature of cognitive models supported by each. Despite this, very little work has been done to compare alternative architectures. This paper attempts to rectify this by offering an initial comparison of two of the most well known cognitive architectures: Act-R (Anderson, 1993; Anderson & Lebiere, in press) and Soar (Laird, Rosenbloom & Newell, 1986; Laird, Newell & Rosenbloom, 1987; Newell, 1990).

This is not the first effort to compare and evaluate Soar and Act. Newell, Rosenbloom and Laird (1989) previously compared Soar to Act*, Act-R's precursor. Their goal, however, was more to use Soar and Act as two different examples of cognitive architectures, not to critically evaluate and compare them. The only serious effort to critically evaluate Soar is Cooper and Shallice's (1995) evaluation of Soar as both a psychological theory and an example of the methodology of unified theories of cognition. Their general conclusion is that Soar fairs poorly as a psychological theory and that the unified theory methodology (at least as exemplified by Soar research) does not offer any advantages over traditional psychological research methodology. In contrast to the Soar approach, Anderson and his colleagues have regularly tested Act-R. Many of these results can help us discriminate between Soar and Act-R.

Theoretical Assumptions

This section briefly reviews the theoretical assumptions for Act-R and Soar. These assumptions are summarized in Table 1. Due to space limitations, I only discuss those mechanisms relevant to the comparison of control.

Act-R

The mechanisms proposed in Act-R are based on two foundational assumptions. The first is that "the implementation of Act-R should be in terms of neural-like computation" (Anderson, 1993, p. 12). The second assumption is that "cognition is adapted to the structure of the environment" (Anderson, 1993, p.14). Consequently, many of the mechanisms in Act-R are designed to reflect the statistical nature of the environment.

Act-R is a parallel matching, serial firing production system with a psychologically motivated conflict resolution strategy. Act-R has a declarative long-term memory containing a network of declarative memory elements (DMEs)[1] and a procedural long-term memory containing production rules. DMEs have activation values and associative strengths with other DMEs. Act-R's working memory consists of the most active DMEs.

The basic cognitive operation in Act-R is a production rule firing. The actions of a production rule modify declarative memory—productions cannot directly test or modify procedural memory.

---

[1] Anderson calls declarative memory elements *chunks*. Since this conflicts with Soar's (nonstandard) usage of the term chunk, I will use the neutral term Declarative Memory Element (DME).

Act-R	Soar
Foundational Assumptions	
Mechanisms should be implemented in neural-like computation	Humans approximate knowledge level systems
Cognition is adapted to the structure of the environment	Humans are symbol systems
Control	
Single goal hierarchy	Single goal hierarchy
Goals originate from task knowledge	Goals are created automatically by the architecture
Adaptive, satisficing conflict resolution	Knowledge-based, least-commitment conflict resolution
Long-Term Memory (LTM)	
Two forms of LTM: Declarative and Procedural	Uniform LTM: All LTM is in procedural form
Procedural memory is represented by production rules	Procedural memory is represented by production rules
Procedural LTM is opaque	LTM is opaque
LTM is permanent	LTM is permanent
Declarative memory is a network with activations and associative strengths	Long-term declarative memory is represented by production rules
Working memory	
Working memory consists of the most active declarative memory elements	Working memory is distinct from LTM
Learning	
The strength of declarative and procedural memory increase as a power function of practice and decrease as a power function of delay	All long-term knowledge arises through knowledge compilation
Procedural knowledge is tuned based on experience	
Procedural knowledge is acquired through knowledge compilation.	
Declarative knowledge is acquired through rules and perception	
Activations and associative strengths are acquired through experience	
Latency Derivation	
Latencies derive from the time needed to match rules, which is the sum of the times needed to match each condition in the rule. The time to match a condition depends on the strength of a rule and the strength of the memory elements it matches.	Constant latency per decision cycle. Latency depends on the total number of decision cycles plus the time for external actions.

Table 1: Theoretical distinctions in Act-R and Soar

Act-R repeatedly follows five steps: 1) Find all rules whose goal conditions match the current goal; 2) Compute the expected utility for each rule found in step 1; 3) Select the rule with the highest expected utility; 4) Attempt to instantiate the remaining (non-goal) conditions in the selected rule. If a rule can be instantiated in more than one way (i.e., because it matches multiple DMEs), take the instantiation with the highest activation; and 5) If the rule can be instantiated, execute its action, otherwise, select the next best production and go to step 4.

Expected utility is defined as *PG-C,* where *P* is the probability that the goal will be achieved if the production is fired, *G* is the value of the goal, and *C* is the cost of achieving the goal by taking the move specified by the instantiation. G and C are often expressed in seconds. This conflict resolution scheme[2] is an adaptive satisficing process. It is adaptive because a rule's expected value and the time to instantiate the rule depend on parameters that are changed through the learning mechanisms discussed below. It is satisficing because it stops trying to instantiate rules as soon as it finds one that can be instantiated and it considers only the instantiation with the highest activation.

Act-R assumes that cognitive behavior is goal-oriented and that goals can give rise to subgoals. A goal in Act-R is a DME that has been pushed onto the architecturally-supported goal stack. As with any other DME in Act-R, a goal has a set of attributes (also called slots) and corresponding values, which are just other DMEs. Goals in Act-R typically contain slots that hold the goal's desired and current problem states. Act-R enforces goal-oriented behavior by requiring every rule to match a goal.

New goals are created by production rules that create a DME representing the goal and then push the DME onto the goal stack. Goal achievement is signaled by a production rule that pops the goal off the goal stack. Goals that are popped off the stack are not deleted: they remain in declarative long-term memory where they can be retrieved by rules.

Act-R has several complementary learning mechanisms that allow it to adapt its knowledge based on experience. These mechanisms serve the five functions described below.

The base-level (or resting) activation of DMEs and the strength of rules increase as a power function of practice and decrease as a power function of delay. These values reflect the log odds of the DME being matched by a rule and the log odds of the production rule firing. The

---

[2] A *conflict resolution scheme* is a mechanism for deciding which of many applicable rules or actions to take when only one can be taken at a given point in time.

equations for estimating these values are based on Anderson and Schooler's [, 1991 #573] analysis of the odds of an item being needed based on its past history of use.

Associative strengths among DMEs are acquired through experience. Associative strengths represent the log likelihood ratio of how much the presence of the DME in the goal increases the chances that a connected DME will be needed. For example, if the number 5 is in the goal, it would spread activation to all addition facts in LTM that contain the number 5. Act-R calculates associative strength as the log of the prior likelihood ratio and the empirical likelihood ratio. The prior value is estimated by m/n, where m is the number of DMEs in declarative memory and n is the number of DMEs to which DME j is associated. DME j is associated to a DME k, if k has j in one of its slots. Thus, prior associative strength from j to k is inversely proportional to the number of DMEs j is associated with. Since associative strength is a weighted average of prior and empirical likelihood ratios, the associative strengths for new DMEs reflect the prior value, but with experience, the empirical value eventually comes to dominate.

Rule-tuning is Act-R's mechanism for altering the importance of procedural knowledge based on experience with that knowledge. Each rule is associated with a strength, a cost, and a probability that the rule will eventually lead to the goal. These parameters are critical to Act-R in two ways. First, the strength of a rule affects its match time. Stronger rules match faster than weaker rules. Second, a rule's probability of success and cost affect the rule's expected utility ($PG-C$), which in turn affects the rules chances of being selected.

The probability of a rule's eventual success P is estimated using a weighted average of the prior probability and the empirical probability derived from a rule's actual history of success and failure. If a rule is fired and Act-R eventually achieves its goal, then the probability of success for that rule will increase, but if Act-R eventually fails, the rule's probability will decrease.

A rule's cost reflects the average cost of eventually achieving the goal by way of the rule. To estimate a rule's cost, Act-R uses a weighted average of a prior cost and an empirical cost. As noted in the previous section, a rule's strength reflects the log odds of it being needed. This is tuned based on the rule's past history of use.

New procedural knowledge in Act-R is acquired through knowledge compilation. Act-R's compilation mechanism builds a rule from a declarative representation of how a resulting problem-solving state depends on an earlier problem-solving state. This representation is called a dependency and can be thought of as an understanding of a problem-solving step. For example, a dependency might encode that a state that encodes the goal to determine 5*0 results in a state which indicates that 5*0=0 and that this result is specific to 0. From this dependency Act-R will build the rule: If the goal is to determine X*0, where X is any number, then make the new state X*0=0. Although rule creation is automatic, building a dependency requires deliberate problem solving with the goal constructing an understanding of why a problem-solving step works.

Declarative knowledge is acquired through rules and perception. A production rule can create new DMEs as part of its actions. Act-R also assumes that perception delivers information into declarative memory. DMEs that arise by either means become a permanent part of LTM.

The time needed to instantiate a production is the sum of the times needed to instantiate each condition in the production. The time to instantiate a condition is a function of the production strength and the activation of the DME to which it matches.

Soar

Soar is based on two foundational assumptions. The first is that humans are (at least to some approximation) knowledge level systems (Newell, 1990, p. 113-117). This means that they apply their knowledge in some rational manner to achieve their goals. The second is that humans are a symbol system (Newell, 1990, p. 113-117). Although Newell admits that the underlying neural level might have substantive effects on the symbol level (Newell, 1990, pp. 113-119), Soar itself has always been based on a strong symbol level and many of its theoretical distinctions reflect this fact.

Soar is a parallel matching, parallel firing rule-based system. Soar's rules represent both procedural and declarative knowledge. Soar's working memory contains only declarative knowledge. Rules cannot test other rules, so they can only match declarative knowledge that other rules have already deposited into working memory. On a given production rule cycle, Soar fires every rule that matches. Rule actions can either propose problem solving operators, register a preference for one or more proposed operators, or make modifications to DMEs in working memory.

All problem solving in Soar is viewed as search in a problem space. A problem space is defined by an initial state, one or more goal states, and a set of operators for transforming states. Soar solves problems by repeating the following steps until the problem is solved or abandoned: 1) Fire rules that propose operators to apply to the current state; 2) Fire rules that register a preference for one or more operators; 3) Select an operator to apply to the current state, then apply it. If no operator can be selected, create an impasse. All of these decisions can be either made by knowledge that is directly encoded in rules or by knowledge generated by searching another problem space.

Soar has a single goal stack that is automatically created and managed by the architecture. Goals arise automatically from an impasse—an architecturally detected lack of direct procedural knowledge that inhibits further progress. Whenever Soar reaches an impasse it automatically generates a subgoal to acquire the relevant knowledge. This is called universal subgoaling because it is an automatic response to all impasses. For example, if multiple operators have been proposed, but other rules have not indicated a clear best operator, then a subgoal is created in which Soar will attempt to determine which operator is best.

Conflict resolution in Soar is concerned with the selection of an operator, not a production rule. Soar fires every production rule that matches in a given cycle, however, only a single operator can be applied to a state at any given time. Unlike most rule-based systems, including Act-R, conflict resolution in Soar is completely knowledge-based. Once operators are proposed, other rules can register preferences for (or against) them. A rule can reject an operator, mark it as the best or worst operator, indicate that it is better or worse than one or more other operators, or indicate that two or more operators are equally good. After this preference phase, Soar determines whether the preferences indicate a single best operator. If so, Soar selects that operator for application to the state[3]. If not, or if there are contradictory preferences, then Soar creates a subgoal to resolve the problem. Like any subgoal, this subgoal is achieved by searching a problem space. Thus, Soar represents the operator tie or contradiction event as declarative knowledge in working memory, which enables Soar's procedural knowledge to detect the event and bring to bear the full problem-solving power of the agent.

---

[3] If the preferences indicate a single set of equivalent operators, then Soar will choose one of those operators at random.

All long-term knowledge in Soar arises through chunking, a learning mechanism that compiles the results of subgoal search into a production rule that can produce the result without subgoaling. Suppose that Soar has a subgoal for multiplying two digits by repeated addition. Given the goal of determining 5*2, Soar would create a subgoal to solve the problem by addition. Once the subgoal returned an answer to the supergoal, Soar's chunking mechanism would build the rule: If the goal is to solve 5*2, then note that the answer is 10.

The reliance on chunking as the only means of acquiring long-term knowledge, implies that Soar can only acquire long-term declarative memory by learning a rule that encodes the appropriate conditions in which the declarative memory will be needed. For example, to recall the sentence "The lawyer is in the park", given either the question "Who is in the park?" or "Where is the lawyer?" Soar would need to learn two rules: 1) If park, then place "The lawyer is in the park" in working memory; and 2) If lawyer, then place "The lawyer is in the park" in working memory.

Soar uses a constant latency per decision cycle, roughly estimated at 50 msec, based on the minimum amount of time needed to make one deliberate cognitive action. Rules that specify external actions are assumed to take additional time consistent with initiating those actions.

Comparison

Control

Both Soar and Act-R organize control around a single goal hierarchy, but their similarities end there. Act-R's production rules are similar to Soar's operators: both are equivalent to a single operator in a problem space. The goal of conflict resolution in Soar is to select an operator, whereas in Act-R it is to select a rule. Goals in Act-R are created by rules, whereas goals in Soar are created by the architecture in response to an impasse.

The distinction between task-initiated goals and architecturally initiated goals becomes important when we consider the architectures' conflict resolution strategies, which are the major theoretical difference between control in Soar and Act-R. Act-R uses an automatic conflict resolution strategy that selects an action (a rule) based on the expected utility of each rule. Other than the expected utility, which depends on the history of procedural memory, no other knowledge can influence conflict resolution. In contrast, Soar uses an open, knowledge-based conflict resolution strategy that selects an action (an operator) based on all available knowledge. Recall that Soar selects an operator by first proposing applicable operators, then collecting preferences that (partially) order the available operators, and finally either selecting the winning operator or creating an impasse (and corresponding subgoal) if the preferences do not unambiguously specify a winner. This subgoal precisely specifies the conflicting operators, so that other knowledge can work at resolving the impasse. Act-R has no architectural mechanism for detecting impasses. If none of Act-R's rules match, then Act-R halts.

What kind of empirical support is there for these different conflict resolution strategies? Soar's control scheme was designed around two general characteristics of human cognition. First, is the observation that people behave flexibly. Newell argues that problem-solving methods (such as the weak methods) emerge during problem solving as a function of available knowledge and task demands (Newell, 1990). For instance, people use means-ends analysis, not because they are deliberately following a means-end strategy, but because they are, at each step of problem solving, trying to reduce differences between their current state and the goal state using whatever knowledge and actions are available to them. Soar's conflict resolution strategy is a least-commitment control scheme that naturally supports this kind of behavior. In fact, some of the earliest work in Soar showed that many of the weak methods emerge by combining Soar's control strategy, a few independent bits of general problem-solving knowledge, and various kinds of knowledge of the task domain (Laird et al., 1986).

Research that is more recent explores the use of Soar for modeling interleaved tasks and interaction with the external world (Nelson, Lehman & John, 1994). Soar's ability to respond to any goal in the goal hierarchy along with its ability to replace goals anywhere in its goal stack, make it well-suited for modeling interleaved tasks. Likewise, Soar can respond to changes in its environment by immediately detecting the changes and switching to a different goal.

The second characteristic in support of Soar is that people generally behave in a rational manner to achieve their goals. According to Newell, intelligent systems behave according to the principle of rationality, which states that "the system takes actions to attain its goals, using all the knowledge that it has." (Newell, 1990, p. 50) Soar's knowledge-based conflict resolution strategy with its automatic impasses supports this kind of behavior.

We must next consider whether Act-R can account for the same phenomena. At first glance, it seems that this might be difficult for Act-R. Since its conflict resolution strategy always picks an action regardless of the number of competing actions and how closely those actions are ranked, only a very limited amount of knowledge is used to select actions.

On closer inspection, however, the situation for Act-R is not as bleak. According to Act-R, cognitive skill acquisition begins with the deliberate interpretation of instructions and examples[4], which are then proceduralized by the analogy mechanism into production rules that directly specify appropriate actions. This means that Act-R must begin to solve a task by placing declarative representations of actions into working memory. Once these actions are in working memory, any available knowledge can be brought to bear on them, including knowledge generated by problem solving in a subgoal. For Act-R to reason in this way, it must have a general set of rules for recalling instructions about the task. Once Act-R proceduralizes some of its knowledge, the general rules will compete with the newly formed rules, which means that Act-R will reason deliberately on some trials and automatically on others. As Act-R gains experience with its new procedural knowledge, it will eventually stop deliberate reasoning. However, if the task environment changes such that the procedural knowledge is no longer appropriate, Act-R will again fall back to deliberate reasoning. Thus, it seems that Act-R is capable of displaying at least some flexible, knowledge-based behavior. By the same means, Act-R can engage in metacognitive reasoning.

Unlike Soar, Act-R's approach to flexible behavior is not directly supported by the architecture. Soar's conflict resolution mechanism would essentially need to be programmed into Act-R's rules. However, the implications of this difference are unclear. B. Chandrasekaran (personal communication) has argued that the Soar architecture might emerge from a lower level architecture because of the need to do problem solving. It is possible that Act-R is one such lower level architecture.

One potential source of difficulty for modeling flexible behavior in Act-R, is that it instantiates only rules that match the current goal. This severely limits Act-R's flexibility in responding to dynamic internal or external changes, because rules related to the current goal have complete control of problem solving, including when to surrender control.

Next, we must consider the evidence in support of Act-R and consider how Soar might account for it. Several results support the Act-R account. First, it is well known that people satisfice—we tend to set an acceptance threshold and then pick the first action that rates above that threshold. This is modeled in Act-R by forcing a decision at each cycle based on comparison among the expected utility of an action. For example, if Act-R is given only a set of rules for making the moves in the Tower of Hanoi along with a rule for detecting the goal state, it will quickly select one of the moves and execute it, without doing any internal lookahead search. In contrast, given the same knowledge, Soar (along with its default knowledge) will do exhaustive depth-first lookahead search until it finds a solution, at which point it will directly solve the problem. Johnson, Zhang and Wang (1994) have produced a modified set of Soar default rules that enables Soar to solve problems with very limited lookahead search, however, the psychological validity of their approach has not been adequately tested.

It is important to understand that Act-R's architectural mechanism for producing satisficing behavior does not apply outside a single rule selection. It is also unclear whether people actually satisfice at the rule matching level proposed by Act-R. However, it is clear that people often satisfice at a higher level by deliberately considering and evaluating options until, at some point, they decide to act rather than continue searching. As with Soar, it is possible to model this behavior in Act-R by deliberately evaluating declarative representations of moves and taking the first move that rises above an acceptance threshold; however, this bypasses Act-R's architectural support for satisficing.

Although the source of satisficing behavior in Soar and Act-R are somewhat different, at present, the evidence does not appear to favor either one. This is in part a consequence of the generality of the evidence supporting satisficing behavior. More detailed quantitative evidence might discriminate between the two architectures.

A second body of evidence supports the use of expected utility and instantiation time in Act-R's conflict resolution strategy. Anderson, Kushmerick, and Lebiere (1993) showed that the distribution of an individual's choices from among a set of moves reflects the expected utility of those moves. Act-R models probabilistic move selection by adding a random amount of noise to the expected utilities of each rule instantiation. This is difficult to model in Soar because Soar's control strategy is largely deterministic. The only exception occurs when two or more operators are given indifference preferences (which is meant to indicate that those operators are equally good), in which case Soar will randomly select from among the operators. It is possible to use indifference preferences to implement probabilistic operator selection. Suppose one wants to model a situation in which operator A is twice as likely to be

---

[4] Soar adopts the same view.

chosen as operator B. By proposing two A operators, one B operator, and making all of them indifferent, Soar will have a 2/3 chance of selecting an A operator, but only a 1/3 chance of selecting B.

There are four problems with the indifference technique. First, it violates the semantics of Soar's indifference preference, which is supposed to mean that the operators are equally good. Second, it requires one to avoid using many of Soar's preferences, such as those that indicate that one operator is better than another, because using such preferences would automatically exclude one or more operators from consideration. Third, since all operators are made indifferent, Soar will never generate an operator tie impasse, effectively bypassing Soar's knowledge-based conflict resolution strategy for selecting among operators. Finally, the technique must be augmented with a theory of learning that shows how chunking can learn new rules that change the distribution of operators in a way that reflects the operators' expected utility. Given that Soar can (theoretically) learn any production that a programmer can write, it seems likely that such a learning theory is possible, but it is unclear how natural or psychologically valid the theory will be.

Anderson, Kushmerick, and Lebiere (1993) also showed that the time to select a rule correlates with instantiation time, not the number of alternative rules. This implies that subjects do not evaluate all available moves, but instead take the first move that exceeds some threshold of acceptability. This is a direct prediction of Act-R's satisficing conflict resolution strategy, which sequentially considers rules, roughly in order of their likelihood of being needed, until it finds a rule that will match.

Soar can produce similar behavior through use of a deliberate satisficing technique as described above. Since this satisficing technique can select an operator without considering all operators, the selection time will depend on the time needed to evaluate only those operators considered before one is selected. This is sufficient to reproduce the general behavior, but it is unclear whether it can model the detailed quantitative data. The predicted times from the Soar and Act-R models stem from different sources. The Act-R model depends on the instantiation time for each rule, whereas the Soar model depends on the number of decision cycles needed to evaluate each operator. If we assume that Soar uses a simple evaluation metric, then each evaluation will take a constant number of decision cycles. In contrast, rule instantiation latencies in Act-R are governed by the number of conditions in each rule, and in the strength of each rule and the matched memory elements.

Lovett and Anderson (1996) showed that the likelihood of selecting a rule instantiation is sensitive to the rule's history of success and distance to goal. In general, people prefer moves that take them closer to the goal and have a higher likelihood of success. In particular, they showed that history and distance to goal independently affect the likelihood of selecting a move. Once subjects gain experience with a rule, their experience will affect their likelihood of selecting instantiations of that rule, regardless of the rule instantiation's distance to goal. This supports Act-R's assumption that history is kept with each rule, without regard for the context in which the rule fires.

Before considering Act-R's explanation of these phenomena, we must first look at Lovett and Anderson's experimental task in detail. Lovett and Anderson used the building sticks task (BST) in which subjects had to build a stick of a desired length by adding or subtracting sticks of three different lengths. For instance, given building sticks of length 1, 2, and 10, and a desired stick length of 5, a subject could solve the problem by adding two sticks of length 2 and one stick of length 1. Alternatively, the subject could solve the problem by first selecting the stick of length 10, then subtracting two sticks of length 2 and one of length 1. The first solution (2 + 2 + 1 = 5) is called the undershoot strategy, because the initial stick selection is less than the desired length. The second solution (10 - 2 - 2 - 1 = 5) is called the overshoot strategy, because the initial stick selection is longer than the desired length. In problems in which both strategies are applicable, subjects tend to select the strategy that gets them closer to the desired length. In the above example, subjects would tend to select undershoot because 5 is closer to 2 than it is to 10. Lovett and Anderson also showed that the likelihood of selecting a strategy was influenced by the magnitude of a problem's bias, which they defined as the difference between the distance to goal for the best undershoot move and the distance to goal for the best overshoot move. In the example above, the bias is 3 - 5 = -2. A negative bias indicates a bias toward undershoot, whereas a positive bias indicates overshoot. As the absolute magnitude of the bias increases, so does the likelihood of selecting the corresponding strategy. Finally, the probability that a strategy will succeed (based on its history) affects its likelihood of being selected regardless of problem bias. Although some BST problems can be solved by either undershoot or overshoot, some can only be solved by one of the strategies. Furthermore, problems can be designed that are biased toward one strategy, but solved by the other.

To model this data, Lovett and Anderson (personal communication) have proposed a model that contains both distance-specific rules, which include a test for distance in their conditions, and general rules which apply regardless of distance. The model contains four production rules: closer-overshoot, general-overshoot, closer-undershoot, and general-undershoot. The closer-x rules suggest x only when x moves closer to the goal than the competing moves. The general-x rules propose overshoot or undershoot moves regardless of relative distance. The computation of distance for BST is assumed to be directly available from perception, so sensitivity to the magnitude of the bias is simulated by adding perceptual noise. The model will initially tend to prefer moves according to the bias, because closer-x rules are given a higher prior probability of success, reflecting subjects' past experience that similarity increases probability of success. The independence of history and distance to goal is also achieved, because the model tends to use both the general-x and closer-x rules, although initially, general-x rules have a lower probability of being used. If on average, the general-x rules have more success than the closer-x rules, the general-x rules will have a higher probability of being selected, regardless of distance to goal.

Modeling the independent influence of history and distance to goal presents a challenge to Soar. Soar can easily make use of distance to goal information, however, Soar does not automatically maintain history of success information for each operator. For example, to model BST in Soar we might produce a problem space with two operators: overshoot and undershoot, and two search control rules: one that prefers the operator that moves closest to the goal, and another that makes overshoot and undershoot indifferent whenever they are equally close to the goal. When this model is run, it will use the move suggested by the distance to goal rule for every problem it is given, regardless of the number of failures and successes it experiences with each operator. Lovett and Anderson's results also suggest that move selection is a stochastic process; however, as shown in the discussion above on expected utility, it is difficult to model such a process in Soar. One could program Soar to remember the number of successes and failures for overshoot and undershoot and then use an operator evaluation metric that combines distance to goal with history information; however, it is unlikely that subjects deliberately keep such counts. Another possibility is to use a model that attempts to categorize each problem as an overshoot or undershoot problem. Soar-based Symbolic Concept Acquisition (SCA) can perform such a task and has been shown to produce graded performance with respect to accuracy and response time (Miller & Laird, 1996). SCA tends to respond faster and more accurately to concepts that are similar to frequently encountered concepts. To use SCA, one could use each BST problem and solution as a training example for category learning. New problems are solved by categorizing the current problem using the classification rules acquired during previous attempts. Continued success with one strategy will result in a number of classification rules for that strategy and relatively few rules for the alternative. Thus, the system will be more likely to classify new examples in terms of the successful strategy, although this depends on the similarity to previously categorized examples. Of course, one would need to construct a detailed SCA model of BST to adequately evaluate this solution.

Learning and Memory

One of the major differences between Act-R and Soar is their theories of long-term memory and learning. Act-R holds that there are separate long-term stores for declarative and procedural memory, whereas Soar is committed to a single long-term procedural store. Act-R's commitment to separate declarative and procedural stores is based on early work on associative memory and on experimental evidence dissociating procedural and declarative memory. Soar's commitment to a single long-term store is based on the goal of minimizing the number of distinct architectural mechanisms. Since a single procedural long-term store can also encode declarative knowledge, Soar is an experiment in trying to determine the limitations of the single-store theory.

Other major differences lie in the architectures' theories of learning. Soar has a single learning mechanism, whereas Act-R has several different mechanisms. Once again, Act-R's learning theories are based on experimental evidence of different types of learning mechanisms, whereas Soar's single learning mechanism was adopted because it can theoretically account for all kinds of learning.

This section compares the Act-R and Soar theories of learning and memory by using recent results on the role of practice on declarative and procedural knowledge. Although, these results do not address all of the issues of interest in a comparison, they highlight some of the major differences in a compelling fashion.

Knowledge compilation, such as Soar's chunking and Act-R's production compilation mechanisms, produce power law speed-up as a function of practice whenever a task is decomposed into smaller and smaller subtasks, such that one or more of the smaller subtasks is used in more than one supertask. When one of these smaller subtasks is compiled, it speeds up any task in which it is used. Supertasks take longer to compile, because they are more complex and require more rules to automate. This combinatorial task decomposition results in power-law learning.

Although knowledge compilation can produce power law speed-up, several results suggest that it cannot be the sole mechanism responsible for power-law learning. First, even simple stimulus response tasks, which are clearly not combinatorial, produce power-law speed-up. Second, knowledge-compilation cannot explain power law slow-down as a function of delay. Finally, several researchers have found evidence that both procedural knowledge and the retrieval of declarative knowledge speed up and slow down as a power law of practice and delay (see VanLehn, 1996 for a review). This result is the focus of the remainder of this section.

Rabinowitz and Goldberg (1995) conducted two experiments that nicely illustrate speed-up of procedural knowledge and declarative retrieval. In the first experiment, one group of participants (who I will call the consistent group) received 33 blocks of training 12 different alphabet artihmetic problems. These are problems of the form A+2=C, where C is the second letter after A. Participants were given a letter and a number and were required to return the letter that was that number of letters away from the given letter. A second group (who I will call the varied group) received 6 blocks of training on 72 different alphabet arithmetic problems. Both groups showed power-law speed-up, but the consistent group was several seconds faster than the varied group. After training, both groups were given a transfer task consisting of 32 new alphabet addition problems. When compared to their response-times at the end of training, the varied group showed no change, but the consistent group slowed considerably and even took longer than the varied group. Rabinowitz and Goldberg explained this result by arguing that the consistent group had simply remembered the answers to the 12 problems and learned to retrieve the answers faster through practice (speed-up of declarative retrieval), whereas the varied group had learned to count up the alphabet faster (speed-up of procedural knowledge).

The results of the first experiment, however, are consistent with knowledge-compilation combined with the speed-up of the acquired rules. Instead of the acquiring and retrieving declarative knowledge of the answers to the 12 problems, it is possible that the participants compiled a rule of the form "If A+2=?" then Press C, and this rule sped up with practice.

To discriminate between compilation and declarative retrieval, Rabinowitz and Goldberg performed a second experiment in which participants in consistent and varied training conditions where transferred to alphabet subtraction problems that were the inverse of addition problems seen during training. Thus, if a participant had seen A+2=C during training, the transfer task would include C-2=A. In this experiment, both groups slowed down during transfer, but the varied group was several seconds slower than the consistent group. Rabinowitz and Goldberg argued that these results supported their assumption that consistent participants were acquiring and retrieving declarative knowledge, whereas varied participants were speeding-up procedural knowledge. Their argument rests on the common assumption that procedural knowledge is subject to asymmetric access, whereas declarative knowledge is subject to symmetric access. According to this assumption, procedural knowledge works from condition to action only, but declarative knowledge can be primed by any part. For instance, the rule "If A+2 then Press C" will only fire when the goal is to solve A+2. However, declarative knowledge "A+2=C" can be retrieved given C-2, since "A+2=C" is primed by both C and 2. In the experiment, Rabinowitz and Goldberg argued that the consistent participants solved the subtraction tasks by retrieving and inverting declarative knowledge of the addition facts, however, the varied participants had practiced counting up through the alphabet, so they needed to develop a new procedure for counting backwards through the alphabet.

These results are consistent with Act-R, but appear problematic for Soar. Anderson and Lebiere (in press) have given a general description of how the results support Act-R, and Johnson (1998) has developed a detailed Act-R model. The Act-R model uses two competing production rules: one to propose a subgoal to compute the answer to the problem and another to solve the problem by retrieving declarative knowledge. Speed-up comes from two of Act-R's learning mechanisms: rule strengthening, which speeds-up rules as a power function of their use, and base-level learning, which speeds up the retrieval of declarative facts as a power function of their use. When given varied training, the same problems are spaced too far apart to retrieve, thus the model must compute the answer to every problem. As a result, the model speeds up the rules needed to count up the alphabet. When given consistent training, however, the model quickly learns to retrieve the answers to the 12 problems. Through continued and frequent retrieval, base-level learning speeds up the retrieval of these facts.

In contrast, these results seem inconsistent with Soar, because of its single long-term memory and its reliance on knowledge compilation as the only learning mechanism. The basic Soar model would consist of a subgoal to solve the problems by counting up (or down) the alphabet. Soar's knowledge compilation mechanism would compile rules that directly encode the answer to each problem. Since a single trial is enough to learn a new rule, this Soar model would predict that the varied group would learn slower than the consistent group, but would arrive at the same asymptote. In addition when given new addition problems for the transfer phase, this model predicts no transfer for either condition, because the rules learned for the first phase apply only to problems seen in that phase. Likewise, when given subtraction transfer problems, this model predicts no transfer, because the acquired rules are specific to addition problems. Both groups would perform equally poorly on the subtraction problems.

Conclusions

This comparison reveals several problem areas for Soar. It is difficult to see how Soar can account for probabilistic move selection as well as the independent effects of history and distance to goal on the likelihood of selecting a move In contrast, Act-R's control mechanism appears to be well supported by empirical data, but does not appear to support the range of flexible control supported by Soar. The comparison also reveals that many of the justifications for each architecture's control structure, such as flexible control and satisficing, are just as easily handled by both. The comparison of learning and memory raises additional problems for Soar. The separate speed-up of declarative and procedural knowledge, and the different access characteristics of the two kinds of knowledge, strongly support two distinct long-term stores and multiple learning mechanisms.

This paper also illustrates several problems that arise when one attempts to compare cognitive architectures. First, because both architectures are Turing universal, it is difficult to prove that an architecture cannot model some phenomena. This situation is not as underconstrained with Act-R and Soar as it is with many other theories. Since both architectures make latency predictions, we can use the time-scale of the behavior under study to further constrain possible models. However, even with this additional constraint, it is difficult to prove that a model is impossible. The best we can do is illustrate how difficult or unnatural it is to model a particular phenomenon within a given architecture. To a large extent, the utility of an architecture, as of any other theory, depends on how easily one can use it to make testable predictions or model phenomena of interest. The problem areas that I have noted for Soar are areas that do not readily admit natural Soar models.

A related problem is what I call the virtual architecture problem. A virtual architecture is one or more mechanisms built on a host architecture, and used in such a way that their constraints dominate modeling, while the theoretical constraints of the host architecture cease to matter. For example, if SCA is used to categorize instances as part of a Soar model, then we can rightly view it as a Soar theory of categorization. However, if we begin to use SCA to implement probabilistic move selection, then we will have effectively bypassed Soar's control mechanism and its constraints. At this point, we might as well talk about the SCA architecture, rather than the Soar architecture, since it is SCA's constraints that matter, not Soar's. Virtual architectures complicate comparisons because they allow modelers to vary the theoretical distinctions with the problem domain.

A third problem with comparative architectural studies arises when models adopt additional constraints that are not part of the primary architectural distinctions. For example, many models, such as Act-R's model of serial recall, require a specific knowledge representation so as to accurately account for the experimental data. However, when modelers attack a different task the architecture does not require them to use the same constraints. Thus, an Act-R model of serial recall and an Act-R model of BST are free to use different representations for lists of DMEs. This is a mini version of the virtual architecture problem—it creates additional theoretical distinctions that vary across tasks, but it doesn't completely override the constraints of the host architecture.

Finally, these problems illustrate how it is possible to build micro-theories inside cognitive architectures. Since it is possible to vary an architecture's constraints, there is no guarantee that two models of separate cognitive capacities in the same architecture are truly based on the same underlying set of theoretical distinctions. What's worse, the models might even be adopting contradictory distinctions.

Acknowledgments

I thank the members of the Soar and Act-R research community for their detailed comments on earlier drafts of this paper. This research was supported in part by grants N00014-95-1-0241 and N00014-96-1-0472 from the Office of Naval Research, Cognitive and Neural Sciences and Technology Division.

References

Anderson, J. R. (1983). *The Architecture of Cognition*. Cambridge: Harvard.

Anderson, J. R. (1990). *The Adaptive Character of Thought*. Hillsdale, NJ: Lawrence Erlbaum Associates.

Anderson, J. R. (1993). *Rules of the Mind*. Hillsdale, NJ: Lawrence Erlbaum Associates.

Anderson, J. R., Kushmerick, N., & Lebiere, C. (1993). Navigation and Conflict Resolution. In J. R. Anderson (Ed.), *Rules of the Mind* (pp. 93-119). Hillsdale, NJ: Lawrence Erlbaum Associates.

Anderson, J. R., & Lebiere, C. (in press). *The Atomic Components of Thought*. Hillsdale, NJ: Lawrence Erlbaum.

Cooper, R., & Shallice, T. (1995). Soar and the case for unified theories of cognition. *Cognition, 55*, 115-149.

Johnson, T. R. (1998). Acquisition and transfer of declarative and procedural knowledge. In F. E. Ritter & R. M. Young (Eds.), Proceedings of the Second European Conference on Cognitive Modelling (pp. 15-22). Nottingham, UK: Nottingham University Press.

Johnson, T. R., Zhang, J., & Wang, H. (1994). Bottom-up recognition learning: a compilation-based model of limited-lookahead learning. In A. Ram & K. Eiselt (Eds.), *Proceedings of the Sixteenth Annual Conference of the Cognitive Science Society* (pp. 469-474): Lawrence Erlbaum Associates.

Laird, J., Rosenbloom, P., & Newell, A. (1986). *Universal Subgoaling and Chunking*: Kluwer Academic Publishers.

Laird, J. E., Newell, A., & Rosenbloom, P. S. (1987). SOAR: An architecture for general intelligence. *Artificial Intelligence, 33*, 1-64.

Lebiere, C. (June 1996). Act-R: A Users Manual [On-line]. Available: ftp://ftp.andrew.cmu.edu/pub/act-r/ftp/release/beta/ACTR3TXT/Manual.rtf

Lovett, M. C., & Anderson, J. R. (1996). History of success and current context in problem solving: Combined influences on operator selection. *Cognitive Psychology, 31*(2).

Miller, C. S., & Laird, J. E. (1996). Accounting for graded performance within a discrete search framework. *Cognitive Science, 20*(4), 499-537.

Nelson, G., Lehman, J. F., & John, B. E. (1994). Integrating cognitive capabilities in a real-time task, *Proceedings of the Sixteenth Annual Conference of the Cognitive Science Society* (pp. 658-663). Hillsdale, NJ: Lawrence Erlbaum Associates.

Newell, A. (1990). *Unified Theories of Cognition*. Cambridge, MA: Harvard University Press.

Newell, A., Rosenbloom, P. S., & Laird, J. E. (1989). Symbolic Architectures for Cognition. In M. I. Posner (Ed.), *Foundations of Cognitive Science* (pp. 93-131). Cambridge, MA: MIT Press.

Rabinowitz, M., & Goldberg, N. (1995). Evaluating the structure-process hypothesis. In F. E. Weinert & W. Schneider (Eds.), *Memory Performance and Competencies: Issues in Growth and Development* (pp. 225-242). Hillsdale, NJ: Lawrence Erlbaum.

VanLehn, K. (1996). Cognitive skill acquisition. *Annual Review of Psychology*, 47, 513-539.

1.2 Evaluating the Design Based Approach

Tim Read

Abstract

The design based approach has been repeatedly advocated by Aaron Sloman as a methodology for Artificial Intelligence and Cognitive Science. This approach is intended to be used for the study of complex control systems such as the mind (a view of mind which differs from the standard computational one). This paper summarises the design based approach together with its supporting philosophical underpinning by drawing together the diverse research work which Sloman has produced over the last seven years. Subsequently, this approach is evaluated both in terms of its relation to mainstream Artificial Intelligence techniques and the research work which has been (and is still being) produced with it.

Introduction

Artificial Intelligence (henceforth AI) is a research area that contains a wealth of techniques and methodologies, each of which comes equipped with its own particular `view of the world'[5]. Developing methodologies is easier than using them; therefore, a larger amount of effort is typically devoted to advocating and outlining a particular approach than to using it. Applications may be piecemeal in nature if regular evaluations are not made of these methodologies (cf. McDermott, 1981).

Furthermore, since design methodologies are not subject to being proved or disproved, it is often very difficult to evaluate a particular approach, its strengths, weaknesses, and the impact it has had or could have upon the problems for which it was developed. For many years Aaron Sloman has been advocating and putting together an approach to the study of mind (within the fields of Philosophy, AI, and Cognitive Science) which is called the `design based approach' (henceforth DBA) (e.g. Sloman, 1989, 1992a, 1992b, 1993a, 1993b, 1993c, 1994, 1995). This approach breaks down boundaries between traditional rivals such as symbolic AI and Connectionism. Furthermore, it provides a framework within which different branches of empirical and theoretical science can be drawn together, and offers a view of the functionality of mind which goes beyond the computational view often implicit in AI. However, as was noted earlier, methodologies like the DBA cannot be proved or disproved. Consequently, the DBA needs to be evaluated in the context of the problems for which it was advocated (namely the problems of understanding the functionality of mind), compared against other approaches (both in terms of its driving assumptions and results of its applications), and considered in terms of the types of problems for which it is applicable. Firstly, the DBA is summarised including the principles upon which it is based; secondly, the way in which the DBA fits into the field of AI is discussed; and thirdly, the results which have been achieved with it up to date are presented.

What is the design based approach?

Before examining the DBA, it is necessary to consider what is meant by a `design`. Sloman (1995) defines a `design` to be an abstraction (including architectural specifications, mechanisms, formalisms, algorithms, etc.) which specifies a complex structure and its interacting components. He goes on to note that a design can be implemented in different `lower level mechanisms`, i.e. he distinguishes between the level at which the functionality of a structure is specified and the level at which it is implemented. This distinction between the abstraction of functional capabilities and their implementation is not new (and, of course, Sloman has never claimed that it is). The seminal article by Newell (1982) introduced the term `knowledge level` to capture this distinction.

Newell characterised a system (an intelligent agent) in terms of different levels of abstraction: a knowledge level, a symbol level, and a device level. He stated that each level can be both considered autonomously (without reference to the other two, e.g. programmers do not need to consider the device level) and reduced to the level below.

A key part of the notion of the knowledge level is that it is assumed by an observer to contain the goals and beliefs which explain the behaviour of the agent, i.e. the role of the knowledge level is assumed to explain agent rationality (since an agent will obtain its goals by making use of the knowledge which is contained at this level). Sloman, however, introduces a different notion of level which is principally concerned with designs (1994a). This differs

---

[5]The author would like to acknowledge Aaron Sloman and Elena Bárcena for helpful comments on earlier drafts of this paper. All errors and idiosyncratic opinions are, as ever, my very own.

from Newell's version of the knowledge level in that the former does not involve rationality (as Sloman correctly notes: systems can result from designs which follow algorithms even where the behaviour may not be described by an observer to be rational). The Slomanian level contains both designed structures and the semantic information stored and used by them. He calls it the `information level´ and states that it lies at a lower conceptual level than Newell's knowledge level.

The concept of the information level is central to the DBA together with Sloman's view of the mind as a control system, and not a computation system (1992). In essence, this distinction is made due to the ambiguities present in the term `computation´ and the tendency of researchers to link it to the concept of algorithm. He arrived at this distinction after realising that non-technical definitions of computation are too vague and general to form part of rigorous explanations and theories, and that the syntactic technical definition of this term was too restrictive (in the sense that these definitions force assumptions about the type of information processing that a system is capable of performing purely based on the current ideas of what is possible). Furthermore, Sloman notes that the standard view of computation forces processes to be discrete and non-continuous, which may not be the case in the brain. Hence, the significant and defining property of a design should be its causal properties, and not only a subset of them, which conforms to the current view of the concept `computational´.

Sloman's view of the mind as a control system, and not a computation system, contains implications for the types of representations which are possible and/or necessary in the design process.
He states that different forms of representation have different roles in control mechanisms (each of them with its own syntax and semantics), and that what is important is not only how information is represented, but also how it is transformed[6] between the functional components in a system. Thus, the types of representation that are required depend greatly on which types of control mechanisms are feasible; something that remains a subject for research.

---

[6]Furthermore, what are the limitations in such transformations? For example, the difficulties of putting the taste of strawberries into words.

We are still at an early stage in the research process of exploring mechanisms and representations. Consequently, as Sloman points out, debates about the relative merits of connectionist versus symbolic mechanisms are largely irrelevant, i.e. the low level details of how a functional control system (or subsystem) is implemented may only make a marginal difference to its functionality. This point is made succinctly in his statement: `architecture dominates mechanism´. In other words, the global design (largely at the information level) of functionally interacting components defines the causal properties of the system, and not the details of how one component or mechanism in that system is implemented. Such information level structures are further defined by Sloman to be `virtual machines´ in the sense that they exist as abstract functional units manipulating complex information states which are largely independent from the lower level physical structures in which they may be implemented. Furthermore, a virtual machine may implement another virtual machine, which implies the existence of hierarchies (many of which may exist within the information level). Finally, he notes that a bottom level may not clearly exist, since below any particular level there may be another one, down to the level of atoms, and below that level, sub-atomic particles, etc.

Given this summary of the assumptions and views of the functionality of the mind, and the general properties of the types of control systems which need to be studied in order to understand such functionality (notions such as design, the information level, the difference between computation and control, and the role of the virtual machine), how do the assumptions form part of the methodology called the DBA?
Central to Sloman's view of how the mind works is the idea of collective functionality, that is, the idea that many different types of mechanisms can operate together (to give rise to one system or architecture) at the information level. A practical problem for researchers is that it is not possible to work with such breadth of design (including such processes as perception, planning, reasoning, action, monitoring, meta-functionality, etc.) and also maintain the functional depth with which each subsystem is specified (in a comparable way to that of a specific research project which is only concerned with one process, e.g. planning).

Consequently, a compromise is required regarding the way designs are produced in the DBA. This compromise can be extracted from the idea that an eventual complete design needs to be both `broad´ and `deep´. `Broad´ in the sense of the range of mechanisms that are considered, and 'deep' in the sense of the functional capabilities with which the mechanisms are specified. Reaching the goal is possible via (at least) two routes: firstly, a researcher may start by producing 'narrow and deep' designs (i.e. considering relatively few mechanisms, which is common in most research projects), and then broaden the work. Secondly, a researcher may start by producing 'broad and shallow'[7] designs (i.e. taking relatively less functionality into consideration), and then deepen the work. Hence, in order to produce the types of designs which Sloman claims to be necessary for both exploring mental functionality and producing an eventual understanding of how the mind works, these designs should initially be 'broad and shallow', and then gradually deepened as future research is conducted.

The final question which remains to be answered regarding the DBA (given the previously outlined goal of developing 'broad and shallow' designs; at the information level) is which process should be used to produce the designs? The actual process of producing designs has not been proposed by Sloman; chiefly, as he notes (1995), both empirical and theoretical science can give rise to designs (or partial designs). The key point is that once a design has been articulated in some form, it needs to be explored and analysed to understand exactly what its capabilities are.

Sloman (1993b) summarises this general process in five steps:

1. Analyse the requirements for an autonomous agent (this might involve both experimental investigation and theoretical postulation).

2. Produce a design specification for a working system to meet the requirements established in step 1.

3. Construct a detailed implementation and computer simulation for the design specified in step 2. Steps 1 and 2 are necessary since whilst the way in which the design specification is implemented in such a simulation may be very different from how it occurs in the brain, it forces a rigorous treatment of all parameters relevant to a design (Daly & Daly, 1991). Furthermore, this process of simulation is directly analogous to that used by control engineers working on, e.g. airplanes, where computer simulations are required to understand exactly how the complex control subsystems interact.

---

[7]The notion of 'broad and shallow' designs was first introduced by Bates et al. (1992).

4. Conduct a theoretical analysis of how the design specification and implementation details meet the requirements established in step 1.

5. Analyse the `neighbourhood design space´ to consider what variations and extensions are possible.

The DBA, therefore, can be seen to be more concerned with defining the types of designs which are relevant to the study of mind than the specific technique by which such designs should be produced. This perspective reflects both the difficulties present in producing designs and the current state of research regarding the types of mechanisms which are theoretically possible, their causal properties, underlying representations, and the way they connect and function together. As the types of control states which arise in intelligent agent architectures are better understood, more can be stated about the types of mechanisms and representations present. It should be noted that, considering Sloman's view about architecture dominating mechanism, artificial versions of the human mental mechanisms are implemented in collections of lower level virtual machines and physical structures. These collections are likely to be different from those in the human brain in both in terms of their functional connection and compositionality (e.g. silicon based circuits versus flesh and blood).

Relating the DBA to other AI approaches

A detailed comparison of the DBA with the large range of individual techniques and principles which have been developed within the AI community would be too large a task. Consequently, in this section the DBA is located within the general area of AI by comparing the DBA with the two standard AI subsets, namely, the symbolic and non-symbolic approaches.

The majority of symbolic approaches relate (either implicitly or explicitly) intelligence and associated abilities to Newell's notion of the knowledge level, involving second generation expert systems[8] and an influential unified theory of cognition such as Soar (e.g. Rosenbloom et al., 1991; Norman, 1991; Ritter, 1993).

---

[8]The difference between first and second generation expert systems is that the former used largely procedural representations of knowledge and the latter, largely declarative knowledge based representations (Steels, 1985).

Furthermore, work has been done to relate the knowledge level to general underlying computer structures (e.g. Vanwelkenhuysen & Rademakers, 1990) and on the types of meta-processes which can make use of the knowledge available at this level (e.g. Maes, 1987; Maes & Nardi, 1988). Non-symbolic approaches relate intelligence with the ability to deal with problems grounded in the real world rather than with the ability to manipulate complex abstract representations. Behaviour based techniques have attempted to specify the types of mechanisms which a robot would need to survive in an unpredictable environment (e.g. Brooks, 1990, 1991; McFarland, 1993; Steels, 1993). Connectionism has also tried to generate principles for the types of mechanisms and representations underlying intelligence. Its relation to Cognitive Theory was recently reviewed by Seidenberg (1993).

The symbolic and non-symbolic approaches differ from the DBA in that the former are essentially ˋnarrow and deep´ approaches, and the latter is a ˋbroad and shallow´ approach. The most significant difference between the three, however, is the philosophy which motivates them, rather than their relative status in terms of breadth and depth.

As was noted earlier, symbolic approaches restrict the notion of intelligence to the types of processes and representations which are possible based upon symbol manipulation. Non-symbolic approaches, on the other hand, restrict themselves to processes and representations inspired by real world demands and so called ˋbrain style´ programming. The DBA does not place such restrictions on processes and representations, although it also does not rule them out either. Sloman´s argument about this issue is that it is far too early in the research process to place aprioristic restrictions upon what we should be studying.

Some critical questions could be raised at this point against the DBA: if the DBA is so flexible that it can accommodate any technique (since there is no reason why the results of any avenue of research cannot be incorporated into designs arising from the DBA), is there not a danger that the approach is too flexible? In other words, if the DBA does not contain assumptions which restrict and determine the type of systems which can be built, is it not the case that the DBA facilitates an all encompassing view of mental functionality without affecting its predictions (therefore, adding nothing)? What is the DBA adding to the mainstream work in AI that is not there already? Furthermore, Sloman has noted that the

DBA and the control view of the mind are not subject to being proved or falsified, in which case why should anyone be interested in them, what value do they have? If researchers conduct `narrow and shallow´ work which aids understanding of the types of mechanisms and representations that are theoretically possible, then what contribution does the DBA make to such understanding, since it is the results of the approaches that give rise to understanding, not necessarily their methodological assumptions?

The global answer to these and other related questions is that the DBA does not attempt to be a methodology in the sense of a handle turning exercise which will give rise to designs for mental architectures. By outlining this approach, Sloman produces a set of guidelines or framework that can be used for the study of mind. He notes that it is too early to make the restrictive statements often present in mainstream AI, since we need to be aware of what is possible before applying limitations and restrictions (we are still in the phase of guided exploration). Placing aprioristic restrictions has been analogised by Sloman to looking for one´s car keys (which were dropped on the pavement by accident on a dark night) only under the street light! (pers. comm.).

As well as trying to remove aprioristic restrictions about the nature of processes and representations, what the DBA adds to the study of mind is a framework in which designs for mental systems can be constructed at the information level. Designs of this nature will consequently provide functional explanation in terms of an understanding of a collection of interacting mechanisms on the assumption that no single `narrow and deep´ approach will (on its own) lead to a functional explanation of mind. An artificial system which can give rise to the functionality of the human mind must be an enormously complicated control system, only some of its internal processes being reproducible by current techniques, an eventual understanding of which is likely to come from an architectural design.

Applications of the DBA

A prime example of the use of the DBA can be seen in the activities of the (past and present) members of the Cognition and Affect research group at the University of Birmingham, under

Sloman´s supervision. The principal aims of the group are the following (Sloman, 1996):

``To understand the types of architectures that are capable of accounting for the whole range of human mental states and processes, including not only intelligent behaviour but also moods, emotions, and the like. In particular we wish to explore the question [of] whether the ability to have emotional states is an accident of animal evolution or an inevitable consequence of design requirements and constraints, for instance in resource-limited intelligent robots.

We are looking at design principles for intelligent autonomous agents, whether natural or artificial, including such issues as:

1. The ontology of a human-like mind: what sorts of states, properties, processes, capabilities can occur in a mind, e.g. beliefs, desires, decisions, deliberation, intentions, plans, suppositions, idle wishes, preferences, ambitions, motive generators, personalities, emotions, moods, loss of control of attention, etc.

2. What kinds of architectures can support agents with different kinds of intelligence, including human-like agents and others. [...].

3. Motives: how they are generated, and how they are managed in autonomous agents.

4. How resource-limited agents cope with time pressures in their deliberations, etc. Does this require meta-management processes?

5. How various kinds of mental states in humans (and presumably other intelligent agents) arise out of the architecture (e.g. emotional states).

6. Various kinds of learning in agents, including acquiring new facts, new rules for internal or external behaviour and perhaps also modifying the architecture itself.

7. How to design interacting communicating agents.

8. How to accommodate hybrid architectures where appropriate, e.g. neural nets

interacting with symbolic reasoning systems. We conjecture that human-like architectures require several different sorts of architectures to coexist and collaborate including a `reactive´ layer, a `deliberative´ layer and a `meta-management´ layer, with different features, constraints and capabilities. Perceptual and action generating systems linked to these mechanisms will also be layered.

9. How to evolve architectures using genetic algorithms and genetic programming.´´

One of the first published results was Beaudoin´s (Beaudoin & Sloman, 1993; Beaudoin, 1994) on the structure of the processes and representations underlying attention and the processing of motives and goals in autonomous agents. This work produced a `broad and shallow´ design of an autonomous agent which operates in a microworld scenario. The implications of the control structures in the design were considered as a starting point in the process of exploring design space.

The author has also used the DBA in three different research areas. Firstly, an application was made to Gray's theory of emotion (Gray 1987, 1990, 1994) which used the DBA to specify a `broad and shallow´ model of a rat called Simrat (Read, 1994, 1995). The resulting computer simulation and analysis enabled mechanisms which were largely defined in neuropsychological terms with empirical data to be understood in terms of their information processing and representational capabilities. This simulation also provided an explanation of behavioural effects which had been largely unresolved in the psychological literature.

Secondly, following an analysis of the types of mechanisms and control structures proposed (in the literature) to underlie animal behaviour and learning, the DBA was used to incorporate these separate lines of research into one design, which was an attempt to explain all the behavioural phenomena (Read, 1996). The process of implementing this design is in progress. Thirdly and finally, the DBA is being used as part of a research project to form a design for a unified theory of perception and action, linking together the structures and types of representations underlying vision, language, and action (Read & Bárcena, 1997).

Sloman & Poli (1996) have produced an agent toolkit which provides researchers with a means of exploring design issues in the context of the DBA (cf. the COGENT tool presented by Cooper and Fox in this volume). The toolkit, call SIM_AGENT enables the rapid design and development of agents. SIM_AGENT has been written in Pop-11 (Anderson, 1989) and will therefore only run in a Poplog Pop-11 environment (which requires UNIX or LINUX on a PC). It has two parts: a rule interpretation mechanism and a rule scheduling library. The former is a condition-action rule interpreter based upon the idea of a forward-chaining production system interpreter. Its funcionality has been augmented by addition of various extensions including an interface to neural networks (or other `sub-symbolic´ mechanisms) through so-called `filter´ conditions, a wide range of condition and action types (both of which are user extendable), and a variety of control options and higher level structuring facilities. Rule sets can be combined to form rule families for selection and deselection as the context changes (which enables Soar like pushing and popping of contexts). The rule families can also be combined to form rule systems which define the funcionality of an agent. A rule system may be an arbitrarily complex collection of interacting rule sets and rule families, with associated databases providing memory stores and communication channels.

The rule scheduling library provides a set of object oriented classes and mechanisms (which are made up of re-usable rule sets and rule families) for running simulations which can be incorporated into agents in order to facilitate the production of agents without having to write all the rules for all the possible types of contexts. Such mechanisms enable the user to allocate differing types of resources between components of an agent and also between agents. For example, a user is able to create agents which plan relatively quickly with respect to their perceptual processes.

This toolkit has been used (in the context of the DBA) by Sloman and Poli in several exploratory scenarios, including the `blind/lazy scenario´ (Poli, 1996). This application was an experiment about the way in which two agents could use a genetic algorithm to evolve rules which enable them to cooperate in the performance of a simple task, making use of a predefined set of mental states and communications protocols.

This toolkit has been used by Wright & Sloman (1997) to implement a protoemotional agent called Minder1. This agent reflects the theoretical work of the authors (e.g. Wright et al., 1996) and is à partial implementation of a form of global processing state (argued by them to occur in human emotional states), which is produced by the repeated surfacing of unsatisfiable motives that disrupt attentive processing. SIM_AGENT is currently being used by researchers both at Birmingham and other institutions (including the U.K. Defense Research Agency for work on simulated army agents).

The DBA has been used by Wright (1996) to explore the question of how hedonic states (which, as he argues, are often absent from information processing theories of emotion) can be subsumed within an architectural context. An attempt is being made to explore the type of control systems present in humans and their relation to attentional and emotional episodes (Wright et al., 1996). This is an ongoing activity of the previously mentioned Cognition and Affect project at the University of Birmingham. Finally, preliminary investigation is being carried out with the DBA as an approach to clinical psychological treatments (pers. comm.).

Conclusion

This article started out by defining the DBA in terms of its philosophical underpinning. The DBA is closer to a set of guidelines or a framework for the study of mind than to a step by step process (although some attempt has been made by Sloman to present it in this fashion). The key notion of this methodology is the emphasis placed on architectural designs specified at the information level of abstraction. Such designs provide explanation in a `broad´ sense since functionality is viewed to emerge from the collective interaction of the individual mechanisms.

In this sense, the implementation details of the mechanisms are far less important than their causal properties and representations at the information level. The DBA was briefly compared to other mainstream AI work and seen to differ not only in terms of the emphasis placed on `broad and shallow´ designs (as opposed to `narrow and deep´ ones) but, more importantly, on the lack of aprioristic restrictions placed upon the types of processes and representations that are typically studied by AI researchers.

It has been demonstrated that the DBA is used to produce designs for control systems which form part of a library of knowledge of what is possible (some of which are being elaborated and explored using the SIM_AGENT toolkit). As this library grows, the information it contains can begin to shape the way in which the DBA will be used in the future and the types of designs that will be produced. A key point in all these applications is that the means by which architectural designs have been produced has been inspired (and derived) from work in a large range of theoretical and empirical sciences, and has not been reduced to a core set of restrictive principles or dogmas.

References

Anderson J. (ed.), 1989. *Popl1 Comes To Age.* Chichester: Ellis Horwood.

Bates J., Loyall A.B., & Reilly W. S., 1991. Broad agents. *SIGART Bulletin*, 2(4), pp.38-40.

Beaudoin L., 1994. *Goal Processing in Autonomous Agents.* Ph.D. Thesis, University of Birmingham.

Beaudoin L. & Sloman A., 1993. A study of motive processing and attention. In A. Sloman, D. Hogg, G. Humphreys, A. Ramsey, & D. Partridge (eds.) *Prospects for Artificial Intelligence (Proceedings of AISB-93)*, pp. 229-238. Oxford: IOS Press.

Brooks R.A., 1991. Intelligence without representation. *Artificial Intelligence* 47, pp.139-160.

Brooks R.A., 1990. Elephants don't play chess. In P. Maes (ed.) *Designing Autonomous Agents: Theory and Practice from Biology to Engineering and Back*, pp.3-34. Cambridge, Mass: MIT Press.

Daly H.D. & Daly J., 1991. Value of mathematical modeling of appetitive and aversive learning: review and extensions of DMOD. In M.R. Denny (ed.) *Fear, avoidance, and phobias. A fundamental analysis*, pp.165-197. London: Lawrence Erlbaum Associates.

Gray J., 1994. A model of the limbic system and basal ganglia: applications to anxiety and schizophrenia. In M. Gazzaniga (ed.) *Cognitive Neuroscience*, pp.1165-1176. Cambridge, Mass: MIT Press.

Gray J. A., 1990. Brain systems that mediate cognition and emotion. *Cognition & Emotion*, 4(3), pp.269-288.

Gray J. A., 1987. *The Psychology of Fear and Stress*, 2nd ed. Cambridge: CUP.

Maes P., 1987. *Computational Reflection.* Ph.D. Thesis, Vrije Universiteit Brussel. Also available as VUB AI-Lab TR-87-02.

Maes P. & Nardi D. (eds.), 1988. *Meta-level Architectures and Reflection.* Amsterdam: North Holland.

McDermott D., 1981. Artificial intelligence meets natural stupidity. In J. Haugeland (ed.) *Mind design, Philosophy, Psychology, Artificial Intelligence*, pp.143-160. Cambridge,

Mass: MIT Press.

McFarland D., 1993. Autonomy and self-sufficiency in robots. In L. Steels & R. Brooks (eds.) *The artificial life route to artificial intelligence. Building Situated Embodied Agents*, New Haven: Lawrence Erlbaum Associates.

Newell A., 1982. The knowledge level. *Artificial Intelligence* 18(1), pp.87-127.

Norman D.A., 1991. Approaches to the study of intelligence. *Artificial Intelligence* 47, pp.327-346.

Poli R., 1996. The Blind/Lazy Scenario and the evolution of mental states, internal processes and communication: *http://www.cs.bham.ac.uk/~rmp/eebic/example2.html*

Read T., 1996. Integrating Behavioural Mechanisms: towards a complete theory of animal learning and behaviour. In submission to *Psychological Bulletin*.

Read T., 1995. *The Use of Systemic Design to Analyse Gray's Theory of Emotion*. Ph.D. Thesis, University of Birmingham.

Read T., 1994. Applying Systemic Design to the study of emotion. In M. Keane, P. Cunningham, M. Brady, & R. Byrne, (eds.) *Proceedings of the Seventh Annual Conference of AI & Cognitive Science '94*, pp.165-178. Dublin University Press.

Read T. & Bárcena E., 1997. El enfoque laberíntico del lenguaje. To appear in *Philologia Hispalensis*.

Ritter F.A., 1993. Three types of emotional effects that will occur in cognitive architectures. In T. Read & A. Sloman (eds.) *Proceedings of WAUME93, Workshop on Architectures Underlying Motivation and Emotion*, University of Birmingham (not paginated).

Rosenbloom P.S., Laird J.E., Newell A., & McCarl R., 1991. A preliminary analysis of the Soar architecture as a basis for general intelligence. *Artificial Intelligence* 47, pp.289-325

Seidenberg M.S., 1993. Connectionist models and cognitive theory. *Psychological Science* 4(4), pp.228-243.

Sloman A., 1996. Details of the Cognition and Affect Project, Cognitive Science Research Centre, University of Birmingham: *http://www.cs.bham.ac.uk/~axs/cog_affect/COGAFF-PROJECT.html*

Sloman A., 1995. What sort of control system is able to have a personality? In R. Trappl (ed.) *Proceedings of the workshop on designing personalities for synthetic actors*, pp.85-97. University of Viena Press.

Sloman A., 1994a. Semantics in an intelligent control system. Invited paper for the Information and Understanding session at *British Academy and Royal Society Conference on Artificial Intelligence and the Mind: New Breakthroughs or Dead Ends?*

Sloman A., 1994b. Varieties of formalisms for knowledge representation. *Computational Intelligence, special issue on computational imagery*, pp.413-423.

Sloman A., 1993a. The mind as a control system. In C. Hookway, & D. Peterson (eds.) *Proceedings of The Royal Institute of Philosophy Conference `Philosophy and the Cognitive Sciences'*, pp.69-110. Cambridge: CUP.

Sloman A., 1993b. Prospects for AI as the general science of intelligence. In A. Sloman, D. Hogg, G. Humphreys, A. Ramsey, & D. Partridge (eds.) *Prospects for Artificial Intelligence (Proceedings of AISB-93)*, pp.1-10. Oxford: IOS Press.

Sloman A., 1992. Silicon souls, how to design a functioning mind. *Cognitive Science Report no. CSRP-92-11*, University of Birmingham.

Sloman A., 1989. On designing a visual system (towards a gibsonian computational model of vision). *Journal of Experimental and Theoretical Artificial Intelligence* 1, pp.289-337.

Steels L., 1993. Building agents out of autonomous behaviour systems. In L. Steels & R. Brooks (eds.) *The Artificial Life Route to Artificial Intelligence. Building Situated Embodied Agents*, pp.511-565. New Haven: Lawrence Erlbaum Associates.

Steels L., 1985. Second generation expert systems. *Future Generation Computer Systems* 1(4), pp.213-221.

Vanwelkenhuysen J. & Rademakers P., 1990. Mapping knowledge-level analysis onto a computational framework. In L. Aiello (ed.) *Proceedings of the 9th European Conference on Artificial Intelligence*, pp.681-686. London: Pitman.

Wright I.P., 1996. Reinforcement learning and animat emotions. In P. Maes, M. Mataric, J.A. Meyer, J. Pollack, & S.W. Wilson (eds.) *From Animals to Animats 4: Proceedings of the Fourth International Conference on Simulation of Adaptive Behaviour*, Cambridge, Mass: MIT Press/Bradford Books.

Wright I.P. & Sloman A., 1997. Minder1: An implementation of a protoemotional agent architecture. *Cognitive Science Research Report CSRP-97-1*, University of Birmingham.

Wright I.P., Sloman A. & Beaudoin L.P., 1996. Toward a design-based analysis of emotional episodes. *Philosophy, Psychiatry and Psychology*, 3(2), pp.101-126.

1.3 COGENT: An Environment for the Development of Cognitive Models

Richard Cooper, Peter Yule, John Fox & David Sutton

Abstract

COGENT[9] is a modelling environment which aims to improve the methodology of computational modelling by providing an integrated approach to model development, description, and evaluation. The environment is explicitly designed to allow psychologists with a range of computational expertise (from very little to a great deal) to develop their own computational models. It achieves these aims by providing the user with a graphical programming language based on the familiar box/arrow notation of informal cognitive psychology. This language draws on parallels between the psychological concept of functional modularity and the computational concept of object-orientation to provide a sound modelling tool in which models may be evaluated through methodologically rigorous computational experiments. COGENT has been used by a number of researchers to develop models in the domains of memory, reasoning, decision making, problem solving, the performance of complex tasks, and concept combination. This chapter presents an overview of COGENT, drawing upon two models to illustrate the system. The first, a production system model of multi-column addition, demonstrates many of the fundamental features of the system. The second, a model of Allen inferencing, uses the new "analogue buffer" features of the system to reimplement the metrical algorithm described by Berendt (1996).

---

[9]COGENT is an acronym for Cognitive Objects within a Graphical EnviroNmenT. For further information, see http://www.psyc.bbk.ac.uk/research/projects/cogent/. We may be contacted by email at: cogent@psyc.bbk.ac.uk.

Introduction

When attempting to develop a cognitive model, a researcher is faced with many issues. Perhaps the first to be addressed concerns the technology to be adopted. There are a bewildering array of alternatives: connectionism (in all its forms), the use of a symbolic cognitive architecture (such as Soar (Newell, 1990) or ACT-R (Anderson, 1993)), or the use of a general purpose programming language (e.g., Lisp or Prolog). If connectionism is inappropriate (because, for example, it is believed that the task being modelled involves overt symbol manipulation), the choice devolves to one between architecture and general programming language. Although the use of a cognitive architecture has unquestionable benefits (e.g., allowing the unitary application of constraints deriving from a range of tasks and domains), it is also fraught with difficulties (cf. Cooper & Shallice, 1995). Given the necessary complexities of cognitive architectures, can, for example, particular behaviour be attributed to specific architectural properties or mechanisms? How should work proceed if a particular behaviour proves intractable in the chosen architecture? Indeed, can any possible behaviour be shown to be intractable in a given architecture? And how should theorists proceed if they adhere to most but not all assumptions underlying their preferred architecture? If one accepts the argumentation behind these rhetorical questions, then one is left with the general purpose programming language option. Although this option has great flexibility, it is generally unconstrained and suffers from a lack of sound methodology. (The most obvious methodological problem is the lack of any principled way of distinguishing implementation detail from theoretical commitment: cf. Cooper, Fox, Farringdon & Shallice, 1996.) In addition, the cognitive modeller requires considerable expertise if the general purpose programming language option is to be adopted. It therefore seems that there is a place in cognitive modelling for a special purpose modelling language which 1) embodies general principles of cognitive psychological theorising, 2) is relatively easy to learn/program, and 3) is underpinned by a sound methodological framework. These concerns have led to the development of COGENT (Cooper & Fox, in press), a modelling environment which aims to improve modelling methodology by addressing the three key areas of model description, model evaluation, and model development. In brief, COGENT addresses model description by providing a graphical interface to a well-defined object-oriented modelling language. The graphical interface allows researchers to specify their models in terms of interconnected boxes.

Such box/arrow diagrams are one of the principal means of theory specification in cognitive psychology, and their use in COGENT is intended to allow psychologists to work with an established theory specification language. The use of box/arrow diagrams in cognitive psychology is, however, generally undermined by the lack of a well-defined operational semantics for the notation: although the diagrams are often annotated with text, the computational assumptions behind the diagrams are rarely, if ever, specified in sufficient detail to allow an objective assessment of the corresponding theory's behaviour. The box/arrow notation embodied within COGENT is supported by a well-defined operational semantics, allowing COGENT box/arrow diagrams to be executed and their behaviour thereby determined.

The basic building blocks of a COGENT model are low-level processing objects (or modules), such as buffers and rule-based processors. These objects are configurable: different processing capabilities can be assigned to different instances of the same class of object. Thus, different buffers can be specified as having different decay characteristics or capacity limitations. This configurability gives the primitive objects a great deal of flexibility, but also encourages a systematic approach to model evaluation. In particular, the sensitivity of a model's behaviour to different values of a given parameter can be assessed by running the model with those parameter values and comparing the resultant behaviours. In this way one can evaluate claims concerning the theoretical relevance of parameters, and thereby distinguish implementation detail (which should not affect behavioural measures) from theory (which, assuming theory falsifiability, will have an effect on behavioural measures).

Model development is supported within COGENT via the notion of a research programme. A research programme is grounded in a specific domain and generally attempts to answer a specific question through the development of a family of related computational models (possibly in association with a series of standard laboratory experiments).

The remainder of this chapter begins with a more detailed presentation of the facilities provided by COGENT. A simple production system model of multi-column addition is used to illustrate this presentation. We then provide a more detailed exploration of the use of COGENT, focusing on the Allen inference task (Knauff, Rauh & Schlieder, 1995) and, in particular, the metrical algorithm of Berendt (1996). We conclude with a general discussion about the role of COGENT and its relation to other approaches to cognitive modelling.

The Basics of COGENT

The complete COGENT environment currently provides four distinct facilities: a set of well-defined configurable object classes (corresponding, intuitively, to types of cognitive module); a graphical interface for specifying models in terms of interconnected instances of these classes (i.e., in terms of box/arrow diagrams); a computational engine for running such models (i.e., a means of executing box/arrow diagrams to determine their behaviour); and a tool for maintaining sets of models within distinct research programmes. We describe and illustrate each of these in turn.

The Primitive Object Classes

Much of the power of COGENT comes from the set of standard object classes built into the system. There are currently five major classes of object: buffer, rule-based process, network, data, and compound. These classes, which are derived from the kind of functional modules used within cognitive psychological theorising, provide the building blocks with which individual models are constructed.

Buffers

A buffer is an information store: a place where items of information may be put for later retrieval. Buffers are appropriate for both short-term storage (e.g., modelling working memory) or long-term storage (e.g., a knowledge base). They may be configured, via a large set of properties, so as to behave in a variety of different ways, allowing, for example, element decay and/or capacity limitations.

In its default form, a buffer will have unlimited capacity, no decay and random access. This means that an indefinite number of elements may be added to the buffer, all elements will be available for later recall unless explicitly deleted from the buffer, and order of recall will be non-deterministic. If capacity limitations are applied (via selection of the "Limited Capacity" property), only a specified number of elements will be allowed in the buffer. The actual number is given by a second property. A third property determines the behaviour of a limited capacity buffer once its capacity is reached. This property can be set, for example, so that when a further element is added the oldest element is deleted, thus providing the functionality of a push-through store.

Spontaneous decay of buffer elements can also be specified through a number of properties. If selected, decay may be deterministic (such that elements will disappear after a given number of processing cycles) or probabilistic (such that elements have a "half life", by which time there is a 50% chance that they will have disappeared).

Yet more properties specify the access characteristics of buffers. Access may be random or based on the order in which elements were added to the buffer (either FIFO, that is, least recent first, or LIFO, most recent first).

The graphical interface to COGENT, as described below, presents the user with all possible buffer properties in such a way that the user may click and select to set the properties as required (see Figure 3 for an example property panel from the multi-column addition model). This approach greatly simplifies the programmatic aspects of modelling storage devices. There are additional benefits, however. The range of properties applicable to buffers makes explicit a range of possible buffer behaviours, and shows that a module's behaviour is not specified merely be labelling that module as a buffer.

Rule-Based Processes

Rule-based processes are devices whose behaviour is determined by a set of symbolic rules. Rules are just condition/action pairs, where the conditions typically involve matching elements in buffers (though advanced users may also include arbitrary Prolog) and the actions allow passing of messages to other boxes.

IF: production(Conds, Acts) is in *Match Memory*

             not production(Conds, Acts) is in *Refractory Memory*

THEN: add production(Conds, Acts) to *Refractory Memory*

             send execute(Acts) to *Fire Production*

TRIGGER: execute(Acts)

IF: add(X) is a member of Acts

THEN: add X to *Working Memory*

Figure 1: Autonomous and Triggered Rules

There are two basic types of rule: triggered rules (which are activated when the process containing them receives a message that matches the rule's triggering pattern); and autonomous rules (which test their conditions on each processing cycle and hence do not require a triggering signal to fire). An example of each type of rule is shown in Figure 1. In these rules, `Conds`, `Acts` and `X` are variables. The first of the rules is autonomous. It continuously monitors *Match Memory* for a term of the form `production(Conds, Acts)` that is not also in *Refractory Memory*. If and when it finds such a term, it adds it to *Refractory Memory* and sends a message of the form `execute(Acts)` to the box named *Fire Production*. The second rule (which might be found in the process named *Fire Production*) is triggered by receipt of a message of the form `execute(Acts)`. `Acts` is understood by this rule to be a list of terms, and, when the process containing the rule receives a message of the form `execute(Acts)`, each term `X` for which `add(X)` is a member of the `Acts` list will be added to *Working Memory*.

COGENT provides a rule-editor which simplifies the process of specifying rules and minimises the risk of syntax errors. (See Figure 4.)

Networks

Network objects provide COGENT with a primitive facility for the development of hybrid and connectionist models. Networks are fully specified via a series of properties, whose values determine input and output vector width, initialisation procedure, activation function and learning rule. At present only simple two-layer feedforward networks are supported, and no special facilities are provided for visualisation of network weights. However, future versions of COGENT are likely to incorporate more complex network objects, together with appropriate visualisation tools.

Data

COGENT provides two subsorts of data box to allow input and output from models. Data sources are intended to allow control over the input to a model. They contain a sequence of message-destination pairs (analogous to the "THEN" side of rules). As processing proceeds, elements are removed from sources and sent to the specified destination. Data sinks are the complement of data sources. They collect messages sent by other boxes and store them in a file. They fulfil no essential role in a cognitive model, but allow output to be collected for later analysis.

Compounds

Compound objects provide COGENT with a bracketing facility, such that other sorts of object can be grouped into higher-order functional subcomponents. In box/arrow terms, a compound is just a box that contains further boxes, and the behaviour of a compound box is entirely determined by the behaviour of its subboxes and their interconnections.

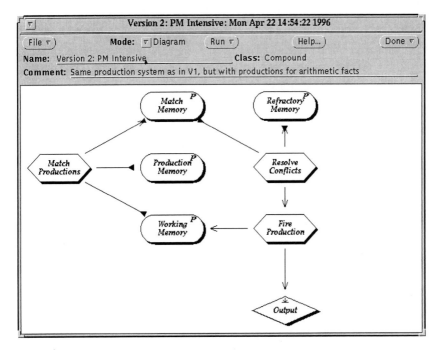

Figure 2: A COGENT Box/Arrow Diagram

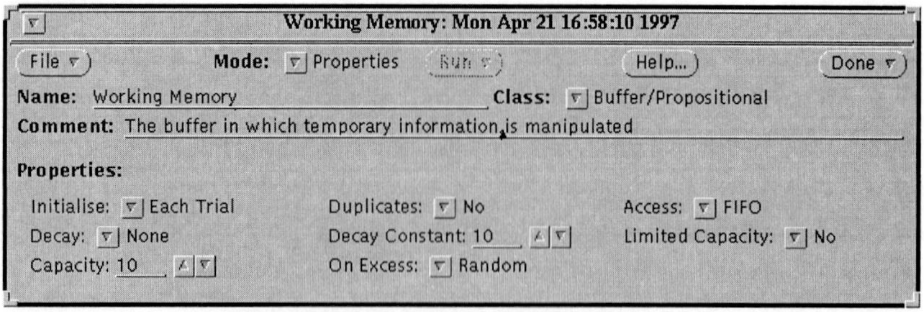

Figure 3: The Properties Panel of Working Memory

It is possible to develop models using COGENT's set of object classes and a standard text editor, and this in fact is how the first model was developed in the embryonic system (Cooper, 1995). However, the usability of the raw class set is hampered by the requisite syntax. COGENT's graphical interface circumvents this potential problem. The interface allows models to be drawn as box/arrow diagrams, which each box in the diagram corresponding to an instance of an object class. Figure 2 shows one such box/arrow diagram. In this (and all COGENT) diagrams, rule-based processes are depicted as hexagonal boxes, buffers are depicted as oblong boxes, and data sinks are depicted as diamonds.

Two different types of arrow on the diagram indicate two forms of communication. Pointed arrows correspond to message passing (including buffer modification). Arrows with a blunt triangular head correspond to buffer reading. Thus, the process *Match Productions* reads from the buffer *Production Memory*. Superimposed arrows indicate both forms of communication: *Resolve Conflicts* reads from and writes to *Refractory Memory*.

The Graphical Interface

The graphical interface provides a palette of object classes, instances of which may be selected and positioned on the canvas. The resulting boxes can then be named and joined by the appropriate arrows as necessary.

In order to fully specify a COGENT model, it is necessary to flesh out the specifications of the boxes which constitute the box/arrow diagram. Double-clicking on any box opens the box to allow setting of class-specific properties and other instance-specific information. Figure 3 shows the properties panel for a typical buffer. As noted above, each property can be set by selecting values from menus, minimising the computational expertise required.

The specification of other instance-specific information (e.g., the rules within processes, or the initial states of buffers) is performed through a series of graphical editors. Each type of box element (e.g., rules, buffer elements, data source messages) has its own structured editor. Figure 4 shows the rule editor with one of the rules from Figure 1 loaded. Note that, as with property specification, most options are provided by menu buttons. Thus, a button to the left of the first condition hides a menu of editing commands which may be applied to that condition (which includes options to delete the condition, add a qualifier (such as a negation), insert a new condition before or after the current condition, or change the condition from a buffer match to some other kind of condition). Similarly, the menu button to the left of "Match Memory" in the first condition allows the selection by menu of the buffer against which the specified term (Production) should be matched. In this (and all) editors, the user's textual input is limited to terms from a general purpose knowledge representation language (which is based on Prolog).

The Execution Model

COGENT's graphical interface maps between the user's representation of a model (expressed in terms of boxes, arrows, properties and rules) and a computationally complete executable representation of the model. COGENT also provides an interface to an execution engine on which the computational representation can be run.

The execution model underlying COGENT is cyclic and based on the parallel operation of subprocesses, with each box operating as a separate subprocess. Communication between

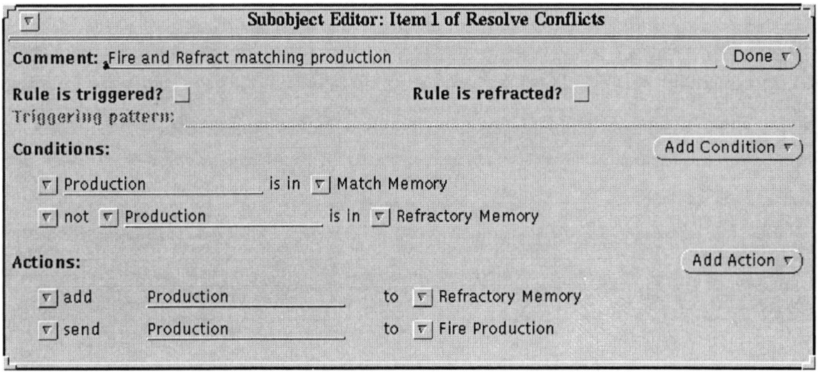

Figure 4: The Rule Editor

subprocesses is effected by message passing. A global data channel is used to store all messages in transit and each processing cycle involves processing and updating this data channel. In brief, each box is considered on every processing cycle. Any messages for that box are removed from the data channel and processed. In the case of buffers, this processing may result in modifications to buffer contents (e.g., the addition or deletion of buffer elements). In the case of processes, messages on the data channel may trigger rules leading to the creation of new messages for processing on the next cycle. Autonomous rules within processes are also checked and, if their conditions are satisfied, the messages corresponding to their actions are added to the message channel for processing on the next cycle. Any messages on the channel destined for data sinks are consumed by copying them to the data sinks' output files and removing them from the channel. Data sources are also checked for the generation of messages, which are moved from the data source onto the global data channel. This processing is repeated for each box (effectively in parallel) on every processing cycle. See Cooper (1995) for more details.

Access to the execution engine is via an interface window (see Figure 5), which provides the user with a series of controls allowing execution of single processing steps, multiple processing steps, complete trials, or blocks of multiple trials.

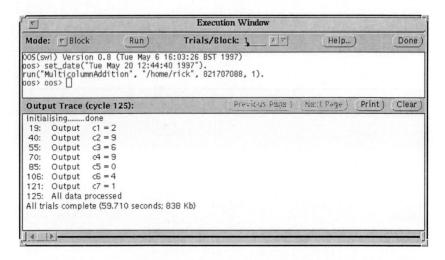

Figure 5: The Interface to the Execution Engine

A complete trial corresponds to the notion of a trial within standard experimental psychology, and a block corresponds to a sequence of trials, also as in standard experimental psychology. The use of language rooted in experimental psychology reflects our commitment to empirical computational research, in which computational experiments and standard laboratory-based experiments go hand in hand. In addition, each function (i.e., step, trial, or block execution) is accessed via menu or panel buttons, eliminating the requirement that the user be familiar with a complex command language and associated syntax.

During model execution, output from data sinks is printed in the lower half of the window shown in Figure 5. The left column of numbers indicates the cycle on which the sink message was received. This is followed by the sink's name and the actual message. Boxes such as buffers and data sources/sinks, whose contents change during processing, may also be opened during model execution to show their evolving contents. (See Figure 6.)

A recent extension to the execution interface is the inclusion of a scripting facility. This facility allows the user to create extended sequences of processing commands. In this way it is

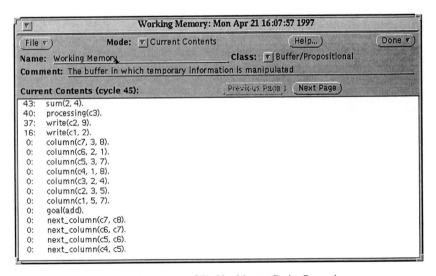

Figure 6: The Contents of Working Memory During Processing

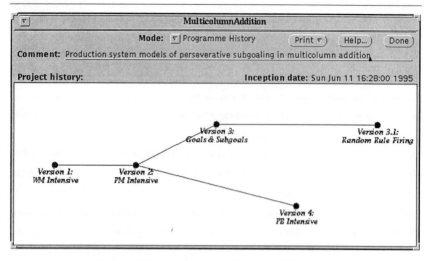

Figure 7: A Research Programme Consisting of Five Models

possible to run, for example, three blocks of 25 trials, each with different decay properties set on some buffer in order to determine the criticality of the decay properties.

Support for Research Programmes

As noted in section 1, we consider model development (i.e., the evolution of models through time) to be an essential element of computational modelling, and further that support for model development should be embodied in the computational tools which support modelling itself.

COGENT supports model development through the concept of a research programme. A COGENT research programme consists of a set of computational models. There is a single "root" model (the first model in the programme), and each other model has a parent model (i.e., the model on which it is based). Multiple models may share a parent, allowing tree-structured programmes. The underlying model of research is that as a programme develops, a number of models will be explored, with possibly many variants on any single model being tested.

This concept of a research programme is supported by COGENT's Research Programme Manager, which provides file management facilities for organising research programmes and a research programme viewer. The viewer (see Figure 7 for an example) provides a graphical depiction of a research programme in terms of a family tree. Each node in the tree corresponds to a model, with the left/right axis being used to represent time. Thus, in Figure 7 the horizontal spacing indicates that work on "Version 4: PB Intensive" began before work on "Version 3.1: Random Rule Firing". This graphical representation provides a simple way of depicting the complexity (or otherwise) of particular research programmes, and the place of individual models within research programmes. Double-clicking on any node in the diagram invokes the above described box/arrow viewing and editing facilities. Individual models may also be copied or deleted.

Modelling Allen Inference: An Extended Example

In this section we provide a more detailed example of the use of COGENT — a model of performance on the Allen inference task as discussed by Berendt & Schlieder (1997). The purpose of this discussion is threefold. Firstly, it provides a concrete demonstration of how COGENT can be used to implement a model that was originally developed by other researchers (Berendt, 1996). Secondly, it links COGENT to models of reasoning (in general) and other work in this volume (in particular). Thirdly, it demonstrates COGENT's flexibility — our initial implementation of the model lead to the development of a new object type (an analogue buffer) which was then incorporated into COGENT's class hierarchy and which is used in the version of the model presented here.

Analogue Buffers

Although the standard buffer type in COGENT is versatile enough for a wide range of models, it does not discriminate between different types of content. Any well-formed Prolog terms can serve as content, and buffer properties such as decay and capacity limitations apply indiscriminately to all types of content. However, there are occasions when psychologists wish to model buffers with content-specific properties.

For example, theories of "mental imagery" typically postulate a specialised imagery store, with properties which apply on the level of metrical representations. There are suggestions (Berendt, 1996) that one such property of the human imagery buffer is a lack of precision in representing location. As a step towards handling such types of models, we have begun developing a specialised buffer type for imagery.

In its present form, the *analogue buffer* is a specialisation of the normal buffer type, which we can call a *propositional buffer*. Analogue buffers impose restrictions on the types of content which they can contain — the only permitted content items are drawn from a restricted set of Prolog structures which specify *graphical objects*, such as points, lines, polygons and circles, in terms of Cartesian co-ordinates. This restriction ensures that each object has a coherent geometrical interpretation, so the contents of the buffer, taken together, specify a picture, which can be displayed using a built-in viewer.

It should be emphasised that there is no "surface" or bitmapped representation like that assumed by Kosslyn (1980), but rather the graphical representation is specified and addressable in terms of significant units. So if conventional buffer decay is enabled, whole objects are lost at once, rather than regions which cut across objects indiscriminately.

Figure 8 shows the Properties view of an analogue buffer. Analogue buffers have all the configurable properties of propositional buffers, as well as *dimensionality* (presently one-dimensional and two-dimensional buffers are supported), *continuity* (which determines whether points can be represented with arbitrary precision or not) and *granularity* (which specifies grain size when continuity is not selected). In addition to these, another two properties permit a kind of imagistic decay, which we can simply call *point movement*. When point movement is selected, points can move on each cycle. Point movement is random but constrained by a *variance* parameter which specifies a normal probability distribution, so if a value of 1 is specified for variance, there is a 0.68 probability that any given point location

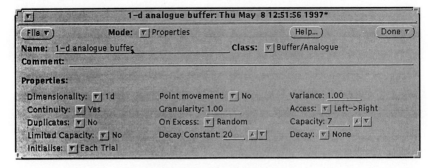

Figure 8: Analogue Buffer Properties

will not deviate by more than 1 scale unit on each cycle. Finally, there are extra access options (in addition to the usual FIFO, LIFO and Random access options) which permit retrieval of items in orders based on their spatial layout: these are Top → Bottom, Bottom → Top, Left → Right and Right → Left. So when Left → Right is selected, the leftmost object is retrieved first, and the rightmost last.

At present the only permissible object types are points, lines, text and markers (in either one-dimensional or two-dimensional buffers), intervals (one-dimensional only), polygons, circles and boxes (two-dimensional only). Each type is represented as a Prolog structure, with two arguments, a name and a geometric specification. In keeping with the restriction that analogue buffer contents must have a graphical interpretation, a special graphical viewer is provided, which depicts the buffer contents pictorially, with a key based on the name fields of the objects in the buffer.

Allen Inferences

A very simple application of COGENT's analogue buffer facility uses a one-dimensional buffer to implement Berendt's model of Allen inferences using metrical representations (Berendt, 1996; Berendt & Schlieder, 1997).

To explain the Allen inference task briefly, participants are presented with inference problems comprising two sentences. Each sentence relates two intervals, one of which is mentioned in both sentences, so the participant's goal is to produce a conclusion about the relation between the remaining two intervals. It is, then, a three-term series task, similar to syllogistic reasoning, but since there is no requirement to produce a conclusion which holds in all possible models of the premises, there is no need for a model revision process as proposed by Johnson-Laird (1983). The set of possible Allen relation types is shown in Figure 9.

For half of the problems, there is only one valid conclusion; however, for the remainder, any of several different configurations of intervals are possible. As Knauff *et al.* (1995) observe, human reasoners show very specific preferences, usually for only one of the possible conclusions to these problems. If one assumes that human reasoners solve these problems via the construction of some kind of mental model (as is assumed here), then this places a strong constraint on the set of acceptable models. Moreover, although many problems can be related by symmetry transformations, human reasoners' responses do not reflect these symmetries. These asymmetry results rule out a class of simple, length-parameterised metrical models, and entail that the model-construction process must be sensitive to the order in which it employs the premises — the representation of a given relation occurring as the second premise will be different from the representation of the same relation occurring as the first premise.

Berendt's solution to the problem takes as its starting point the assumption that the mental imagery system cannot represent position accurately. Reasoners are assumed to be aware of this limitation, so they use strategies to circumvent it, for example, avoiding (where possible) models which represent points as having identical position. By making small length adjustments when representing intervals, it is possible to construct models which are robust with respect to small changes in point location.

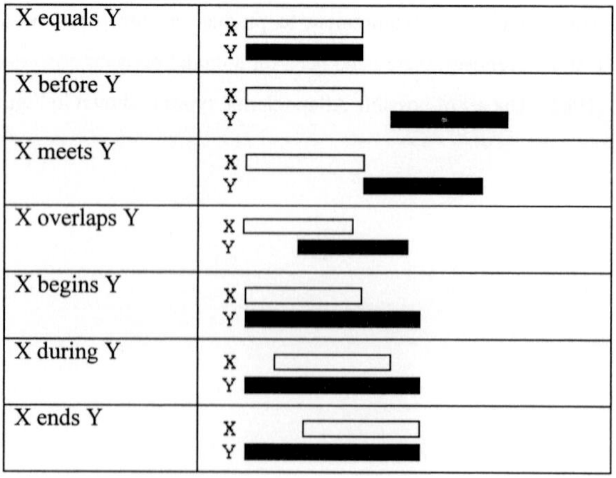

Figure 9: The Set of Allen Relations

Since the length adjustments must be sensitive to the pre-existing contents of the imagery store, relations are represented differently if they occur as the second premise than if they occur as the first, so the model accounts for the empirical asymmetry results in a natural fashion, giving it a high degree of both descriptive and explanatory adequacy.

The COGENT Implementation

The COGENT implementation of Berendt's metrical model of Allen inferencing uses the analogue buffer facilities described above to clarify and simplify the processes assumed to be operating on the imagery store. In order to implement the model, we developed a set of symbolic rules to represent the Allen relations as configurations of metrical intervals in a one-dimensional analogue buffer. A further set of rules reads a conclusion off from the resulting total configuration. Since the order in which relations are constructed is an important variable, model construction must be implemented as a serial process, so there is a third set of rules to

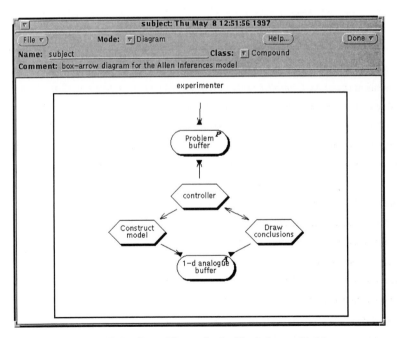

Figure 10: Box/Arrow Diagram for the Allen Inferences Model

schedule the construction and inspection of models.

Figure 10 shows the COGENT box/arrow diagram for the inferencing model. It consists of two buffers (one analogue buffer for the metrical image, and one propositional buffer for linguistic representations of premises and conclusions), as well as three distinct processes (a controller, and two slave systems for constructing and interrogating the metrical image).

After giving an overview of the time-course of problem solution below, we present details of the construction of representations in the analogue buffer, and the drawing of conclusions on the basis of the representation.

Overview of Processing within the Model

A trial begins when the problem sentences are input to the *Problem buffer*. The *Problem buffer* can be considered as the simulation of a sheet of paper, containing the premises, and eventually the conclusion of the problem.

The *Controller* has read/write access to the *Problem buffer*, and waits for the premise pair to appear. When this occurs, a refracted rule (i.e., a rule which fires just once for any instantiation of its variables) annotates the premises, builds a model construction plan and triggers the *Construct model* process to initialise the *1-d analogue buffer*. The process also recurrently triggers itself (by sending itself a message) with the model construction plan. On subsequent cycles the *Controller* reads each annotated premise in turn according to the plan, and sends the premise to the *Construct model* process for integration into the model.

The *Construct model* process contains rules for each forward and inverse Allen relation. To integrate a premise, it selects the interval which forms the subject of the premise and reads the corresponding interval specification from the analogue buffer. It then computes the position and length of the predicate interval, and adds (a representation of) this interval to the *1-d analogue buffer*. The initialisation rule (which is triggered before integration of the first premise) ensures that the presupposition of this process — that the subject interval for the premise is already in the buffer — is satisfied.

Figure 11 shows a graphical view of the contents of *1-d analogue buffer* after both the premises *A before B, B begins C* have been integrated into the model. The underlying representation is shown underneath, illustrating how graphical objects, specified as Prolog structures, are interpreted graphically. Note the COGENT interface uses colour to allow the three intervals to be distinguished.

Because the *Controller* module is operating in parallel according to a construction plan, and the *Construct model* process takes a single cycle to integrate each premise, the *Controller* can predict when the model will be complete and when it should trigger the *Draw conclusion* process (i.e., there is no need for an acknowledgement message from the *Construct model* process back to the *Controller*).

Thus, on the cycle after the second premise is sent to the construction process, the *Controller* triggers a conclusion-drawing process to read off any valid conclusions from the completed model.

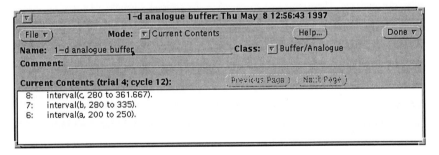

Figure 11: Graphical (above) and Textual (below) Views of Analogue Buffer Contents

Like the construction process, the *Draw conclusions* process contains a rule for each distinct conclusion type. These test for satisfaction of truth conditions relating to point ordering. Each candidate conclusion is tested in parallel, and any rules whose truth conditions are satisfied send the appropriate conclusion back to the controller module.

On receiving any conclusions, the *Controller* writes them to the *Problem buffer*. At this point there are no outstanding triggers, so the model halts.

Model Construction and Inspection Details

To illustrate the use of the analogue buffer, it is worthwhile going into some detail about how the model construction and conclusion drawing processes operate. Figure shows one of the model construction rules. This rule constructs a representation for the "overlaps" relation.

The rule is triggered by receipt of a message consisting of a Prolog structure, `premiss/2`, whose arguments are a list representing the premise and a number representing the construction number (i.e., first or second premise). This number is used for calculating the length adjustment, `epsilon`. When triggered, the antecedent conditions are tested; if they satisfy (in this example they always will), then the production fires, and executes its consequent actions.

The first condition retrieves the interval representation corresponding to the grammatical subject of the premise from the analogue buffer, incidentally instantiating its start- and end-point, `Sx` and `Ex`. These are used to calculate the interval's length, then the `delta_1` constant is retrieved, specifying the distance between the subject and object intervals' start-points. This must be adjusted with the parameter `epsilon`, which is calculated on the basis of the construction number. Having retrieved all relevant parameters, the start- and end-points are calculated, exhausting the conditions. The consequent action adds the new interval, corresponding to the grammatical object of the premise, to the analogue buffer.

Figure shows a conclusion-drawing rule. This rule draws the conclusion *X overlaps Y* if its conditions are satisfied. When triggered with the appropriate trigger pattern, it retrieves the interval representations for `X` and `Y` from the analogue buffer, then tests for the appropriate relations among the intervals' start- and end-points. If these conditions are satisfied, the conclusion is sent to the controller.

It should be evident that minor modifications of each of these rule types suffice to cover all the possible Allen relations, both in the model construction and conclusion drawing processes.

The effect of point movement

Provided the analogue buffer property controlling Point Movement is switched off, the model produces valid conclusions for almost all possible pairs of Allen relations, and the conclusions it produces are the ones that Berendt's model predicts; however, if Point Movement is switched on, the range of valid conclusions produced by the model increases, and more invalid conclusions are also produced, depending on the setting of the Variance parameter.

```
TRIGGER:   premise([X, normal(overlaps), Y], Construction)
IF:        interval(X, Sx to Ex) is in 1-d analogue buffer
           Length is Ex - Sx
           delta_l(Delta)
           epsilon(Construction, E)
           Sy is Sx + Delta + E
           Ey is Sy + Length
THEN:      add interval(Y, Sy to Ey) to 1-d analogue buffer
```

Figure 12: The Construction Rule for *X overlaps Y*

```
TRIGGER:   conclusion([X, normal(overlaps), Y])
IF:        interval(X, Sx to Ex) is in 1-d analogue buffer
           interval(Y, Sy to Ey) is in 1-d analogue buffer
           Sx < Sy
           Sy < Ex
           Ex < Ey
THEN:      send conclusion([X, normal(overlaps), Y]) to controller
```

Figure 13: Rule for Drawing the Conclusion *X overlaps Y*

For example, given the premises *A before B, B before-inverse C*, the model will ordinarily produce only the conclusion *A overlaps-inverse C*. But with Point Movement enabled, the model will sometimes produce alternative conclusions: for example, in a sample of 15 trials with these premises, the model produced *A overlaps-inverse C* 12 times, and the alternative valid conclusion *A during C* 3 times. This illustrates how Berendt's model is robust with respect to point movement, since the overwhelming majority of conclusions were still the predicted ones, but also that occasionally the amount of degradation of the metrical representation is great enough to result in an alternative conclusion.

Unfortunately, space limitations preclude a more thorough analysis of the model's sensitivity to Point Movement and Variance here; see Berendt & Schlieder (1998) for more discussion of the subject.

Discussion of the Allen Inferences Model

In its present form the model implements Berendt's (1996) metrical algorithm quite straightforwardly, for a task in which natural language conclusions are drawn on the basis of natural language presentation of premise pairs. This is similar to the task employed by Knauff *et al.* (1995), except that in that task participants were required to specify their conclusions using a graphical computer interface.

The present implementation draws natural language conclusions since it was constructed with a view to modifying the model to investigate "Figural effects" in the Allen inference task, by analogy with the syllogistic reasoning task (Johnson-Laird, 1983, Johnson-Laird & Bara, 1984, Stenning & Yule, 1997).

In the Knauff *et al.* paradigm, premises are always presented with the same term arrangement (or "Figure") in the premises — notated as ab/bc, where the terms a, b and c denote the three intervals — whereas in the syllogistic reasoning task, four different term arrangements can be used — ab/bc, ba/cb, ab/cb and ba/bc. These Figures are known to affect human reasoners' preferences among valid conclusions in the syllogistic reasoning task — this is known as the Figural effect (Johnson-Laird & Bara, 1984).

It is possible that if Allen inference problems were presented using these Figures that similar effects would be observed. There is a straightforward mapping between the set of problems used by Knauff *et al.* and the set generated from the uninverted Allen relations and the four

Figures: inverting term order in a premise corresponds to transforming the semantics of the relation from normal to inverse.

In terms of the COGENT model, premise integration must be modified by changing the rules in the *Controller* process to be sensitive to the four possible term arrangements in the premises, permitting integration of a semantic inverse of the premise where term order is inverted, but also, permitting integration of the second premise first when appropriate. This manipulation permits new predictions of the model to be derived and tested.

We are currently investigating human performance on a Figural variant of the Allen inferences task, in tandem with the development of appropriate COGENT models.

Other Applications of Analogue Buffers

As well as the Allen Inferences model described here, analogue buffers can be used to model a wide variety of reasoning and mental imagery processes. We anticipate that the one-dimensional analogue buffer will be useful for modelling a range of temporal reasoning and seriation tasks. The two-dimensional buffer type has already been used for a model of mental rotation of random two-dimensional polygons (cf. Cooper, 1975), and for a model of syllogistic reasoning using Euler Circles (cf. Stenning & Yule, 1997).

The analogue buffer is a recent addition to the COGENT object hierarchy, and we anticipate that the range of analogue buffer functionality will be substantially increased in the near future; as well as adding more graphical object types, for example icons, we intend to introduce configurable limits on image size, and modify the handling of buffer access to give greater flexibility in directional scanning. Moreover, it is likely that we will introduce a more general set of configurable buffer properties governing activation levels for buffer contents. Used in an analogue buffer, this should permit construction of imagery models using "fading" decay, a common feature of theories of human imagery processes (e.g. Kosslyn, 1980).

Discussion

The previous sections have described COGENT as a piece of technology and shown how it can be used to implement a model of reasoning. We now return to general issues concerning methodology, COGENT's role within computational modelling, and our future plans for COGENT development.

Methodology

A central theme of work on COGENT has been support for a systematic methodology within cognitive modelling (Cooper *et al.*, 1996). In contrast to empirical psychological work, models are frequently published in a poorly specified form (and hence are not replicable), bear no strict correspondence to the cognitive theory which they are intended to implement, and hide numerous potentially influential implementation decisions. COGENT embodies several methodological principles which alleviate these problems.

Firstly, COGENT achieves a degree of methodological rigour through the strict one-to-one mapping between COGENT boxes and functional models. The graphical interface ensures that a strict correspondence is maintained between the theoretically justified box/arrow diagram and the executable code (which COGENT itself generates). At the box/arrow level, all functional elements must be made fully explicit and there is no scope for hiding implementation detail.

Secondly, by providing a range of standard object classes, COGENT systematises the definitions of standard boxes (e.g., buffers, rule-based processes, networks). This standardisation assists communication by preventing ambiguity and vagueness in specification. At the same time, instances of the standard object classes may be configured for individual applications by a range of parameters which fully determine their behaviour. Thus, modellers cannot ignore or overlook the range of computational properties possible of an instance of any particular object type.

Thirdly, COGENT allows the systematic exploration of parameter spaces so that any dependencies of behaviour on parameter values can be fully determined. If the value of a parameter is found to affect simulated behaviour then clearly that parameter must have some theoretical import. Only if behaviour is independent of a parameter's value can the parameter be said to be irrelevant.

Finally, COGENT provides some support for the development of computational research programmes (paralleling the empirical research programmes common in current cognitive psychology), whereby sequences of successively more adequate models can be explored and developed.

Environments and Architectures

As emphasised in the introduction, COGENT is not an architecture like Soar or ACT-R. It does not, for example, embody any specific assumptions about control processes (see Johnson (1998) for a comparison of the architectural control processes in ACT-R and Soar), and it does not contain any pre-specified learning mechanisms. Thus COGENT imposes minimal theoretical constraints on the modeller. Proponents of architectures have argued that such theoretical constraints are necessary, and furthermore that they are one of the great strengths of the architectural approach (see, for example, Newell, 1990). We are not wholly convinced by these arguments. While there is a place for a well-defined research programme investigating possible architectures of cognition, it frequently appears that architectures are used primarily as programming environments solely in order to lend credibility to an otherwise unrelated cognitive model. The use of an architecture solely for programmatic support is not in itself dangerous, but it promotes the (false) beliefs that a) a model implemented in the architecture is somehow superior to one which is not, even if the two models are based upon the same psychological assumptions; and b) a model implemented in an architecture somehow adds support to the psychological pretensions of that architecture. These issues are discussed in more detail in Cooper & Shallice (1995).

COGENT is not susceptible to these arguments. A model implemented in COGENT truly *is* superior to an equivalent model which is implemented in some other technology precisely because of COGENT's preoccupation with methodological concerns. And a model implemented in COGENT only adds to COGENT's psychological pretensions to the extent that any model stated in box/arrow terms adds to the psychological pretensions of the box/arrow notation. As a general cognitive modelling environment, COGENT does not embody any computational constraints over and above those embodied in the box/arrow notation itself. Our approach is to provide optional facilities, such as the various buffer properties, which facilitate exploration of alternative assumptions about a given theory's implementation, rather than to impose any overarching general theory of cognition upon the theorist.

A model implemented within COGENT gains clarity and succinctness (through the use of the familiar box/arrow notation supplemented with object-oriented concepts and a computationally sound operational semantics) and methodological rigour (through the requirement of a one-to-one mapping between components of box/arrow diagrams and computational mechanisms and the support for computational experiments and research programmes). Thus, COGENT is most appropriate for the development of cognitive models which are not clearly rooted in any specific architecture (either because the model is conceived of independently of any particular architecture or because the modeller is not willing to accept any existing architecture in full). The range of models which have to date been implemented within COGENT — including models of child memory (Barreau, 1997), multi-column addition (Cooper, 1996), medical diagnosis (Fox & Cooper, 1997; Cooper & Fox, 1997), as well as the reasoning models discussed above — are testament to this position.

Future Directions

Development work on COGENT is progressing in three main areas: models; methodology; and software. Much of COGENT's development has been driven by generalising the needs of particular models. The various buffer properties, for example, have arisen through generalisations of buffers required by models of child memory, multi-column arithmetic and decision making, and analogue buffers were introduced when we turned our attention to models of imagery-related tasks. We are actively developing further models (primarily in the areas of reasoning and decision making) to provide motivation and support for further system enhancements.

It is anticipated that further methodological support will be incorporated into COGENT at both the level of individual models and the level of research programmes. At the level of individual models, it is possible to treat the experimental environment as a separate compound box. This allows greater control over the presentation of stimuli and the collection of data from the model in question. We intend to provide further support for this approach in terms of 1) extensions to the scripting language facilities so that computational experiments can be specified in the same terms as standard laboratory based experiments (i.e., by specifying trial order, block order, stimulus randomisation, etc.); 2) extensions to the capabilities of data sinks so that output can be interactively tabulated, graphed and analysed; and, ultimately, 3) capabilities for replacing models by real subjects so that the same experimental environment can be used to collect and maintain both human and computational data. Our goal here is to allow the same input data files to be used for both human and computational experiments, and for both types of experiment to generate output files which may be automatically compared and analysed. This will provide methodological support at the level of research programmes by ensuring a close relation between computational and laboratory work.

Finally, development of the COGENT software is continuing in order to extend the potential user base. The version of COGENT described and shown here is implemented using the XView widget set and requires a Sun Workstation or similar machine running UNIX/X windows. COGENT is also available for the LINUX operating system. A port of the software to the Microsoft® Windows™ environment has recently been completed, and a version compatible with Windows 95/NT is now available.

References

Anderson, J.R. (1993). *Rules of the Mind*. Hillsdale, NJ., Lawrence Erlbaum Associates.

Barreau, S. (1997). *Developmental Constraints on a Theory of Memory*. PhD Thesis. Department of Psychology. University College London.

Berendt, B. (1996). Explaining preferred mental models in Allen inferences with a metrical model of imagery. In G. W. Cottrell (ed.) *Proceedings of the 18th Annual Conference of the Cognitive Science Society.* San Diego, CA. pp. 489–494.

Berendt, B. & Schlieder, C. (1998). Mental model construction in spatial reasoning: A comparison of two computational theories. This volume.

Cooper, L.A. (1975). Mental rotation of random two-dimensional shapes. *Cognitive Psychology*, **7**, 20-43.

Cooper, R. (1995). Towards an object oriented language for cognitive modelling. In J.D. Moore & J.F. Lehman (eds.) *Proceedings of the 17th Annual Conference of the Cognitive Science Society.* Pittsburgh, PA. pp. 556–561.

Cooper, R. (1996). Perseverative subgoaling in production system models of problem solving. In G.W. Cottrell (ed.) *Proceedings of the 18th Annual Conference of the Cognitive Science Society.* San Diego, CA. pp 396–402.

Cooper, R. & Fox, J. (1997). Learning to make decisions under uncertainty: The contribution of qualitative reasoning. In M.G. Shafto & P. Langley (eds.) *Proceedings of the 19th Annual Conference of the Cognitive Science Society.* Stanford, CA. pp 125-130.

Cooper, R. & Fox, J. (in press). COGENT: A visual design environment for cognitive modelling. To appear in *Behavior Research Methods, Instruments and Computers.*

Cooper, R., Fox, J., Farringdon, J. & Shallice, T. (1996). A systematic methodology for cognitive modelling. *Artificial Intelligence*, **85**, 3–44.

Cooper, R. & Shallice, T. (1995). Soar and the case for Unified Theories of Cognition. *Cognition*, **55**, 115–149.

Fox, J. & Cooper, R. (1997). Cognitive processing and knowledge representation in decision making. In R.W. Scholtz & A.C. Zimmer (eds.), *Qualitative Aspects of Decision Making.* Lengerich, Germany, Pabst Science Publishers.

Johnson, T. (1998). A comparison of ACT-R and Soar. This volume.

Johnson-Laird, P.N. (1983). *Mental Models.* Cambridge, UK, Cambridge University Press.

Johnson-Laird, P.N. & Bara, B. (1984). Syllogistic Inference. *Cognition,* **16**, 1–61.

Knauff, M., Rauh, R. & Schlieder, C. (1995). Preferred mental models in qualitative spatial reasoning: A cognitive assessment of Allen's Calculus. In J.D. Moore & J.F. Lehman (eds.) *Proceedings of the 17th Annual Conference of the Cognitive Science Society.* Pittsburgh, PA. pp. 200–205.

Kosslyn, S.M. (1980). *Image and Mind.* Cambridge, MA., Harvard University Press.

Newell, A. (1990). *Unified Theories of Cognition.* Cambridge, MA., Harvard University Press.

Stenning, K. & Yule, P. (1997) Image and language in human reasoning: a syllogistic illustration. *Cognitive Psychology,* **34,** 109-159.

1.4 Reusable models and graphical user interfaces: Realising the potential of a unified theory of cognition

Frank E. Ritter, Randolph M. Jones & Gordon D. Baxter

Abstract

Many results and techniques applicable to human-computer interaction (HCI) have been discovered by using cognitive modelling. However, few of these lessons have been applied to improve the explanation and illustration of cognitive models themselves. We have started to redress this imbalance by developing for a well-known cognitive architecture (Soar) a graphical user interface and reusable models. The general displays in the interface facilitate understanding by showing the models' behaviour in architectural terms; model-specific displays help explicate the concepts and results of the models at the task and knowledge level. We also illustrate how external displays can be used to model interactive behaviours. Developing these models demonstrates that existing models can be replicated and integrated within a unified theory of cognition, and, where appropriate, be made into a high level modelling language that includes learning. Their use in cognitive science courses suggests that the understanding of cognitive models and cognitive modelling could be greatly improved if similar displays and reusable models were more widely available.

Introduction

Cognitive models suffer from usability problems. Few lessons from the field of human-computer interaction (HCI) have been re-applied to increase the understanding of the models themselves, even though many results and techniques in HCI have been discovered using cognitive modelling (John, 1996).

There are also serious problems restricting the reuse of cognitive models. It is probably fair to say that cognitive models are not generally reused, even when they have been created in a cognitive architecture designed to facilitate their reuse. It is also probably fair to say that cognitive models can often be difficult to explain and understand. There are exceptions,[10] but overall cognitive modelling does not have the level of system reuse and visual displays that the artificial intelligence and expert systems communities now take for granted.

We have started to address these related limitations by developing a graphical user interface for a well-known cognitive architecture, Soar (Newell, 1990). We also describe here the replication and extension of several cognitive models, which have been translated into Soar productions and modified to make them easier to understand and to reuse as a high level modelling language. We will further motivate each of these issues and then present how they are achieved with the graphical user interface and the models themselves.

Graphic displays make behaviour visible

Graphic displays are often useful aids when solving problems (Larkin & Simon, 1987). This is also true in cognitive modelling. When a graphical user interface was previously available for Soar (Ritter & Larkin, 1994), it led to some new understandings about Soar models. We found, for example, that few extant models did extensive search *in* problem spaces, but rather did search *through* problem spaces, using relatively few operators in each space. When Soar was reimplemented in C, the graphical user interface was lost. However, the recent inclusion in Soar of the Tcl/Tk scripting and graphics language (Ousterhout, 1994) made it practical to create a new graphical user interface.

General architectural displays and model-specific displays are both necessary. The general displays are useful for developing, understanding, and explaining any model by showing the behaviour in architectural terms. The displays also facilitate an understanding of the architecture itself. Model-specific displays may be necessary for higher level behaviour, such as specific knowledge level (Newell, 1982) or task level information.

---

[10] Pearson's Version 2 of the Symbolic Concept Acquisition model and its explanatory displays is an exception that helped inspire this work (available at http://ai.eecs.umich.edu/soar/soar-group.html). Other exceptions include PDP toolkits such as O'Reilly's PDP++ (http://www.cnbc.cmu.edu/PDP++/PDP++.html).

Explicit interfaces support building models of interaction

Support for graphical user interfaces can also encourage cognitive modellers to make explicit the model's task and its representation and interaction with the external environment. An excellent example of this is provided by our reimplementation of Brown and VanLehn's (1980) subtraction model based on repair theory. In the original model, there was a uniform representation of the concepts and knowledge used in the task. This representation included symbols that presumably came from a perceptual process (e.g. the digits and structure of a subtraction problem), internal goals and operators used to solve the problem, and symbols representing intentions that could map onto physical motor commands (e.g. writing down a digit). All of these symbolic representations were lumped together in a way that made the actual inputs and outputs of the task somewhat unclear.

In our reimplementation of the subtraction model, we made a clean division of perception, reasoning, and external action. Although it is not a high-fidelity model of human perception or motor control, it makes explicit the inputs and outputs of the task. It precisely defines when information goes into the reasoning system and what the reasoning system must do with it. For the subtraction task, this means there is a simulated world with a blackboard containing a subtraction problem. There is an explicit focus of attention for the model, which can only perceive the symbols representing a single column at a time (i.e. the simulator only sends the reasoner information about the current focus). There is a precise set of actions the model can use to effect change in the simulated world (scratching out and writing down numbers). In addition, the various parts of the world simulation are represented graphically, so an observer can watch the model solve a problem, see the model's focus of attention and its marking on the blackboard, and generally follow the model's behaviour as if it were a human solving subtraction problems. We have found making other cognitive model's behaviour visible useful as well (e.g. Bass, Baxter, & Ritter, 1995; Jones & Ritter, 1998).

Reusable cognitive models

There are several goals to consider when developing models for reuse. The models should be clear, easy to run, and easy to integrate with other models. Many of these desires are consonant with the call for unified theories of cognition (Newell, 1990).

Competitive argumentation (VanLehn, Brown, & Greeno, 1984) proposes that modellers should know which mechanisms in their model provide the power—which mechanisms lead the model to fit the data. The reuse of cognitive models allows us to extend competitive argumentation and the simple reuse of existing code, by packaging mechanisms as a general explanation of particular patterns of behaviour and for application to other tasks.

Computational modelling of psychological phenomena starts with developing a model that performs the task. This model is then analysed empirically or theoretically in an attempt to explain experimental data relating to the phenomena of interest. The need to develop a computer program—a model—that actually performs the task often forces the designer to make assumptions that do not necessarily contribute to the psychological theory. When these models are reimplemented, however, different design assumptions may be made, and it (hopefully) becomes clearer which parts of the implementation are theoretically important, and which are simply scaffolding. Building reusable models further clarifies these distinctions so that future users of the model can readily see which aspects of the model are meant to be explored. In addition, once the important parts of a model are explicitly identified, they should be more easily reused in further research on cognition.

How Soar supports building reusable models

In order to construct a library of reusable, additive cognitive models, it is necessary to develop the models within a uniform, integrated cognitive architecture. For our current efforts, we used Soar (Newell, 1990), which was explicitly designed as an architecture to model cognition. Soar models behaviour down to the level of deliberate actions that take of the order of hundreds of milliseconds for humans to perform. Because the vast majority of existing models and data are at this time-scale or above, Soar is appropriate. In addition, Soar dictates that all cognitive tasks be viewed as search through problem spaces, stressing the importance of perceptual and internal symbols, operators, and goals.

Soar supports the development of a wide variety of models within a single representation scheme and performance paradigm, so we should also expect it to be of use in reimplementing existing cognitive models. This expectation was realised when the reimplementations of the subtraction model and Able, which serve as example models here, both proved to be relatively straightforward.

Some cognitive models may map less easily onto Soar's assumptions than others. For example, the reasoning paradigms used in the repair theory system in the subtraction model were slightly awkward to implement within Soar. However, rather than viewing such difficulties as a reason not to use Soar, we view them as opportunities to learn more about the explicit claims of the cognitive model and about the power and characteristics of the Soar architecture. If something seems difficult to implement within a uniform architecture, we may question whether it is an important theoretical aspect of the model. If it does seem important, it is worth exploring how Soar might be made to incorporate similar cognitive constraints, or whether such constraints might arise out of Soar's existing principles. For example, behaviour that takes tens of milliseconds (mostly perceptual and motor processes), would most likely be better modelled in some other architecture or would require extending Soar to that level.

Reusing the models presented here

If a unified theory of cognition (such as Soar) is to provide an approach that supports the integration of models (Newell, 1990), then the models have to be reusable. The first step to support this is to make the model and its associated documentation publicly available, which we do.[11] The next step is to implement models in a way that fosters reuse.

Brown and VanLehn's (1980) theory of systematic errors in subtraction problem solving makes it clear that errors may arise from the combination of poorly learning a particular problem-solving strategy together with using a fixed set of mechanisms for repairing knowledge gaps. Reimplementing Brown and VanLehn's model allowed us to make an explicit distinction between the general problem-solving regime and the repair theory. In addition, we built a number of different specific subtraction procedures, which further emphasised the distinction between theories and their parameters (in this case, knowledge of a specific subtraction procedure).

---

[11] The models described here and the graphical user interface are available from "http://www.nottingham.ac.uk/ pub/soar/nottingham/".

The reimplemented subtraction models are useful for understanding subtraction and exploring buggy behaviour. They are particularly useful for examining extensions to Brown and VanLehn's work by studying different subtraction procedures or different repair methods in order to explain the variety of errors that humans exhibit.

Our first reimplementation of Able, from Soar 4 to Soar 6, was not difficult, but the result was not as general as one might want in a utility. We reused Able's principle application mechanism to develop a simple reasoning component that learned as part of a model that performed a simple air traffic control-like task (Bass et al., 1995). The bulk of the effort creating the next version, Able III, the one presented here, went into rewriting Able's general mechanism so that it could be routinely reused in other models of formal domains by adding domain principles. We demonstrate below how we managed to reuse it very quickly to model a simple task.

The subtraction models and Able both serve as educational examples of how the Soar architecture works, and how it can be used to model different types of human behaviour. The displays provided with them are also reusable. The general graphical user interface will be useful to anyone wanting to increase their understanding of Soar or particular Soar models. The displays specific to these models serve as exemplars and can be modified for use with other models. We now describe in detail the interface and then the models.

General Architecture Displays

We have built a graphical user interface for Soar, called the Tcl/Tk Soar Interface (TSI). The TSI consists of a set of general displays that are available as an extension to Soar. The graphical user interface currently runs with the latest Soar releases (7.0.4 and 7.0.5) under Unix, Linux, and MacOS. An interaction console with menus replaces a command line interface, as shown in Figure 1. The current version of Soar allows multiple models (agents) to be run in the same process. The Soar Control Panel (inset) is used for selecting, creating, and running these agents. The ten most commonly used Soar commands (Nichols & Ritter, 1995) are either directly supported by the displays, bound to keystrokes, or on menus. The set of available commands can also be restricted for novices.

The interface includes context-sensitive pop-up menus for inspecting the various memories in Soar. When the mouse is clicked over a string in the console window, the interface determines which type of object is selected (e.g. long-term-memory production rule, short-term-memory attribute, short-term-memory object) and pops up a menu of appropriate options for viewing that object. This interface helps a novice understand the different types of memories in Soar, and allows the experienced user to search for useful information quite rapidly.

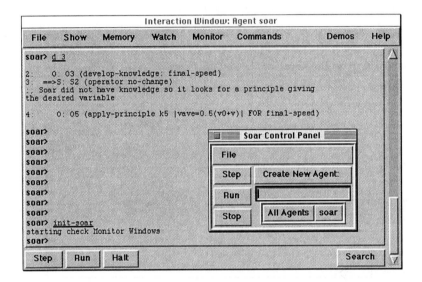

Figure 1: The TSI console window that replaces the simple command line interface. The agent control window ("Soar Control Panel") is overlaid.

A complete Tcl/Tk interpreter is included in the interface, together with methods for the command interpreter to communicate with a Soar agent. Integration with a Tcl/Tk interpreter allows for the fairly rapid prototyping and development of external simulation environments in which to situate a cognitive agent. This assists in clarifying the distinction between cognitive models and their external environments.

There are three optional displays that are continuously updated as the model runs. They show the current goal stack, the rules that are about to fire, and the details on how the next operator will be selected. In each of these displays the user can also bring up a help menu and directly run the model. Figure 2 shows two of these displays. The continuous goal stack display, shown at the top of Figure 2, indicates the order of operator applications and the current goal stack. Users can examine the substructure of objects in the stack using a separate window (not shown). Users can also select how much detail is displayed, printing several layers of substructure by default or examining substructures one level at a time. The continuous match set display, at the bottom of Figure 2, provides a display of the rules that have matched the current working memory and will fire in the next architectural cycle. Users can display the structure of the matching rules in a separate window.

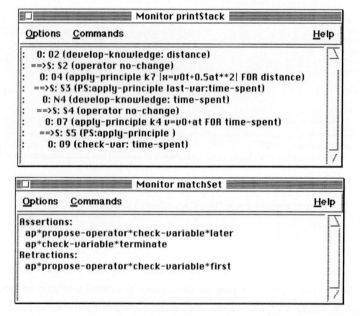

Figure 2: Selectable TSI display windows updated every cycle when they are open, showing the current goal stack (top window) and the rules that will fire next (bottom).

Only anecdotal evidence about the usefulness of these displays is available so far. When an early version was introduced to a psychology class on programming cognitive models, all of the students elected to use the displays rather than the original command line interface. Subsequent classes that have also used the displays have not reported any problems and appear to have learned Soar more readily than previous classes.

A Teaching Tool: The Subtraction Models

Our version of the subtraction model was initially developed for a graduate course on symbolic cognitive modelling at the University of Michigan, and has subsequently been used for undergraduate courses on AI and cognitive science at Bowdoin College and the University of Nottingham. The subtraction systems supplemented theoretical discussion and analysis with hands-on design, implementation, and experimentation with a specific computational model.[12]

The subtraction model was derived from Brown and VanLehn's (1980) paper on repair theory. Brown and VanLehn gathered data from a large number of children learning to do multi-column subtraction. From this data they created a catalogue of the different types of systematic errors (or bugs) that children make when learning to do subtraction and proposed a theory for the source of some of those bugs.

In repair theory, people can exhibit systematic errors (errors that persist due to the same incorrect knowledge or procedure) either because they have an incorrect procedure that still allows them to compute answers or because they consistently use particular repairs to overcome their incorrect knowledge when it leads them into impasses. Later work by VanLehn (1983; 1989) focused on learning and how the incorrect subtraction procedures could be acquired in the first place. In contrast to this work (and the Able model described below), the subtraction model we developed did not address learning.

The basic idea of repair theory is that children initially acquire a correct or nearly correct procedure for solving subtraction problems. Children who have a nearly correct procedure can still solve some problems, but other problems reveal gaps in their knowledge, and so they

---

[12] This model is available from "http://ai.eecs.umich.edu/people/rjones/subtract/index.html".

encounter impasses where they cannot proceed. In the face of these impasses, there are a number of courses of action the children might take to find a solution to the subtraction problem. If a child did not know how to borrow, for example, and came across the task of subtracting 9 from 7 in a particular column, they might decide to subtract 7 from 9 instead. Subtracting 7 from 9 is something the child knows how to do, and it allows them to continue working on the problem. However, it also leads to an incorrect answer. If the child exhibits this particular behaviour systematically, it is a bug that can be used to predict errors that the child would generate on specific problems. A collection of potential repair mechanisms that result in observed bugs are at the heart of Brown and VanLehn's repair theory.

The revised subtraction models

The interface to the revised subtraction model (developed using Tcl/Tk) is shown in Figure 3. This interface allows students to select three different subtraction procedures for analysis. Multiple subtraction procedures were developed to allow cognitive modelling students to explore how different procedures might lead to different types of systematic errors, even given the same set of repair strategies for each procedure. In addition, the three subtraction procedures use the same production rules for most of their representation and differ only in some operator preconditions. This provides one example of the benefits of reusable cognitive models: they can be used to highlight the general aspects of models and to explore alternatives.

The interface also allows students to experiment with the models by deleting operator proposals. When impasses arise, they can select among tied repair operators. The models then give (usually) incorrect answers corresponding to one of the subtraction bugs that Brown and VanLehn identified in children's subtraction procedures.

To implement Brown and VanLehn's subtraction model within Soar, we divided the model into three major components. The first component consists of the general regime for reasoning assumed by Brown and VanLehn: reasoning involves the (possibly conditional) execution of steps in a solution strategy in a forward manner (i.e. there is no internal search and no explicit backward chaining from goals to actions). Some execution steps involve the creation of new goals, which in essence invoke a new procedure that constitutes part of the overall problem-solving strategy. Other execution steps involve explicit intentions in solving the problem, such as writing down a number, scratching out a number, or explicitly shifting focus of attention from one column to another. Our version of the subtraction model interacts with the external blackboard simulator, so the explicit intentions translate directly into output commands sent to the simulator. In response, the simulator changes state and sends a representation of the new state (subject to the model's current focus of attention) back to the reasoning process via a symbolic, perceptual input link.

The second component of the Soar implementation includes the specific set of operators that constitute each particular procedure for solving subtraction problems. This includes knowledge of particular subtraction goals, like "borrow from a column", and knowledge of "primitive" reasoning steps, like "write the difference of two numbers" or "shift focus to the left".

The third component consists of a set of operators that implements the various types of repair strategies Brown and VanLehn propose in repair theory. In the Soar implementation, the repair operators become applicable when execution of the subtraction strategy encounters an impasse (execution cannot proceed) during a problem. Each repair operator makes some change to the internal representation of the problem that (usually) allows the model to continue executing the subtraction procedure. Repairs include operations like skipping a column, swapping numbers in a column, and incrementing a number in a column.

Brown and VanLehn's general reasoning paradigm maps quite nicely onto the existing Soar architecture. In general, reasoning steps in Brown and VanLehn's subtraction model consist of operator preconditions, operator applications, subgoals, and subgoal satisfaction conditions, each of which map directly onto the representation of knowledge and reasoning in Soar. The primary difficulty in implementing Brown and VanLehn's model arose from the fact that their subtraction procedure has script-like portions, which are basically an ordered set of steps to follow, without dependencies between steps. With this reasoning formulation, one can delete an intermediate step without disturbing the flow of processing. Implementing such a script-like mechanism in Soar is not difficult, but there are simpler ways of achieving the same effect of implementing a problem-solving procedure. In addition, we could not ignore this aspect of Brown and VanLehn's reasoning paradigm, because it leads directly to the model's explanation of where systematic problem-solving errors arise.

Brown and VanLehn's subtraction procedure assumes a strictly internal representation for subtraction problems. Thus, even though their procedure can only use information from one column of the problem at a time, the whole of the problem's representation is always accessible in memory. The main impact of this arises when the model traverses columns during a borrow. In Brown and VanLehn's procedure, this occurs by pushing and popping columns on an internal stack. A pop can shift the focus of attention directly back to the appropriate column, and the procedure knows it is done with a traversal when the stack is empty.

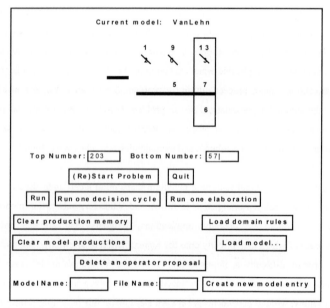

Figure 3: The blackboard display and interface for running the subtraction models.

We built an external environment—a simulated blackboard—for the subtraction model to use. It provides a more realistic representation of how an external display supports children's solutions of subtraction problems on a worksheet. The blackboard used by the model appears at the top of Figure 3. Using the simulated blackboard forced us to make internal intentions and external actions explicit in the model. The blackboard is also useful because it makes the task state visible and allows student modellers to directly observe the model's task level behaviour.

The blackboard restricts the model's access to the information in the current focus column. In order to switch columns, a physical action operator of MOVE-LEFT or MOVE-RIGHT must be executed. In the external environment there is no analogue to an internal stack. Although the model can still use a goal stack to keep track of how many columns have been shifted, the actual shifting has to occur as a physical, external action, with no backtracking possible. This meant our implementation of Brown and VanLehn's subtraction procedure had to be altered slightly. A pseudocode description (in the style used by Brown and VanLehn) appears in Table 1 with the primitive operations (i.e. operations that involve output commands to the blackboard interface) listed in italics. All other operations are internal constructs that effectively just create subgoals. The interested reader should compare this algorithm with that of Brown and VanLehn (1980). Table 2 presents an example trace of the VanLehn procedure on a particular subtraction problem and a buggy trace of the same problem when the step proposing a BORROW-FROM-ZERO is missing from the BORROW-FROM procedure.

Table 1: Brown and VanLehn's subtraction procedure with external focus operations included. Possible application conditions for each step are surrounded by {..}. Thus, {} means "always execute this step". A satisfaction condition of TRUE means to apply only one step of the procedure. FALSE means apply *every* applicable step of the procedure in sequence. Otherwise, the procedure terminates when the satisfaction condition is satisfied.

subtract () SATISFACTION CONDITION: *true*
  {} --> column-sequence

column-sequence () SATISFACTION CONDITION: *TOP IS BLANK*
  {} --> subtract-column
  {} --> move-left
  {} --> column-sequence

              subtract-column () SATISFACTION CONDITION: *ANSWER IS NOT BLANK*
  {BOTTOM IS BLANK} -->   write-answer
  {TOP < BOTTOM} --> borrow
  {} --> difference

borrow () SATISFACTION CONDITION: *false*
  {} --> move-left
  {} --> borrow-from
  {} --> move-right
  {} --> add-10

borrow-from () SATISFACTION CONDITION: *true*
  {TOP IS ZERO} -->   borrow-from-zero
  {} --> decrement

borrow-from-zero () S   : *false*

The basic model was presented to students as the *VanLehn* model. We also provided the students with two alternative subtraction procedures. The first, which we call *Neo-VanLehn*, is the same as the *VanLehn* procedure, except that it eliminates the special BORROW-FROM-ZERO operation. Instead, if the top digit is zero when doing a BORROW-FROM operation, the procedure does a BORROW followed by a DECREMENT. The second alternative procedure has a flatter structure, eliminating both the BORROW-FROM-ZERO and SUBTRACT-COLUMN operations from the *VanLehn* model and collapsing their primitive actions into other operators. This procedure was called *Neches*, because it is loosely based on a subtraction procedure presented by Neches, Langley, and Klahr (1987).

Table 2: A sample trace on the problem 205 - 47 for the VanLehn procedure and a buggy version of it with the BORROW-FROM-ZERO step missing from the BORROW-FROM procedure. Operations in italics represent external actions.

Original VanLehn Procedure

```
SUBTRACT
    COLUMN-SEQUENCE
        SUBTRACT-COLUMN
            BORROW
                MOVE-LEFT
                BORROW-FROM
                    Borrow-From-Zero
                    Write-9
                    MOVE-LEFT
                    BORROW-FROM
                        DECREMENT
                    MOVE-RIGHT
                MOVE-RIGHT
                ADD-10
            DIFFERENCE
        MOVE-LEFT
    COLUMN-SEQUENCE
        SUBTRACT-COLUMN
            DIFFERENCE
        MOVE-LEFT
        COLUMN-SEQUENCE
            SUBTRACT-COLUMN
                WRITE-ANSWER
            MOVE-LEFT

ANSWER: 158
```

Buggy VanLehn Procedure

```
SUBTRACT
    COLUMN-SEQUENCE
        SUBTRACT-COLUMN
            BORROW
                MOVE-LEFT
                BORROW-FROM
                    Decrement
                    IMPASSE:
                    PLEASE CHOOSE A REPAIR
                    1. DEMEMOIZE
                    2. INCREMENT
                    3. WRITE-9
                    4. ADD-10
                    5. REPAIR-QUIT
                    6. REPAIR-SKIP
                    7. REPAIR-SWAP
                    CHOICE: 3
                    WRITE-9
                MOVE-RIGHT
                ADD-10
            DIFFERENCE
        MOVE-LEFT
    COLUMN-SEQUENCE
        SUBTRACT-COLUMN
            DIFFERENCE
        MOVE-LEFT
        COLUMN-SEQUENCE
            SUBTRACT-COLUMN
                WRITE-ANSWER

ANSWER: 258
```

How student modellers used and extended these models

For a cognitive modelling course at the University of Michigan, the students read Brown and VanLehn's (1980) paper and a paper on Soar, and attended an hour-long tutorial on Soar. They were then shown how to use the subtraction interface. In addition, they were given descriptions of the three subtraction procedures and the repair strategies we implemented using Soar. The students divided into groups of two or three (each including one person already familiar with Soar), and were allowed two weeks to complete the assignment shown in Table 3.

Table 3: Task given to students working with the subtraction models.

1. Examine two of the provided subtraction procedures and try to identify about ten of Brown and VanLehn's bugs that could arise from each procedure. Make a list of the predicted bugs, then run the system and try to generate the bugs with appropriate deletions of operator proposals and use of repair strategies.

2. Find a way to generate a few bugs that the models presented by Brown and VanLehn (1980) could not generate. This could be done either by implementing a new procedure for doing subtraction, or by developing and implementing a new repair strategy (or a combination of the two). Demonstrate each of the new bugs with the newly implemented procedure and/or repair.

3. Write a report on the findings in steps 1 and 2, and give us feedback on the overall project.

The results of the project were an unqualified success. Every group completed the first part of the project, with no two groups generating the same set of bugs. For the second part, each group came up with a unique solution. Three groups created new subtraction procedures. One of the new procedures was the subtraction procedure taught to a group member who grew up in India. In this procedure, instead of decrementing the top digit of a column for a borrow, one increments the bottom digit. The other new procedure was designed to be an "anytime algorithm" for subtraction, basically working the problem from left to right instead of right to left. The third group modified the VanLehn procedure to treat borrowing into zero as a special case, allowing this to become a point at which bugs could occur. Another group focused on what new bugs could be generated if some of the operators were actually changed rather than simply deleted. Finally, one group explored the use of some new, rather specific repair strategies, which seemed necessary for generating some of the trickier bugs. All of the groups were able to generate bugs that were found in Brown and VanLehn's catalogue of bugs, but that were not generated by Brown and VanLehn's model.

All of the students clearly improved their understanding of Brown and VanLehn's work, and gained some insight into the internal workings of Soar. They also appeared to gain an increased appreciation of the design and analysis of computational models of human processing. The project provided an excellent complement to the theoretical frameworks being discussed in class. Students were excited about the ability to combine different procedures and techniques in order to increase the coverage of bugs discovered by Brown and

VanLehn. The exercise suggested that a similar interface could be used to analyse a number of different subtraction procedures, which combined may be able to generate a larger number of the bugs.

A Rule Learning Utility: Able III

Able III is a substantially revised version of Levy's Able-Soar, Jr. (Levy, 1991). As part of the revision, the code was substantially updated and documented. The model was extended to cover more problems, and we created graphic displays to illustrate its specific behaviours. Most importantly, we modified Able's principle application mechanism so that it can be used as a building block for other models.

The initial Able model and how it works

Able is a model of physics problem solving (Larkin, 1981; Larkin, McDermott, Simon, & Simon, 1980b). Able's predictions at the level of applying physics principles have been matched to extensive amounts of protocol data of subjects solving kinematics problems. Able initially works backward from the target variable(s), using means-ends analysis to find which principles to apply; after learning, it ends up with a more expert behaviour, working forwards from the known variables without search.

Able does not provide as detailed a model of physics problem solving as some more recent models (Elio & Scharf, 1990; Ploetzner, 1995; VanLehn, Jones, & Chi, 1992), for it does not model as much of the complete process, such as learning the principles, setting up the problem, or performing the algebraic manipulations. The novice to expert transition in formal domains like physics is modelled fairly well by Able, albeit on the high level of principle application. The model emphasises how the order of principle application in formal domains changes with practice.

Able was first written as two related models: ME to simulate novice physics problem solvers (barely able); and KD to simulate expert problem solvers (more able) in kinematics (Larkin et al., 1980b) and fluid statics (Larkin & Simon, 1981). These models matched problem solving protocols very well. The models were later unified by a chunking mechanism that allowed the model to learn while solving problems, thereby showing how the novice model could become an expert model through practice (Larkin, 1981). This unified Able model was translated by Levy (1991) into the Able-Soar, Jr. model that ran in Soar 4. His translation suggests that Able's learning mechanism was essentially the chunking mechanism in Soar (Newell, 1990). Levy's work remains an interesting example of how quickly someone can learn and model in Soar, for he wrote it in two weeks. His model is where we started.

The revised Able model

In Able III we have updated Able-Soar, Jr. to run under Soar 7 (Congdon & Laird, 1995). There have been several small changes to the Soar architecture and its implementation since Levy's model, including allowing the reuse of state representations and making the representation of problem spaces more implicit. Some of the rule syntax, firing, and support mechanisms have changed slightly as well.

At the start of a problem, unlike the subtraction models, Able has all the known and unknown variables in its working memory (its top problem solving state). Its problem solving ends when the target variable(s) are known. Also on the top state are the physics principles. Able III has eight principles, such as $F = m a$ and $x = v_0 t + 0.5 a t^2$. These equations are represented in a simple way as sets of variables (e.g. F m and a) because Able only models results at a relatively abstract level, such as if F and m are known, then a would be known as well.

Figure 4 shows the operators and their relationships. After a problem has been retrieved with FETCH-PROBLEM, problem solving proceeds with a top-level operator proposing to solve the problem. DEVELOP-KNOWLEDGE will later implement single inference steps that directly solve the problem, but initially, nothing can be done, and an impasse is noted by the architecture. In this impasse, the target variable is selected as the variable to solve. APPLY-PRINCIPLE operators are proposed to apply each of the principles on the state. There is some fairly powerful heuristic knowledge used to select which APPLY-PRINCIPLE operator to use first. Not all problem solvers necessarily have such heuristics, but all of Larkin's subjects appear to have had them. Operators that apply principles with more known variables are preferred, but more importantly, operators that propose principles including the target variable are highly preferred. Operators that apply principles with the same number of unknowns and relationship to the target are made equivalent. If the model has available additional domain knowledge about which principles to apply first, it could be used here as well.

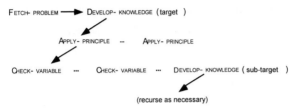

Figure 4: The structure of the operators in Able III. Arrows indicate order of application and relationships in the hierarchy. Ellipses (...) indicate that multiple applications of the previous operator may occur.

Although Able III may know that it needs to apply a particular principle (using APPLY-PRINCIPLE), it may not know initially *how* to apply that principle. However, Able III learns how to apply each principle with experience. Another impasse occurs, and lower level CHECK-VARIABLE operators check each of the variables in the principle. If all variables except the target are known, the target can be derived, and this result is passed up to the higher APPLY-PRINCIPLE operator. If variables other than the target are unknown, DEVELOP-KNOWLEDGE is applied recursively, with the unknown variable as a target. This leads to behaviour that is typical of novices in this domain, working backwards from target variables (Larkin, McDermott, Simon, & Simon, 1980a; Larkin et al., 1980b).

During problem solving, new, learned productions (chunks) are created that encapsulate the essential aspects of the impasse and the result that was used to resolve the impasse. These new rules allow APPLY-PRINCIPLE to be applied atomically when similar circumstances occur. With additional problem solving, because the bottom-most operators must be learned first, the derivation of unknown variables from known variables eventually occurs directly with the DEVELOP-KNOWLEDGE operator.

Learning changes how Able solves problems. With enough practice, fully learned behaviour occurs with the DEVELOP-KNOWLEDGE operator solving problems directly through application of the learned rules, working forward, using the known variables to derive additional known variables. The model changes from being driven in a goal-directed way, applying principles to derive the target variable, to being data-driven, where the known variables are used to directly derive additional known variables.

Practice also drastically decreases Able's problem-solving time. Able III initially takes 27 architectural (decision) cycles to solve a typical problem (number 5) on the first attempt. This time includes time to find the principles to apply, to check each of the variables, and recursively solve for variables where necessary. After practice over 7 trials with the same problem, Able III takes just 2 cycles to solve the problem and does not improve with further practice. The learning curve that is generated for a single problem does not even approximately fit the power law of learning (Rosenbloom & Newell, 1987), but it is difficult to comment further—there are multiple aspects of the task not yet included in the model; the learning curve when computed across multiple problems looks more like typical subject data; and solution times were not reported for the original subjects.

The relative ease with which Able-Soar, Jr. was translated shows that Able was not fundamentally affected by the changes in the Soar architecture in the last five years. While Able's functionality has basically stayed the same (Able-Soar, Jr. solved 13 unique dynamics problems, Able III solves 16), the number of rules has slightly decreased from 51 basic rules (excluding monitoring and problem generating rules) to 48 rules. The rules have not become more complex—the number of clauses and their complexity have both decreased dramatically, from 371 to 223 clauses and from 684 to 477 patterns, respectively. The differences in these rule sets suggest that the syntax for specifying models in Soar has become simpler without substantially changing the architecture, which is indeed what its architects endeavoured to do (Laird, Huffman, & Portelli, 1990).

One of the valid criticisms of Soar suggested by Cooper and Shallice (1995) was that as the architecture was modified, older models must be carried forward for their results to remain valid. This has not typically happened each time the architecture has been released as new software. The Soar community has not been convinced of the need because they understood the changes, and theoretically the changes have nearly always been small with limited impact on existing models. Able is a relatively straightforward model, but the absence of difficulties suggests that the approach Cooper and Shallice put forward to classify changes to an architecture did not correctly classify changes. Many of the changes they noted were changes in the implementation and interface rather then changes in the theory. More complicated models, however, have a greater chance of suffering from changes to the architecture.

Application-specific displays

There are two model-specific displays included with Able III to help explain how its behaviour. The first display, shown in Figure 5, describes the problem Able III is working on, including the text of the physics story problem, the target variables, and the current status of all variables (known or unknown). This display currently only works with the physics variables in Able III.

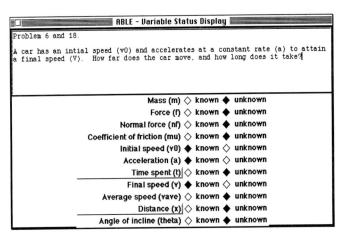

Figure 5: The problem display in Able III, showing the problem (as text in the top pane) and the current status (known/unknown) of the variables. The target variables, Time spent (t) and Distance (x), are in raised text on the screen, which appear here as underlined text.

The second display, shown in Figure 6, indicates the order of principle application. It shows that Able III when it is a novice (really an apprentice, since it knows something) works backward from the target variable. The more expert Able III, after it has solved problems and has nearly doubled its number of rules, does not appear to apply principles at all, but works

103

forward, immediately deriving what is known. Because the display is based on the application of principles, it works with any set of principles loaded into Able III.

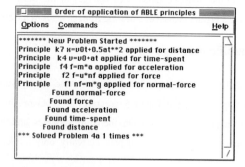

Figure 6: The principle application display in Able III shows the order that principles are applied. With practice on this problem, explicit reference to principles disappears.

Using principles as high level language

Previous work on Able did not treat its principles and their application mechanism as a high level programming language for cognitive models, but they can be used that way. Such reasoning occurs often enough that the principle application mechanism should be available as a general utility. Based on our work it is now straightforward to add new principles to model another domain. Students in cognitive modelling classes at Nottingham, as a single week's homework assignment, are routinely able to create models of problem solving in new domains such as electronics and rotational motion.

New problems can be included by representing their features on the top state. New principles are represented one per production rule. The principle application mechanism in Able III can then demonstrate how unknown problem variables would be derived through principle application. Additional knowledge ordering principle application can be added, but the weak methods of search in Soar and Able III's existing knowledge will otherwise solve the problem if it is solvable.

The principle application mechanism could be used to model novice-expert transitions in other domains, and it provides a way to include routine learning in models. With any set of domain principles, choosing and applying the principles will initially be effortful. With practice, the model's performance will become situation driven and faster. This approach may make it easier to create Soar models by providing a mechanism that more closely resembles the highest conceptual level, the knowledge level (Newell, 1982), and it provides a mechanism for moving from declarative to procedural knowledge.

To test how easy it would be to create a new model using the principle application mechanism, we created and tested in 30 minutes a model that solved a gas physics problem noted as one that should show novice/expert differences (vanSomeren, Barnard, & Sandberg, 1994, p. 14-15). The model consists of three production rules to be added to the existing Able III mechanism—a simple model for a simple problem, but it demonstrated that models can be created quickly.

Difficulties remain with using Able III as a utility, however. The novice-expert transition, which takes well under 100 trials on our problem set, normally takes years of practice. The transition that is modelled—the order in which to apply principles—may be learned this quickly, but the model does not include the full spectrum of knowledge that makes up an expert. The principle application mechanism is also unrealistic in the way it uses working memory. It keeps the problem and all the principles on the top state, which is not appropriate. These flaws should not be seen as reasons to reject the model, but rather clear indications about where it can be improved (Grant, 1962).

Able's novice/expert performance characterisation is similar in some ways to Klein's (1989) widely applied theory of recognition-primed decision making (which might more correctly be called "recognition-guided problem solving in dynamic tasks" because experts typically do not simply make a single decision but a series of decisions based on interaction with the environment). Like Klein's theory, expert Able works forward from known information; its behaviour is based on previous problem solving, and Able does not consider alternative actions. Able is different in that it is spelled out in enough detail to implement some of the structural details of behaviour in a limited area, whereas Klein's theory remains descriptive.

Able was developed to model behaviour in formal domains. So far, Able has only been applied to formal domains: those "involving a considerable amount of rich semantic knowledge but characterised by a set of principles logically sufficient to solve problems in the domain" (Larkin, 1981, p. 311). So, mathematics, physics and sophisticated games (e.g. chess) are formal, whereas biology and English literature are much less so. Whether Klein's domains (e.g. fire fighting) are formal or can be formalised is unclear. The field of cognitive science assumes that they could be, and the attempts to build expert systems in these areas are consistent with that belief. Able III suggests that it may be possible to create a wide range of cognitive models that start to explain novice/expert differences through models that improve through performing tasks.

Summary

The models presented here as exemplars suggest two useful and eventually necessary steps in creating cognitive models. The first addition is that models and architectures should routinely include graphic displays. The general displays presented here will be useful when developing any Soar model because they make the architectural behaviour visibly explicit. The utility of the specific, knowledge level displays suggests that similar displays should be provided for other models. Both types of displays may also provide suggestions about useful displays for other architectures.

The displays have once more told us something about Soar. Soar proposes that there are three levels of theoretical interest: the knowledge level, the problem space level, and the symbolic or implementation level (Newell, 1990). Implementing the TSI has emphasised that the problem-space level does not explicitly exist in the code that makes up Soar models—it is an emergent feature arising from production firings. Creating a new interface has highlighted this—there are numerous commands to manipulate productions but few commands to manipulate problem space objects to be included in the interface. A graphical user interface helps modellers to visualise each of these three levels and encourages us to support the higher levels more directly. We have already included a facility to allow users to apply a specified operator. We need to extend the TSI to list objects on the problem space level and to show how often they have been used, as is already provided for productions.

The second addition these exemplars suggest for cognitive modelling is that a powerful way to clarify and resuse a model is to abstract and export its fundamental mechanisms for inclusion in other models, and to do this by working within a cognitive architecture. Here, the principle application mechanism in Able III becomes a utility as a new programming language. This is an important exemplar, for cognitive models as sets of knowledge should be reusable, including their knowledge based mechanisms. The subtraction blackboard and operator implementations provide a similar framework for models of arithmetic. This extends the view of competitive argumentation (VanLehn, Brown, & Greeno, 1984), encouraging one not only to know what gives the model its power, but also to package the mechanism for explanation and reuse. With both models, by providing general mechanisms we have seen that cognitive models can be created more easily and that they can also be extended in interesting ways by relative novices.

We believe that for cognitive modelling to thrive, rather than just survive, more models will have to be developed in the ways we have described. Models must be made easier to understand, easier to extend, and easier to reuse. Packaging models and associated displays as utilities or as high level programming languages within a cognitive architecture provides one way of facilitating this.

Acknowledgements

Initial versions of some of the graphical displays were created by Karl Schwamb. Moritz Baumann, Pete Bibby, Fernand Gobet, and Rolf Ploetzner have provided useful comments. The domain-specific interfaces for the subtraction model were developed with the aid of Peter Wiemer-Hastings. John Laird and Clare Congdon helped design the course assignments for the subtraction model. Support for this work has been provided by the DRA, contract 2024/004, and by the ESRC Centre for Research in Development, Instruction and Training. Any errors remain the fault of the authors, and an acknowledgement here does not constitute an endorsement of this article from those listed.

References

Bass, E. J., Baxter, G. D., & Ritter, F. E. (1995). Using cognitive models to control simulations of complex systems: A generic approach. *AISB Quarterly, 93*, 18-25.

Brown, J. S., & VanLehn, K. (1980). Repair theory: A generative theory of bugs in procedural skills. *Cognitive Science, 4*, 379-426.

Congdon, C. B., & Laird, J. E. (1995). *The Soar user's manual, Version 7*. Ann Arbor, MI: Electrical Engineering and Computer Science Department, U. of Michigan.

Cooper, R., & Shallice, T. (1995). Soar and the case for unified theories of cognition. *Cognition, 55*, 115-149.

Elio, R., & Scharf, P. B. (1990). Modeling novice-to-expert shifts in problem-solving strategy and knowledge organization. *Cognitive Science, 14*(4), 579-639.

Grant, D. A. (1962). Testing the null hypothesis and the strategy and tactics of investigating theoretical models. *Psychological Review, 69*(1), 54-61.

John, B. E. (1996). Cognitive modeling and human computer interaction. In *Proceederings of the First European workshop on Cognitive Modelling*, p. 6-7, Technical report No. 96-39, Forschungsberichte des Fachbereichs Informatik, Technische Universität Berlin.

Jones, G., & Ritter, F. E. (1998). Initial explorations of modifying architectures to simulate cognitive and perceptual development. In *Proceedings of the Second European Conference on Cognitive Modelling*. 44-51. Nottingham: Nottingham University Press.

Klein, G. A. (1989). Recognition-primed decisions. In W. B. Rouse (Ed.), *Advances in man-machine systems research (vol. 5)*. 47-92. Greenwich, CT: JAI.

Laird, J., Huffman, S., & Portelli, M. (1990). Status of NNPSCM and S-support. In T. Johnson (Ed.), *Thirteenth Soar Workshop*. 49-51. The Ohio State University: The Soar Group.

Larkin, J. H. (1981). Enriching formal knowledge: A model for learning to solve textbook physics problems. In J. R. Anderson (Ed.), *Cognitive skills and their acquisition*. 311-334. Hillsdale, NJ: Lawrence Erlbaum Associates.

Larkin, J. H., McDermott, J., Simon, D. P., & Simon, H. A. (1980a). Expert and novice performance in solving physics problems. *Science, 208*, 1335-1342.

Larkin, J. H., McDermott, J., Simon, D. P., & Simon, H. A. (1980b). Models of competence in solving physics problems. *Cognitive Science, 4*, 317-345.

Larkin, J. H., & Simon, H. A. (1981). Learning through growth of skill in mental modeling. In H. A. Simon (Ed.), *Models of thought II*. 134-144. New Haven, CT: Yale University Press.

Larkin, J. H., & Simon, H. A. (1987). Why a diagram is (sometimes) worth ten thousand words. *Cognitive Science, 11*(1), 65-99.

Levy, B. (1991). Able Soar, Jr: A model for learning to solve kinematic problems. Unpublished.

Neches, R., Langley, P., & Klahr, D. (1987). Learning, development, and production systems. In D. Klahr, P. Langley, & R. Neches (Eds.), *Production system models of learning and development.* 1-53. Cambridge, MA: MIT Press.

Newell, A. (1982). The knowledge level. *Artificial Intelligence*, 18, 87-127.

Newell, A. (1990). *Unified theories of cognition.* Cambridge, MA: Harvard University Press.

Nichols, S., & Ritter, F. E. (1995). A theoretically motivated tool for automatically generating command aliases. In *Proceedings of the CHI '95 Conference on Human Factors in Computer Systems.* 393-400. New York, NY: ACM.

Ousterhout, J. K. (1994). *Tcl and the Tk Toolkit.* Reading, MA: Addison-Wesley.

Ploetzner, R. (1995). The construction of coordination of complementary problem representations in physics. *J. of Artificial Intelligence in Education, 6*(2/3), 203-238.

Ritter, F. E., & Larkin, J. H. (1994). Using process models to summarize sequences of human actions. *Human-Computer Interaction, 9*(3&4), 345-383.

Rosenbloom, P. S., & Newell, A. (1987). Learning by chunking, a production system model of practice. In D. Klahr, P. Langley, & R. Neches (Eds.), *Production system models of learning and development.* 221-286. Cambridge, MA: MIT Press.

VanLehn, K. (1983). Human skill acquisition: Theory, model and psychological validation. *Proceedings of the Third National Conference on Artificial Intelligence.* 420-423. Cambridge, MA: MIT Press.

VanLehn, K. (1989). *Mind bugs: The origins of procedural misconceptions.* Cambridge, MA: MIT Press.

VanLehn, K., Brown, J. S., & Greeno, J. (1984). Competitive argumentation in computational theories of cognition. In W. Kintsch, J. R. Miller, & P. G. Polson (Eds.), *Methods and tactics in cognitive science.* 235-262. Hillsdale, NJ: Lawrence Erlbaum Associates, Inc.

VanLehn, K., Jones, R. M., & Chi, M. T. H. (1992). A model of the self-explanation effect. *Journal of the Learning Sciences, 2*, 1-59.

VanSomeren, M. W., Barnard, Y. F., & Sandberg, J. A. C. (1994). *The Think Aloud Method: A practical guide to modelling cognitive processes.* London/San Diego: Academic Press.

1.5 Modelling Motivation and Action Control in Cognitive Systems

Gerhard Strube

The traditional way to define – and model – cognition, from the mid-fifties onward, has been to focus on *deliberation*, i.e., on those inferential processes that operate on well-defined symbolic mental representations in order to get a task accomplished that would require intelligence for human beings to solve. Consequently, AI programs, as well as computer models of psychological processes, were largely confined to a world of symbols. Only a few projects attempted to overcome these limitations and take a step towards more realistic interaction, such as Winograd's famous SHRDLU (Winograd, 1972). Still, the seminal work accomplished in GPS (Newell & Simon, 1963) and STRIPS (Fikes & Nilsson, 1971) continues to be the anchor point for most of AI and cognitive science alike. Recent years, however, have brought a veritable paradigm shift: interaction with the 'real' environment – physical, or human users, or other 'agents' – has been brought to the fore; and 'situatedness' (Suchman, 1987) and the ability for communication and co-operation (as in distributed AI) have become important criteria. The basic nature of biological cognitive systems, including humans, has been recognised (and redefined) as autonomous and situated. Cognitive systems, in short, are understood as agents existing in the real world (Strube, 1996).

The recent shift of paradigm has important consequences for cognitive modelling. The most important aspect for AI is that in the real world unforeseeable things happen all the time. Therefore, instead of pre-programming solutions to every possible conflict into large programs committed to one single top goal, AI programmers now have to think about programming policies for negotiating goal conflicts, or impasses in action control, and about implementing facilities for learning from experience. In the words of Pattie Maes (1991a, p. 51):

> *A complex agent has complex goals. First of all, it has many goals, second the goals it has vary over time, third they have different priorities, and fourth their priorities vary according to their interrelationships. So it is definitely important that an autonomous agent can mediate among goals and handle their conflicts or even try to exploit their interrelationships to optimize their achievement over time.*

The most important consequence for cognitive modelling is that we will never understand the adaptive and flexible behaviour of biological cognitive systems if we continue to play down or plainly ignore motivational aspects and the way they interact with cognition. But for deploying AI technology in natural, and hence, dynamic environments, we must consider actions and action control in (natural or technical) cognitive systems as well. This implies that the behaviour and the architecture of the whole system (and at least of parts of its environment) have to be taken into account, not just some domain of expert knowledge and rules for inference and heuristic search. Practically all cognitive models, even the ambitious 'big' ones, like ACT* (Anderson, 1983) and SOAR (Laird, Newell & Rosenbloom, 1987), have addressed *only one task at a time*. This does not imply that production rule systems could not be used for a wide variety of tasks; indeed, the opposite has been amply demonstrated. But 'application systems' have usually been built in order to model a single task, like solving the Tower-of-Hanoi problem. And they get into trouble whenever a problem requires multiple goals to be handled – goals that cannot be organised into a single goal–sub-goal hierarchy.

In this chapter I propose a diagnosis and a therapy. The diagnosis is that AI, psychology and cognitive science all went up the wrong track when they subscribed unreservedly to the theory of rational decision. My suggested therapy is to realise that deliberation and decision are only a part of what is needed to endow a cognitive system with the capacity for goal management and real-world action control. Cognition, at least in Nature, can exist only in organisms that are able to live without it. In other words, cognition comes as an enhancement to existing mechanisms of action regulation, not as the sole means by which organisms control their behaviour. Therefore, it is necessary to integrate deliberation with automatic and non-cognitive (e.g., physiological or 'reactive') control, and I am going to propose a framework for that, which is inspired by human motivation and action control.

Rational decision

The paradigm of human behaviour as governed by rational decision originated in the forties and permeated the whole field of the psychology of motivation in the course of the ensuing decades. (One could even trace the basic idea back to Pascal in 1662.) Herbert A. Simon, psychologist, economist and one of the founders both of AI and of cognitive science, was

awarded the Nobel prize in 1978 for his work in the fifties on formalising rational choice.
The basic tenet of rational decision theory is that people choose to act so that they maximises
their profits. In psychology, each behavioural alternative is assigned a utility, or (subjective)
valence, V. According to Lewin, Dembo, Festinger and Sears (1944), V equals the sum of the
valences of the possible outcomes of an action, each outcome weighted by its estimated
probability of occurrence:

$$V_r = V_s \cdot P_s + V_f \cdot P_f \ (1)$$

where V_r is the resulting valence of an action, split into valence and probability of success
(index s) and failure (index f). The probabilities add up to 1; the valence for failure is usually
negative. The theory predicts that a subject, when presented with two or more behavioural
alternatives, will compute the valence of each alternative and decide in favour of the action
that will result in the maximal expected valence. Note that the theory was cast from the very
beginning to work in a world of uncertainty: any action can succeed or fail, and in the absence
of objective knowledge about outcome probabilities, the decision has to be based on the
(subjective) estimates. The model thus came to be known as 'risky choice'.

Atkinson (1957) conceived of valence as the product of personal motive strength M (e.g.,
'need achievement') and incentive strength I (e.g., of a task to be performed). The well-known
model by Atkinson and Feather (1966) integrated this view with Lewin et al.'s formula to
define the 'resultant tendency' T as:

$$T_r = M_s \cdot P_s \cdot I_s + M_f \cdot P_f \cdot I_f \ (2)$$

This is the formulation that came to dominate the psychology of motivation for the next
twenty years or so.

Psychological theories of decision, intention, and action control

The risky choice model has been applied with considerable success in the field of
achievement motivation, most notably by the research groups of John Atkinson in the U.S.
and of Heinz Heckhausen in Germany. In the course of this research, many variations and
embellishments of the model were devised (see Kuhl, 1994, for an overview).

For need achievement, the motive strength term M in formula (2) can be regarded as a
personality trait, which means as a stable value over time. This is not the case with other
motives, e.g., hunger, thirst, sleep, sex – needs that generally grow over time of deprivation,
and are lowered by a consumatory act. While this may be one reason that risky choice theory

has not gained much ground in these domains, the main obstacle was that in achievement research, all parameters were measured either by explicit judgements given by the subjects, or by means of a modified version of the Thematic Apperception Test (TAT), which requires subjects to look at a series of pictures and then to tell a short story which the pictures evoke in them. Obviously, these kinds of measures are possible only with human subjects and rely on introspection and, in the case of TAT measures, on interpretation as well.

From about 1980 on, the Heckhausen school focused on the path from decision to action, noting that decision marks a kind of *Rubicon*, before but not after which subjects tend to be open-minded and information-seeking (Heckhausen & Gollwitzer, 1987). Decision leads to the formation of an *intention* to act, and intention in turn may lead to planning before actual action occurs (Gollwitzer, 1993). This usage of the term 'intention' is well compatible to Bratman (1987; 1990), whose insights into the organising powers of intentions (e.g., as sources providing criteria for what is relevant) have met with broad approval in AI. Kuhl (1985) and has shown that there is need to shield ongoing action against competing intentions, at least to some degree, and has suggested augmenting motivation by attention-manipulating action control mechanisms.

Belief, desire, intention: an AI approach to deliberation

Rational choice also permeates AI. For instance the well-known AI textbook by Russell and Norvig (1995) devotes two chapters to utility theory and its derivations. They even make rationality the very foundation of AI, defining it as 'an *ideal* concept of intelligence' (p. 4, authors' italics). What I have introduced above as a cognitive system, Russell and Norvig call a rational agent, but the aims are similar.

One well-known approach to building autonomous agents is the BDI architecture developed by Rao and Georgeff (1991; 1995), where B stands for beliefs, or informational states, D for desires (motivational states), and I for intentions (deliberative states of the agent, with explicit reference to Bratman, 1987). As far as can be seen from the conference papers now available, a BDI system is implemented by decision trees with choice nodes (providing information about utilities or valences) and chance nodes (providing estimated probabilities). In fact the BDI model restates, basically, the assumptions of the risky choice model, albeit without the dynamic assumptions typically made in psychological theories.

Limitations of purely rational approaches

The BDI interpreter (Fig. 1) is an endless loop at the top level of control. Each time the loop is traversed, the agenda is scanned for active goals, from which goals are selected and intentions are generated and then executed. It is only after these complex processes – sometimes it may take quite some time to deliberate options and to execute the one selected for action – that new information from the environment is perceived ('get-new-external-events', which leads to an update of the event-queue). Then goals achieved are dropped, as well as those that proved impossible to achieve.

Had Nature built its creatures according to that specification, scarcely a species would have survived, as far as I understand it. This loop certainly provides too much shelter for ongoing action – urgent needs for incompatible action, e.g., reacting quickly to a warning cry, cannot be fulfilled in a system like that.

```
BDI-interpreter
initialize-state ();
repeat
        options := option-generator (event-queue);
        selected-options := deliberate (options);
        update-intentions (selected-options);
        execute ();
        get-new-external-events ();
        drop-successful-attitudes ();
        drop-impossible-attitudes ();
end repeat
```

Figure 1: BDI interpreter as given in Rao & Georgeff (1995).

The solution to this problem that SOAR provides is to have rules that 'perceive' the state of the world (as far as it is reflected in working memory) in each cycle and, whenever a specialised rule recognises the urgent need for which it was designed, it pushes its goal directly on top of the goal stack. This allows for almost immediate action (say, a few tenths of a second, which seems to be enough even in as complex an application as air combat, according to Tambe et al., 1995). The possible cost is that everything connected with the top goal of the action thus interrupted may be lost, due to the clearing of the (one and only) goal stack available (ibid., p. 30).

It is somewhat depressing to see that obvious weaknesses, as shown in the BDI interpreter loop, are present in modern psychological theories as well. Dörner (1996, p. 343) presents quite a similar flow diagram for action control, in which only after all the processes needed for selecting goals, planning and execution are completed, a procedure is called to check whether the present state of the environment might be dangerous!

In a nutshell, rational choice, planning and execution can just take too long for survival. Even the quick polling procedure that SOAR uses may be too slow for some cases. True interrupts and automatic, non-deliberative control structures are needed in order to come to grips with the real world.

Cognition and levels of control in cognitive systems

Natural cognitive systems are biological organisms, comprising a huge amount of regulation well beneath the level we usually call 'cognitive'. In this respect my views differ markedly from the proposal made by Maturana and Varela (1987) which regards living systems *per se* as cognitive. In fact, many organisms are not cognitive at all. Take an amoeba, for example: it displays genetically built-in behaviour, like retracting a pseudopod (extension vaguely looking like a foot) when pricked with a needle. This kind of behaviour is not modifiable; we may regard it as the effect of a direct coupling between sensors and motor effectors. Although it has been shaped by evolution to be adaptive in general, there is no adaptation on a shorter time-scale (i.e., no learning). It is a simple, non-cognitive system (Figure 2a).

Cognition, as a relatively recent development of evolution, provides adaptive (and hence, indirect) coupling between the sensory and motor sides of an organism. This adaptive, indirect coupling provides for the ability to learn (as demonstrated by conditioning, a procedure that in its simplest variant works even in flatworms), and in higher organisms, the ability to deliberate (Figure 2b).

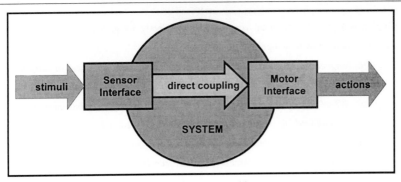

Figure 2a: A simple, non-cognitive system.

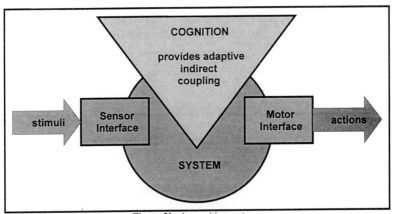

Figure 2b: A cognitive system.

The most important characteristic of a cognitive system with respect to the present discussion, however, is that cognitive control does not just 'take over' from non-cognitive control, but coexists with non-cognitive control in the same organism. This is, of course, also true for humans: the greater part of our bodily functions is controlled by sub-systems (like the one associated with the *nervus vegetativus*) that are non-cognitive and cognitively impenetrable (in the sense of Fodor, 1983). The same holds true for simple motor reflexes, which are usually implemented by only three neurons (one afferent and efferent each, coupled by a spinal interneuron).

Cognition can provide additional adaptability, if properly integrated with the 'automatic' behaviour produced by non-cognitive subsystems:

> 'Well-designed morphology and automatic behavior can produce intelligent behavior if the environmental conditions can be anticipated during the design phase. Where this is not possible, cognitive (planning and reasoning) processes can be employed to respond intelligently to unpredictable environmental changes.' – 'In any complex animal there is likely to be a mixture of autonomous and automaton-like control.' (McFarland & Bösser, 1996, p. 281, p. 286)

An example: Regulation of food intake

Food intake in animals and the regulation of body weight is controlled by feedback loops (Kandel, Schwartz & Jessell, 1995, ch. 33). Indeed, rats have been demonstrated to return to 'normal' weight within about ten days, after two weeks of having either been force-fed, or placed on a restrictive diet (Keesey, Boyle, Kemnitz & Mitchel, 1976). This demonstrates how effective non-cognitive, physiologically implemented feedback can be. So why does it seemingly not work with us? Why do humans so often have problems maintaining a healthy body weight?

It's because cognition interferes. Admittedly, there are cognitive processes that go along well with the physiological regulation of food intake: hunger (a proprioceptive stimulus) lets us know that we should eat, a feeling of satiation signals when we should stop. However there is a host of other cognitive processes that also controls eating. These are called learned, or secondary motives. Excitatory ones, instigating the consummation of food, are, for instance: expectation of tasting good (by the smell and looks of food), memories of former gratifying eating experiences, social norms like 'clean your plate', and in rare cases, other motives like achievement (breaking the Guinness record of sausage-eating within ten minutes). Negative, or inhibitory motives are good manners and other social norms (e.g., against stealing food), desires to stay or become healthy (dieting) and slim (eating less), and sometimes also religious reasons (fasting).

Cognitive control of eating can completely offset the homoeostatic process: people have starved themselves to death for higher reasons. However this is not typical for the interrelation of cognitive and physiological control of bodily functions in general. On the contrary, most vital functions are only marginally influenced by cognitive control (like intake of air, where you can willingly hold your breath a few minutes at most), or not at all, as with blood pressure. The latter example tells us that cognitive control depends on suitable information – in the case of body functions, proprioceptive information – like the feeling of hunger. When proprioceptive stimuli are not available we cannot become aware of our internal state. But when suitable information is made available by special bio-feedback techniques (like visualising blood pressure by measuring it and displaying the value on a computer screen), people can exert cognitive control over their blood pressure.

Non-cognitive control in AI: reactivity

Basic physiological regulation bears some similarity to the 'behaviour-based', or 'reactive' approach to robotics proposed by Brooks (1986; 1991). Rodney Brooks' famous insectoid robots have simple sensomotoric control loops (e.g., for avoiding obstacles). These control loops he calls behaviours. Behaviours may be built on top of each other, leading to a layered control architecture. Ultimately, the research programme calls for integration with high-level layers that implement cognitive functions, but the present state, after a decade of research, is still pretty low-level. Interaction between behaviours typically consists in the higher level behaviour temporarily suppressing the lower level one.

A second open issue with the behaviour-based approach is the 'blending' of behaviours on about the same level, as in guiding a robot around an obstacle (behaviour A) while targeting in some specified direction (behaviour B). The scheme advocated by Konolige and Myers (1996) still calls on the programmer to decide which behaviours might be combined and how. However, on the whole this approach shows at least how non-cognitive control could be modelled.

A three-level framework for action control

In this section, I present a much simplified picture of action control sub-systems in humans and higher animals, which nevertheless may be useful as a theoretical framework to organise future work on modelling both cognitive and non-cognitive management of goals and control of action. The framework consists of three levels of control (see Figure 3), the lowest of which is non-cognitive physiological regulation and reflexes. The highest level is the deliberative one, and in between a second cognitive level is proposed, the level of stimulus-driven associative regulation and activation of action schemata.

The basic level: non-cognitive control

This is the level for cybernetic regulation (usually feedback loops for control of homoeostatic processes), for reflexes (specialised, hard-wired responses to highly specific stimuli), or 'behaviours' in the sense in which the term has now come into use in robotics. We must assume that on this level (which may be partitioned into a considerable number of layers) a multitude of semi-autonomous control systems exist.

Of special interest is the chemical communication used in natural organisms. By means of the circulation of blood in the body of vertebrates, hormones and other substances can be 'broadcast' through the whole system within a few seconds. This system complements communication within the neural system, which is highly specific with regard to sender and receiver. Recently, broadcasting of messages has also been discussed in Distributed AI (DAI), and, of course, control through a blackboard architecture (Hayes-Roth, 1985) might be regarded as a direct forerunner.

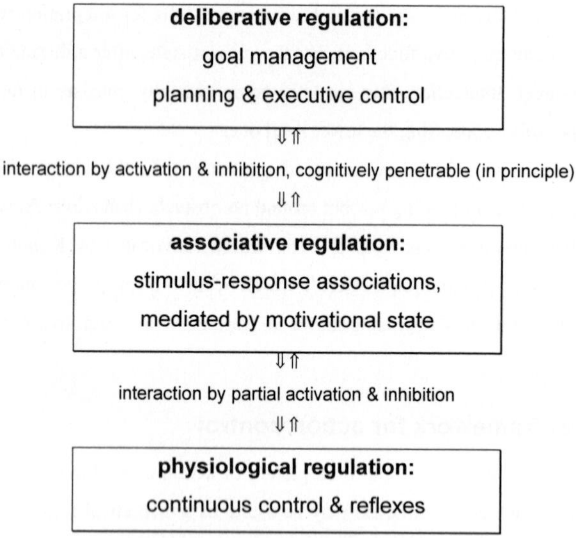

> **deliberative regulation:**
>
> goal management
>
> planning & executive control

⇓ ⇑

interaction by activation & inhibition, cognitively penetrable (in principle)

⇓ ⇑

> **associative regulation:**
>
> stimulus-response associations,
>
> mediated by motivational state

⇓ ⇑

interaction by partial activation & inhibition

⇓ ⇑

> **physiological regulation:**
>
> continuous control & reflexes

Figure 3: Three levels of action control.

The cognitive level proper: deliberation

On this level, conscious decision, planning and action control take place. Many of these processes have already been modelled successfully in the symbol processing paradigm (Newell & Simon, 1976). This means that processes take the form of production rule execution or other sorts of inferential processes (e.g., deduction), operation upon structured mental representations of any sort: frames, propositions, rules, or even depictions (i.e., image-like representations).

Attempts to devise representations of motives and intentions and integrate them with existing architectures, have (as far as I can see) not yet met with success. Kuhl (1983), for example, suggested 'motivation nodes', comprising three elements: (i) a pointer to the 'subject node', apparently something like the self concept, (ii) a pointer to an 'object node' (a plan, or an action), and (iii) a pointer to a 'relation node' such as *want, can,* or *must*. Especially the last characteristic makes these nodes look very similar to what philosophers call propositional attitudes: the subject is in a relation of willing, fearing, believing, etc. something that can be expressed as a logical proposition, e.g. *I want P,* with *P = I talk to Catherine on the phone.* While there is no problem to define representations structured like that, the open issue is how to process them: What makes the difference between *wanting P* (an intention) and, e.g., *believing that P*? How should the representation (and the procedural semantics, say) of *want* be defined so that *wanting P* triggers me to reach for the phone, while *believing* does not?

Within the ACT* framework (Anderson, 1983), Westermann and Heise (1996) have proposed representing motivational aspects in analogy to emotion nodes à la Bower (1981) and Branscombe (1988). This amounts to a purely cognitive representation in semantic memory on the one hand, and special emotion- or motive-related productions on the other. However, it seems that none of these proposals has actually been implemented. Endorsing an intention for immediate action would mean, of course, to trigger a production (or rather, a package of production rules) that normally should lead to actual behaviour. Any conflicts with other, concurrent processes, like stimulus-driven activation of a well-learned behavioural schema (see below), would occur outside the cognitive level. Indeed, we are sometimes surprised that we don't do what we intend to do (Norman, 1981), which testifies to the fact that at least the final stage of conflict resolution in action control is not itself part of the processes occurring on the symbolic-cognitive level. The 'takeover' of non-cognitive or associative control may be registered at the deliberative level as failure to execute what was intended, or may even be missed, as in the case of action slips. The between-level 'brokering' process that ultimately decides which action is executed in case of between-level conflict, is not itself open to conscious inspection (in contrast to goal conflicts within deliberation).

In between: associative control

Associative control links stimuli (which may be quite thoroughly analysed sensory inputs, matched to patterns in memory) with already well-established patterns of (motor) behaviour. This formulation comprises classical as well as operant conditioning (in the latter, actions are linked with evaluated consequences), and also stimulus-driven activation of complex action schemas (as in Norman, 1981). Simple associative control has been observed even in rather primitive animals (even some non-vertebrates), for which it is, in the absence of deliberation, the only cognitive control, usually expressed as a learning mechanism that links species-typical behaviors to novel stimuli. In higher animals, which also have deliberation, associative control seems to serve as an independent means of control, as well as a means of supporting deliberative processes (e.g., by proceduralization of action schemas, and linking them to classes of stimuli for automatic execution).

Action schemas are the product of extended training. Motor programs, in particular, are built in the cerebellum through many repetitions of the movements they contain, i.e., through training (Schmidt, 1975). Within production system approaches, these processes have been modelled as 'knowledge compilation' (Anderson, 1982; 1983), or chunking (Laird, Newell & Rosenbloom, 1987); these models, however, do not provide for a procedural layer beneath that of production rules.

How cognitive is associative control?

Not everyone will share my opinion that this stimulus-driven, associative control should indeed be regarded as cognitive, because it is not clear which kind of mental representations are used by these processes, nor that we should speak of mental representations at all in this context. As I view it, there are two ways out of this dilemma:

Solution 1: The term 'cognition' will be reserved for only those processes that go along with conscious representations (e.g., event representations, as in episodic memory). This usage is consistent with early AI and cognitive science, especially with the Physical Symbol System hypothesis (Newell & Simon, 1976). It is also the usage of McFarland and Bösser (1996), who distinguish between cognition and intelligent behaviour: 'Intelligent behavior is behavior the consequences of which are judged to be intelligent' (p. 1) and: 'Intelligent behavior is not necessarily the result of cognition' (p. 16). But as their ensuing discussion (pp. 17-20) shows, they also feel unsure as to whether associative processes are cognitive or not.

Solution 2, which I advocate here: Learned and modifiable stimulus-response associations should be regarded as cognitive, although we are often not aware of the mental representations used by our own associative processes, and some may not be cognitively penetrable at all. (Remember that Jerry Fodor argued that language processing is cognitively impenetrable as well, but surely no one would hesitate to call language processing a cognitive process.) In addition, modern accounts of conditioning show how much cognition (e.g., stimulus categorisation) is involved (see Mackintosh, 1983). That conditioning happens automatically, i.e. without conscious attention, is true of most undisputedly cognitive processes as well (Norman, 1981). One could also regard 'implementation intentions' *sensu* Gollwitzer (1993) as cognitively constructed associations, as in 'When I pass the campus gate tomorrow, I'll remember to post this letter'.

Discussion

Mental representations and interactions between levels

The central question for an integrated multi-level system concerns between-level interaction. Deliberation, i.e., all that is going on at the symbolic-cognitive level, needs suitable mental representations. I have already mentioned the example of blood pressure: If there is no valid perception (usually, proprioception: a feeling) of a physiological state of affairs, no deliberate control of it will be possible. Generalising from there, we may assume that cognitive control is dependent on the existence of valid mental representations, which are at least potentially conscious.

The existence of action slips testifies to the fact that for successful deliberative control, even that is not enough: We must indeed be actually aware of (all) the relevant action-guiding stimuli and intentions, which means that we must attend to our ongoing action. Without attention, automatic processes (like the execution of a well-practised action schema) may take over (Norman, 1981). Reason (1990, p. 51) emphasises that in the presence of competing action schemas, 'the conflict ... is generally resolved in favour of contextually-appropriate, high-frequency knowledge units'. On the other hand, frequency of action is how action schemas develop, i.e., through repeated (and deliberate!) execution. They are open to wilful control as long as we are aware of the stimulus pattern that elicits their execution. The same holds for automatically acquired stimulus-driven associations that provide a certain readiness for behaviour (e.g., for aggression, or flight). It seems that the mental representation of such readiness is emotion (e.g., anger, or fear). Emotions, in as far as they are a feeling (proprioceptive stimulus), provide a hook for deliberative control to influence – but again, we need to be aware of the emotion. (Emotions are also linked on the associative level to provide behavioural readiness for general ways of action, like aggression, or taking flight. They are probably functional in operant conditioning as well. Their function is not constrained to provide a means for deliberative control.)

Deliberative control is not necessary throughout most of the life of an animal. All basic bodily functions are controlled automatically at the level of physiological regulation. Essential action patterns are innate, many bound to eliciting stimuli. It therefore does not come as a surprise that it is possible to build a floor-cleaning robot, foraging for garbage in a purely non-cognitive way (Brooks, 1986). Cognition starts with acquisition of new stimulus-driven behaviour sequences by learning, which also requires categorical perception and mental representation of stimuli. Deliberation needs all this (especially valid mental representations of the stimulus patterns guiding the other levels of control), and inference (e.g., for planning action sequences).

So far we have considered interactions from the lower levels 'up' to the deliberative one, but what about the other direction? Clearly, symbol structures would be useless, except for (mostly numerical) parameters specifying motor programs (Schmidt, 1975). Action schemas on the associative level provide some local adaptation of their own and would not need parameterisation. Since they also deactivate themselves automatically when their goal has been reached (Norman, 1981), there is only a need for triggering action schemas. Triggering might be provided by the deliberative level as well as it is usually provided automatically by some pattern of external and internal stimuli. Processes controlled at the physiological level, however, tend to be continuous and homoeostatic; there is no need to trigger them. They may be inhibited (and sometimes, activated as well) from the higher levels. So it seems that action control in organisms could do with limited interaction between levels.

AI architectures and the multi-level approach

Traditional AI (planning) has taken to deliberation alone. In recent years, however, several models have focused on the associative level and although exclusively (i.e., not within a multi-level framework). In AI, the best-known approach is that by Maes (1991a, b; 1994). Action schemas are represented as STRIP-like structures, with specifications of propositions to be added or deleted after execution, with precondition lists, etc., but on the other hand, these 'competence modules' interact in a connectionist way, i.e., they have a level of activation, they have activating or inhibiting connections with other units, and by means of a meta-level network (which is not an extra level in the sense discussed here), the strengths of these connections can be adjusted by non-supervised learning procedures.

The most detailed cognitive science model of action control on the associative level up to now has been presented by Balkenius (1995). It follows faithfully the psychological literature on conditioning, and has also been combined with a reactive layer (as in Brook's robots) and implemented in robots that engage in exploration. Thus it exemplifies an action control scheme without deliberation, but with an associative layer on top of purely reactive control.

In AI, at least one multi-level control architecture that combines different ways of action control has been proposed by Hayes-Roth (1995), the AIS (architecture for intelligent systems). AIS distinguishes direct coupling 'through reflex arcs or through perception-action co-ordination processes' from the 'cognition system' (Hayes-Roth, 1995, p. 335). AIS has no counterpart to our intermediate level of associative control, so it is basically cognition (deliberation) and the rest. About the non-cognitive part, however, nothing more can be said other than that which has just been cited, although AIS is described in considerable detail, referring to an application system that monitors patients in an intensive care unit. The 'cognition system' of AIS consists of a blackboard architecture with (unlimited?) parallelism of ongoing activities and some selective influence on the kind and speed of incoming medical measurement data. As a potential model of human action control, therefore, AIS is both too weak (lacking interaction with lower levels of control) and too strong (e.g., allowing the system to execute several attention-demanding activities in parallel, which is beyond human capacity).

AIS contains cognitively interesting ideas for goal management and action control, especially an 'adaptive meta-control strategy' and different modes of control. The meta-control strategy is always given highest priority; thus it can influence the control of all ongoing action. It monitors system resources and 'may also decide to suspend competing activities if a critical problem arises' (p. 333). It may even change the current control mode. Among AIS' several control modes, there is also a 'reactive' mode, in which 'the agent commits in advance to a set of specific notions and conditions for their execution' (p. 343). This sounds like associative control, but not quite, because it is always monitored (i.e. the system cannot be unaware of it), and the commitment is only made in order to save time on decision and planning. Much the same holds for 'what we might call a pure "reflex" mode' (p. 344), which turns out to be identical to reactive mode, with the exception that not all incoming information is monitored, but only sensory information that is relevant to the activity.

Adaptive and flexible control within a purely deliberative approach can be successful, as in the intensive care unit application of AIS. For mobile robots, non-cognitive control will be inevitable, though probably not enough. Reflexes, for instance, are orders of magnitude faster than cognitive control, but in organisms rightly limited to very basic behavioural reactions: since reflexes operate locally, it would soon become extremely difficult to co-ordinate them all (and central co-ordination would destroy their speed advantage). Therefore, their scope must be limited and there must be only a few of them. In order to speed up control, a flexible yet speedy coupling of perceived stimulus patterns and behavioural patterns is very useful: the intermediate, associative level. A step in that direction are knowledge compilation of production rules (Anderson, 1982), or the chunking mechanism provided in SOAR; AIS could integrate such learning facilities as well. Still, it falls short of what is needed to model the associative level in organisms. Associative learning, both classical and operant conditioning, rely on an organism's built-in evaluation of its state (at the physiological level), which may become cognitively available as emotion. Temporal correlation of perceived events or the organism's own actions on the one hand, and the evaluative proprioceptive signal on the other, are sufficient for associative learning and the most efficient means of action control in most organisms. By linking classes of stimulus patterns to actions of arbitrary complexity, associative learning can also make use of the results of learning at the symbolic level (e.g., complex behavioural schemas). No single-level approach, neither a combination of deliberation and 'behaviors', as advocated by Konolige & Myers (1996), can be as powerful as the multi-level control architecture we find in living cognitive systems.

To summarise, there is AI work which is highly relevant to models of action control in cognitive science. Future research in AI and in robotics will certainly prove influential on our view of animal and human motivation. On the other hand, cognitive modelling should not blindly import what works in AI. The acclaim of the BDI approach in traditional AI does not imply that viewing the world as a giant discrete state space will give us the best model of how we, or other animals, perceive it. On the other hand, agent architectures integrating complex action control with learning, as advocated by Maes (1994) and others, may complement contributions from psychology and biology in order to arrive at valid computational models of motivation and action control in organisms.

References

Anderson, J. R. (1982). Acquisition of cognitive skill. *Psychological Review, 89*, 369-406.

Anderson, J. R. (1983). *The Architecture of Cognition.* Cambridge MA: Harvard Univ. Press.

Atkinson, J. W. (1957). Motivational determinants of risk-taking behavior. *Psychological Review, 64*, 359-372.

Atkinson, J. W., & Feather, N. T. (1966). *A Theory of Achievement Motivation.* New York: Wiley.

Balkenius, C. (1995). *Natural Intelligence in Artificial Creatures* (Lund University Cognitive Studies, vol. 37). Lund: Lund University.

Bower, G. H. (1981). Mood and memory. *American Psychologist, 36*, 129-148.

Branscombe, N. R. (1988). Conscious and unconscious processing of affective and cognitive information. In K. Fiedler & J. Forgas (Eds.), *Affect, Cognition and Social Behavior* (pp. 3-24). Lewiston, NY: Hogrefe.

Bratman, M. E. (1987). *Intention, Plans, and Practical Reason.* Cambidge, MA: Harvard Univ. Press.

Bratman, M. E. (1990). What is intention? In P. R. Cohen, J. Morgan & M. E. Pollack (Eds.), *Intentions in Communication* (pp. 15-31). Cambridge, MA: MIT Press.

Brooks, R. A. (1986). A robust layered control system for a mobile robot. *IEEE Journal of Robotics and Automation, 2*, 14-23.

Brooks, R. A. (1991). Intelligence without representation. *Artificial Intelligence, 47*, 139-159.

Dörner, D. (1996). Eine Systemtheorie der Motivation [A system theory of motivation]. In J. Kuhl & H. Heckhausen (Eds.), *Enzyklopädie der Psychologie (Ser. C 4: Motivation, Volition und Handlung*, vol. 4, pp. 329-357). Göttingen: Hogrefe.

Fikes, R. E., & Nilsson, N. J. (1971). STRIPS: a new approach to the application of theorem proving. *Artificial Intelligence, 2*, 189-208.

Fodor, J. A. (1983). *The Modularity of Mind.* Cambridge, MA: MIT Press.

Gollwitzer, P. M. (1993). Goal achievement: The role of intentions. In W. Stroebe & M. Hewstone (Eds.), *European Review of Social Psychology* (pp. 141-185). London: Wiley.

Hayes-Roth, B. (1985). A blackboard architecture for control. *Artificial Intelligence, 26,* 251-321.

Hayes-Roth, B. (1995). An architecture for adaptive intelligent systems. *Artificial Intelligence, 72,* 329-365.

Heckhausen, H., & Gollwitzer, P. M. (1987). Thought contents and cognitive functioning in motivational vs. volitional states of mind. *Motivation and Emotion, 11.*

Kandel, E. R., Schwartz, J. H., & Jessell, T. M. (1995). *Essentials of Neural Science and Behavior.* London: Prentice Hall International.

Keesey, R. E., Boyle, P. C., Kemnitz, J. W., & Mitchel, J. S. (1976). The role of the lateral hypothalamus in determining the body weight set point. In D. Novin, W. Wrywicka & G. A. Bray (Eds.), *Hunger: Basic Mechanisms and Clinical Implications* (pp. 243-255). New York: Raven Press.

Konolige, K., & Myers, K. (1996). *The Saphira Architecture for Autonomous Mobile Robots* (Manuscript, Artificial Intelligence Center). Menlo Park, CA: SRI International.

Kuhl, J. (1983). *Motivation, Konflikt und Handlungskontrolle* [Motivation, conflict, and action control]. Berlin: Springer.

Kuhl, J. (1985). Volitional mediators of cognitive-behavior consistency: Self-regulatory processes and action versus state orientation. In J. Kuhl & J. Beckmann (Eds.), *Action Control: from Cognition to Behavior* (pp. 101-128). Berlin: Springer.

Kuhl, J. (1994). Motivation and volition. In G. d'Ydewalle, R. Bertelson & V. Eelen (Eds.), *Current Advances in Psychological Science: An International Perspective* (Vol. 2, pp. 311-340). Hillsdale, NJ: Erlbaum.

Laird, J. E., Newell, A., & Rosenbloom, P. S. (1987). SOAR: An architecture for general intelligence. *Artificial Intelligence, 33,* 1-64.

Lewin, K., Dembo, T., Festinger, L., & Sears, P. S. (1944). Level of aspiration. In J. McV. Hunt (Ed.), *Handbook of Personality and Behavior Disorders* (pp. 333-378). New York: Ronald.

Mackintosh, N. J. (1983). *Conditioning and Associative Learning.* New York: Oxford Univ. Press.

Maes, P. (1991a). Situated agents can have goals. In P. Maes (Ed.), *Designing Autonomous Agents* (pp. 49-70). Cambridge, MA: MIT Press.

Maes, P. (1991b). *Adaptive Action Selection.* Proceedings of the 13th Annual Conference of the Cognitive Science Society (pp. 108-113). Hillsdale, NJ: Erlbaum.

Maes, P. (1994). Modeling adaptive autonomous agents. *Artificial Life, 1,* 135-162.

Maturana, H., & Varela, F. J. (1987). *The Tree of Knowledge. The Biological Roots of Human Understanding.* Boston: New Science Library.

McFarland, D., & Bösser, T. (1996). *Intelligent Behavior in Animals and Robots.* Cambridge, MA: MIT Press.

Newell, A., & Simon, H. A. (1963). GPS, a program that simulates human thought. In E. A. Feigenbaum & J. Feldman (Eds.), *Computers and Thought* (pp. 279-293). New York: McGraw-Hill.

Newell, A., & Simon, H. A. (1976). Computer science as empirical enquiry: Symbols and search. *Communications of the ACM, 19,* 113-126.

Norman, D. A. (1981). Categorization of action slips. *Psychological Review, 88,* 1-15.

Rao, A. S., & Georgeff, M. P. (1991). Modelling rational agents within a BDI architecture. In J. Allen, R. Fikes & E. Sandewall (Eds.), *Principles of Knowledge Representation and Reasoning* (pp. 473-484). San Mateo, CA: Morgan Kaufmann.

Rao, A. S., & Georgeff, M. P. (1995). BDI agents: from theory to practice. In V. Lesser (Ed.), *Proceedings of the 1st International Conference on Multi-Agent Systems* (IMACS-95), San Francisco, CA (pp. 312-319). Menlo Park, CA: AAAI Press / MIT Press.

Reason, J. (1990). *Human Error.* Cambridge: Cambridge University Press.

Russell, S. J., & Norvig, P. (1995). *Artificial Intelligence. A Modern Approach.* Englewood Cliffs, NJ: Prentice Hall.

Schmidt, R. A. (1975). A schema theory of discrete motor skill learning. *Psychological Review, 82,* 225-260.

Strube, G. (1996). Kognition [Cognition]. In G. Strube et al. (Eds.), *Wörterbuch der Kognitionswissenschaft* (pp. 303-317). Stuttgart: Klett-Cotta.

Suchman, L. A. (1987). *Plans and Situated Actions: The Problem of Human-machine Communication.* New York: Cambridge University Press.

Tambe, M., Johnson, W. L., Jones, R. M., Koss, F., Laird, J. E., Rosenbloom, P. S., & Schwamb, K. (1995). Intelligent agents for interactive simulation environments. *AI Magazine, 16*(1), 15-39.

Westermann, R., & Heise, E. (1996). Motivations- und Kognitionspsychologie: Einige intertheoretische Verbindungen [Motivation and cognition: some connections between psychological theories]. In J. Kuhl & H. Heckhausen (Eds.), *Enzyklopädie der Psychologie* (pp. 275-327). Göttingen: Hogrefe.

Winograd, T. (1972). Understanding natural language. *Cognitive Psychology, 3*(1) complete issue.

Address for correspondence:

Prof. Dr. Gerhard Strube

IIG

Friedrichstr. 50

D-79098 Freiburg

Germany

Tel. (xx49-761) 203–4934 / secr. –4933 / fax –4938

email: strube@cognition.iig.uni-freiburg.de

Section II

Reasoning and Discovery

2.1 Mental model construction in spatial reasoning: A comparison of two computational theories

Christoph Schlieder & Bettina Berendt

Abstract

Evidence suggests that many spatial relational inference tasks are solved by integrating premise information into a single mental representation, the mental model, which is then inspected to find a conclusion. For most tasks, little is known about the representational details of the mental model. Consequently, the relation between mental models and mental images has hardly been discussed. Although, in principle, a mental image could be used as mental model, no conclusive evidence has been provided that this is the strategy reasoners actually adopt. This paper discusses the construction of mental models for a particular spatial relational reasoning task, the three-term series using Allen's interval relations. We have proposed two alternative computational theories for the obtained data: one based on ordinal information only and not committed to a specific modality (Schlieder, 1995), and one based on metrical information, claiming that the mental models used are mental images (Berendt, 1996a). Both explain the data equally well. The present paper compares the two computational theories with respect to their underlying strategies, which aim at optimizing ease of inspection (ordinal) versus stability of representation (metrical).

Spatial relational reasoning

Although cognitive modelling has become an accepted tool in psychological research on reasoning, different computer simulations are rarely based on the same set of empirical data. For instance, the two competing computational accounts for propositional reasoning, one in terms of mental proofs (Rips, 1994) and one within the framework of mental model theory (Johnson-Laird, Byrne & Schaeken, 1992), argue upon decisive issues with evidence from different experiments.

Yet it is generally recognized that a strength of cognitive modelling as a theory buildung tool consists in making psychological theories that describe cognitive processes of a complex dynamic behavior (e.g. reasoning) comparable. Obviously, the results of the comparison are more telling if the theories rely on exactly the same empirical basis. Such cases are rather rare in the literature. We thought a joint presentation of our two alternative cognitive models for spatial relational reasoning could be of interest: both cognitive models account for data coming from an experiment on spatial three-term series described in Knauff, Rauh and Schlieder (1995) and its replication study (Strube et al., 1997).

Interval relations as material for studying relational reasoning

Spatial reasoning has been studied mainly as a special type of relational reasoning. The classical relational reasoning task is the so-called *three-term series task,* which consists of two premises, $X r_1 Y$ and $Y r_2 Z$, together with a conclusion $X r_3 Z$ (Hunter, 1957; DeSoto, London & Handel, 1965; Huttenlocher, 1968; Johnson-Laird, 1972). Premises and conclusion specify relations (r_1, r_2, and r_3) holding between some entities (X, Y, and Z). These tasks come in two versions: as a *verification task,* in which subjects are asked to verify a given conclusion, and as a *generation task,* in which subjects are asked to generate a valid conclusion. *Spatial relational reasoning* is studied by using tasks in which spatial relations appear in the premises and the conclusion. More complex tasks arise if premises are added that relate further entities: four-term series or, generally, n-term series.

Much research has been concerned with one-dimensional spatial relations such as *left-right, in front of-behind, east-west, north-south* (Maki, 1981; Ehrlich & Johnson-Laird, 1982; Mani & Johnson-Laird, 1982; Byrne & Johnson-Laird, 1989). All these relations are understood in a geometrical sense, that is, as relations between idealized point-like entities.

A slightly more complex type of one-dimensional geometrical objects is obtained by considering intervals on a straight line, each interval being defined by a starting point and an end point. Relations holding between intervals have been described in an AI context by James Allen (1983). He proposed a system of 13 relations which encode the relative position of two intervals in a qualitative, that is, non-metrical, way.

Originally, the interval relations had a temporal interpretation, i.e., intervals represented events, but they were soon used in spatial reasoning as well (Güsgen, 1989; Mukerjee & Joe,

1990, Hernández 1994). Fig. 1 illustrates all the situations that can be distinguished with respect to the linear order of the starting points (s_X, s_Y) and end points (e_X, e_Y) of two intervals (X, Y). The point ordering is used to define the relations.

In the AI literature, the interval relations are usually referred to by the symbols shown in the second column of the table. These symbols are mnemonics for the meaning of the relations in a temporal context (e.g. $X s Y$ for X *starts* Y) — with a spatial interpretation, the symbols loose their intuitive appeal. Therefore, we will use the verbalizations of the relations listed in the first column where possible. Note that each relation has an inverse, the *equals* relation being its own inverse. The inverse relation is obtained by exchanging the roles of the X and Y interval in the defining point ordering.

Three-term series can be built using the interval relations. They constitute spatial layout problems in which a configuration of three intervals, X, Y and Z is specified by the interval relations of the premises, $X r_1 Y$ and $Y r_2 Z$. We will consider generation tasks in which the interval relation of the conclusion $X r_3 Z$ is unknown and has to be produced by subjects. Generally speaking, r_1 and r_2 impose a restriction on the relation r_3 that may hold between X and Z. For example, if X *overlaps* Y *from the left* and Y *overlaps* Z *from the left* then the relation between X and Z is restricted to one of the following: X *lies to the left of Z, X touches Z from the left* or X *overlaps Z from the left*. To put it differently, there are only three ways to arrange the starting points and end points of X, Y, and Z in a linear order consistent with the definitions of r_1 and r_2. We will call such point orderings *models of the problem's premises X r_1Y and Y r_2 Z*. In each model a different interval relation r_3 holds between X and Z. Any of these relations is considered a correct answer, a *'conclusion' of the problem*. Thus, there is a one-to-one correspondence between the models of the premises and the conclusions.

The task of finding a conclusion $X r_3 Z$ for given premises $X r_1 Y$ and $Y r_2 Z$, where r_1, r_2, and r_3 are interval relations, is called the *interval three-term series ($X r_1 Y$, $Y r_2 Z$) $\triangleright$ $X r_3 Z$*. A total of 12 x 12 = 144 interval three-term series can be built from the interval relations, not counting series in which the trivial relation *equals* appears in the premises. It turns out that half of the problems have a single model (conclusion).

The remaining 72 multiple-model problems fall into four classes: problems with 3, 5, 9 and 13 models (conclusions). Using interval three-term series as material for studying spatial relational reasoning has several methodological advantages from which we will only mention one: the relation system is much more complex (13 relations) than the ones previously used (2 relations). As a consequence, more three-term series tasks can be formulated yielding a much more constraining set of data for the cognitive modelling. A detailed discussion of methodological issues related to the material is given by Rauh and Schlieder (1997).

verbalization	relation	inverse	diagram	point ordering
X lies to the left of Y	X < Y	Y > X		$s_X < e_X < s_Y < e_Y$
X touches Y on the left	X m Y	Y mi X		$s_X < e_X = s_Y < e_Y$
X overlaps Y from the left	X o Y	Y oi X		$s_X < s_Y < e_X < e_Y$
X lies left-justified in Y	X s Y	Y si X		$s_X = s_Y < e_X < e_Y$
X is contained in Y	X d Y	Y di X		$s_Y < s_X < e_X < e_Y$
X lies right-justified in Y	X f Y	Y fi X		$s_Y < s_X < e_Y = e_X$
X equals Y	X = Y	Y = X		$s_X = s_Y < e_Y = e_X$
X contains Y right-justified	X fi Y	Y f X		$s_X < s_Y < e_Y = e_X$
X contains Y	X di Y	Y d X		$s_X < s_Y < e_Y < e_X$
X contains Y left-justified	X si Y	Y s X		$s_X = s_Y < e_Y < e_X$
X overlaps Y from the right	X oi Y	Y o X		$s_Y < s_X < e_Y < e_X$
X touches Y on the right	X mi Y	Y m X		$s_Y < e_Y = s_X < e_X$
X lies to the right of Y	X > Y	Y < X		$s_Y < e_Y < s_X < e_X$

Figure 1: The 13 interval relations, adapted from Allen (1983).

Evidence for the use of mental models in interval three-term series

Premise integration is a phenomenon observed not only in relational reasoning but also in syllogistic reasoning and reasoning with conditionals. We will, however, restrict our attention to relational reasoning. *Premise integration* occurs in a three-term series task if there is evidence that reasoners do not encode the premises separately in working memory, but rather that they encode instead a unified representation from which it is generally impossible to recover the premises.

Typical evidence for premise integration in spatial relational reasoning is provided by the fact that in an incidental memory task following reasoning, subjects cannot discriminate between the premises and valid conclusions of a spatial four-term series (Mani & Johnson-Laird, 1982). Direct evidence for premise integration in interval four-term series — about 80% model-consistent conclusions among the correct conclusions — has been reported by Rauh and Schlieder (1997).

The theoretical framework best adapted to account for premise integration is mental model theory (Johnson-Laird & Byrne, 1991; Evans, Newstead & Byrne, 1993). Mental model theory assumes that the information conveyed by the premises of a reasoning task is integrated into a representation in visuo-spatial working memory, *the mental model*, which is then inspected in order to draw the conclusion. For interval three-term series it is possible to state precisely what kind of spatial information the mental model will have to encode: namely, a specific linear order on the starting points and end points of the three intervals, in other words, what we called a (logical) model of the problem's premises. However, the mental model is not restricted to encoding just the point ordering. Additional spatial information may also be represented. This would be the case if a mental image of the interval configuration (which specifies the relative size of the intervals and the distances between them) is used as a mental model. As we will see, the two computational theories described below will differ exactly in this respect.

According to mental model theory, two processes are involved in solving an interval three-term series task. First, a model construction process which integrates the premises, and second, a model inspection process which determines the conclusion that holds in the model. As we have seen, certain reasoning tasks allow for the construction of different models (conclusions). Knauff, Rauh, and Schlieder (1995) have conducted an experiment on interval three-term series that provides evidence that not all these mental models play the same role in reasoning. Since the present article is concerned with the problem of specifying the computational model of the model construction process, the experimental method and procedure is described only briefly.

The experiment was devided into three consecutive phases. In the *definition phase* the subjects read definitions of the interval relations. They were also shown pictures with intervals in an appropriate position. A *learning phase* followed in which one-sentence descriptions of premises (e.g. "The red interval lies to the left of the blue interval") were presented, and subjects had to graphically localize one interval with respect to the other on a computer screen. The learning phase lasted as long as it took the subject to reach a certain success criterion. In the *inference phase* of the experiment, subjects had to solve all 144 interval three-term series tasks that can be formed without using the equal relation. Presentation order in the inference phase was random. The premises of the three-term series were displayed verbally using their one-sentence descriptions, and the conclusion had to be characterized graphically by the subjects, just as in the learning phase.

A detailed description of the results is given in the paper describing the experiment. We will only mention the most important finding: as a chi-square test shows, the correct conclusions produced by the subjects do not distribute equally over the different possible correct solutions. There are preferred conclusions, or, since there is a one-to-one correspondence between conclusions and models, there are preferred models. Fig. 2 summarizes the preferences. The preferred conclusion (model) for an interval three-term series with the premises $X r_1 Y$ and $Y r_2 Z$ is found in the row indexed by r_1 and the column indexed by r_2. Three cells of the table contain two relation symbols. In those cases two preferred conclusions with equal answer frequency were found. It is interesting to note that there was no preferred answer which was not a conclusion. In other words, the table of the empirical model preferences is a "simplification" of Allen's original composition table: for the single-model entries (white cells in fig. 2), both tables are identical, and for the multiple-model entries (shaded cells in fig. 2), the table of empirical model preferences selects one out of the several alternative models.

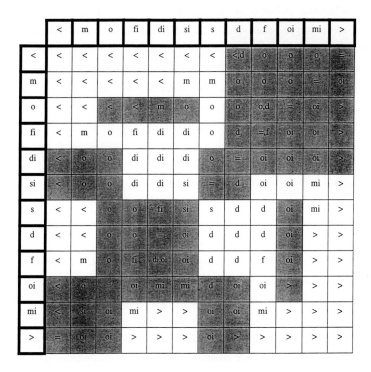

Figure 2: Empirical model preferences, from Knauff, Rauh and Schlieder (1995)

The ordinal computational model

Logically speaking, none of the models of an interval three-term series is more preferable than the others. An explanation for the empirical model preference must be sought in the cognitive processes that construct the mental model. We expect a computational model of the model construction process to reproduce most of the empirical model preferences.

Agreement between theory and data is then easily quantified as the number of empirical model preferences reproduced by the computer simulation.

Order effects in the construction of preferred mental models

A seemingly simple way to explain the preferences consists in assuming that the subjects used some kind of metrical prototypes of the relations to build their mental model. As fig. 3 illustrates, such prototypes would specify the distances by which intervals of unit length standing in a specific interval relation must overlap or separate. We assume that the distance parameters d_1, d_2, d_3, and d_4 are chosen in a way to achieve the best fit with the data. A classical imagery account of spatial reasoning which postulates the existence of pictorial prototypes for relations would be very close to this type of parametrized theory. There are several sources from which the distance information needed to build up mental images could be drawn. It is possible that subjects used the distances in illustrations of the relations presented in the definition phase. We find, however, that no distance-parametrized theory of the described type can give a satisfactory account of the preferences found.

Choosing the parameters in a way that accounts for the preferred model of a specific interval three-term series task has immediate consequences for the predictions for a number of other three-term series. There is a general dependency between three-term series problems due to symmetry. The relevant group of symmetry transformations is known from the analysis of the computational properties of the interval relations (see Ligozat, 1990). This group is generated by two transformations which we will call *reorientation* and *transposition*. When diagrams of interval configurations similar to those in fig. 3 are used as models, the symmetry transformations can be given a simple geometrical interpretation. Reorientation is equivalent to reflection of the diagram about the horizontal axis, and transposition is equivalent to reflection about the vertical axis. For some problems, applying reorientation or transposition amounts to the same thing. That is to say, a maximum of four models can be generated from a model by applying the symmetry transformations.

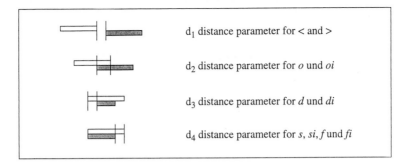

Figure 3: Metrical relation prototypes

As can easily be seen, the distance-parametrized account of model construction predicts symmetry with respect to both symmetry transformations, namely reorientation and transposition. This twofold symmetry is not reflected in the data. The empirical model preferences show the first kind of symmetry, in most cases (4 symmetry violations) but certainly not the second (13 symmetry violations). Fig. 4 illustrates the consequences of the violation of transposition symmetry for the distance-parametrized theory of model construction. Both three-term series are related by transposition symmetry. The model in the first row is constructed by using first the distance d_1 and then d_2. While this model corresponds to the empirical model preference, the model in the fourth row does not. It is built by using the distances in the inverse order: first d_2 then d_1. Obviously, the order in which the distances are processed matters for the empirical model construction process. We will therefore call the remarkably high number of violations of transposition symmetry the order effect.

No matter how the distance parameters are chosen in this computational model, the order effect will never be reproduced. We may therefore say that no such theory can give a satisfactory account of the empircal data. A process with more dynamic behavior is needed to reproduce the effect: the result of integrating a premise into the mental model should somehow depend on the structure of the model that has been built up so far.

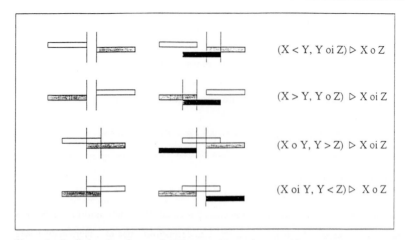

Figure 4: Predictions based on reorientation symmetry and transposition symmetry

Showing only 4 reorientation asymmetries, the empirical model preferences strongly support the assumption that model construction essentially follows the same spatial layout principles in the left-right direction as in the right-left direction. However, any computational model committed to reorientation symmetry will not be able to account for at least 4 of the multiple-model entries in fig. 2, namely those violating the symmetry. But symmetry is not the only distinctive answer pattern found in the data. The 12 three-term series in the diagonal of the table arise from the composition of inverse relations, e.g. *X lies to the left of Y, Y lies to the right of Z*. We find that 9 of these series have the *equal* relation as the preferred conclusion (for the remaining 3 it was the second preferred conclusion). Now such three-term series could have been solved easily without constructing a mental model. Just comparing the linguistic form of the second premise with the linguistic form of the first premise reveals that the relations are inverses in which case *equal* is always a correct solution. Because of the plausibility of this rule-based account, we will not try to explain these preferences by model construction. However, a computational model of the process should also provide correct (but not necessarily the preferred) conclusions. Note that the analysis of symmetry violations in the data and its consequences, the assumption of reorientation symmetry for model construction as well as the assumption of a rule-based strategy for compositions of inverses — all originally proposed by Schlieder (1995) — are shared by both computational theories described in this paper.

Point ordering representation and scanning rules

We have seen that a particular computational model based on metrical information fails to explain the empirical preferences because it does not capture the procedural aspects of model construction which lead to the order effect. Schlieder (1995) formulates an alternative account of the model construction process in terms of a more abstract type of spatial information, namely ordering information. We cannot go into all the details of this theory, but we will state some of its central representational assumptions.

In AI research on qualitative spatial reasoning, it is common practice to distinguish different types of spatial information according to the degree of determination. A relation conveys *metrical information* if it can be defined in terms of metrical invariants, e.g., distances between points. If the relation is already definable in terms of the linear order relation on a finite set of points, we will say that it encodes *ordering information*. (This is just a working definition limited to the one-dimensional case. In this sense, the interval relations encode ordering information about the relative position of intervals. It should be mentioned that the relations are sometimes classified among topological relations. We will not bother with conceptual issues here; but for a general definition of n-dimensional ordering information and a discussion of the differences to topological information, see Schlieder (1996a).

In the ordinal account, the mental model is encoded by means of a *point ordering representation,* in which points are the representational primitives. They occur in two types, as *starting points* and *end points* of intervals. Only the direct succession and the identification of points is represented explicitly. These relations are encoded by two kinds of relational elements, *identification links* and *successor links*. A peculiarity of the representation is the *spatial focus*. Modifications of the representation always occur at the focus position. In order to insert a point, the focus has to be shifted to the appropriate place, an operation which is called *scanning*. Essentially, the computational model describes the sort of scanning which is required to insert the starting point and the end point of the interval for each interval relation (see fig. 5).

Two scanning rules are associated with each of the 12 interval relations used in the experiment (remember that the *equals* relation was not used). The first scanning rule describes how to shift the focus to insert the starting point of the interval and the second the end point of the interval. Some focus shifts are completely determined by the semantics of the relation. For instance, to insert the endpoint of an interval Y with the *relation X touches Y from the left*, the focus has to be shifted to the starting point of the reference interval X. From 24 (2 x 12) scanning rules, 6 are determined in this way by the relation's semantics. The remaining 18 are reduced to 9 scanning rules by postulating a model construction process that is symmetric with respect to reorientation, i.e., a scanning process which works in the left-right direction according to the same rules as in the right-left direction.

Only 9 scanning rules are not determined by the relation's semantics or the symmetry assumption, and only these scanning rules constitute "degrees of freedom" of the ordinal computational model. Each scanning rule shifts the spatial focus across the point order representation until a specific goal point is reached. During scanning, the goal may change; but such changes are local in the sense that they depend only on the point currently focussed. We will illustrate this with a scanning rule called LIN which is used to insert interval end points for the relations *touches from left* and *overlaps from left*. Note that some of the interval relations share scanning rules so that actually only 6 (not 9) scanning rules are specified by the ordinal computational model.

(LIN) *Shift the focus to the right. Stop left of the end point that corresponds*
    to the starting point first encountered during scanning.

The left column of fig. 5 illustrates the kind of scanning and insertion steps that may occur during model construction. Only the integration of the second premise during the three-term series task $(X \text{ oi } Y, Y \text{ m } Z) \triangleright X \text{ o } Z$ (premises: *X overlaps Y from the right, Y touches Z from the left*; preferred conclusion: *X overlaps Z from the left*) using the LIN rule is shown. The semantics of the relation *touches from the left* does not constrain the position of the end point: it could be placed before e_X, incident with e_X or after e_X. Only the last position corresponds to the empirically preferred mental model — it is also the position determined by the LIN rule.

model construction	image generation
◄ s_Y s_X < e_Y < e_X ►	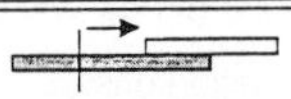
◄ s_Y < s_X e_Y < e_X ►	
◄ s_Y < s_X < e_Y = s_Z e_X ►	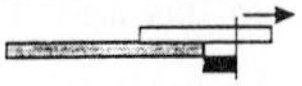
◄ s_Y < s_X < e_Y = s_Z < e_X ►	
◄ s_Y < s_X < e_Y = s_Z < e_X < e_Z ►	

Figure 5: Application of the LIN scanning rule

A scanning rule should yield correct results for all tasks to which it applies. In other words, the LIN rule must handle the relation *touches from the left* as well as the relation *overlaps from the left*. It has to work both if these relations appear in the first premise and if they appear in the second premise of a three-term series (regardless of which relation was processed before). Considering these tight constraints, the agreement of the ordinal computational model with the data can be rated very high. For all 72 single-model three-term series the correct model is constructed. Equally, a correct model is constructed for the 12 three-term series arising from the composition of inverses. Most important, for the remaining 60 multiple-model three-term series, that is for those multiple-model tasks in which we expected that preferred mental models were constructed, the ordinal computational model reproduces 54 of the 60 preferences. Among the 6 cases where theory and data disagree there are 4 violations of reorientation symmetry which in any case the theory could not have reproduced anyway. We may therefore consider the ordinal compuational theory to be descriptively adequate.

The metrical computational model

The fact that there is an ordinal computational model of the data of course does not rule out that imagery is involved in the solution of Allen inferences tasks. Self-reports made by subjects in the experiments indicate that, subjectively, imagery was involved for most subjects. This further motivates a search for a computational model based on imagery.

Imagery could be involved in different ways. It could be a mere epiphenomenon, in which case there is no need for a different computational model. It is also possible that imagery is not causally effective in model construction. As posited by the ordinal computational model, construction could operate on an ordinal point ordering, from which an image is generated, which is then inspected. In this case, the metrical information contained in the image is irrelevant, because once the order of points is fixed, any distance could be assigned to a connection between a pair of consecutive points: since the inspection process only evaluates ordering, its results are invariant with respect to metrical distances.

So in this case too, there is no need for a different computational model. Only if the incremental construction process operates on an image can the metrical information implied by the involvement of imagery become relevant for the computational model.

If these construction processes involve the specification of absolute distances (absolute with respect to the image and/or a fixed reference entity like the length of the preceding interval), a computational model is truly metrical, and different from the ordinal model. It is this third possibility that is considered in the model by Berendt (1996a) that we will describe here. That it is possible to construct mental images using metrical information when the underlying information is a verbal description, has been demonstrated for example by Denis and his colleagues (e.g., Denis et al., 1995). In a metrical model, inspection also operates on the image.

A second requirement for a metrical computational model is that the construction processes be simple. It has been shown above that the simplest metrical computational model, involving only distance parameters, cannot account for the data, because it cannot generate the order effect. So some modification is necessary to obtain the simplest model which can account for the data. The metrical computational model is based on the observation of a side-effect of (constant) distance parameters: the construction process often causes the construction of a new point such that it is equal to an already existing point, when this equality is not necessary. As an example consider fig. 6. The premises "X contains Y justified to the right" (in the following: $X \, fi \, Y$) and "Y is contained in Z" ($Y \, d \, Z$) allow three different models: "X is contained in Z," "X lies left justified in Z," and "X overlaps Z from the left" ($X \, d \, Z$, $X \, s \, Z$, and

$X \ o \ Z$). Constant distance parameters[13] construct $X \ s \ Z$. But this is a very unstable relation: Small inspection errors will make the starting points of X and Z appear different. The other two relations are more stable: they are invariant with respect to small metrical divergences.

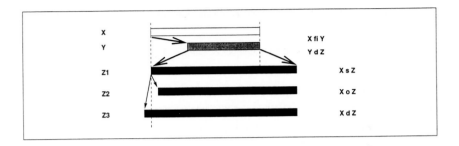

Figure 6: Example of an Allen inference with more than one solution.

This shows the instability of images containing solutions like "lies left-justified in" (s): small metrical divergences between constructed and inspected values change the Allen relation obtained by inspection.

Why should there be small metrical divergences between constructed and inspected values? Our background theory is based on the assumption that mental images are inexact, i.e. that it is not possible to represent and/or process fine details which are sensitive to small metrical changes. This theory of inexactness is corroborated by evidence of a failure to make discoveries in rotated mental images (= find emerging shapes) that are immediately obvious if the same image is rotated in perception (Reisberg & Chambers, 1991; Slezak, 1991). This contrasts with findings that this kind of discovery is possible when different images are used (e.g. Finke & Slayton, 1988). One explanation for these findings is that discoveries are possible if the images are simple enough and impossible otherwise (e.g., Logie, 1995).[14]

---

[13] assuming they are the same for the relations fi and d; different parameters for all relations seem to be forbidden by parsimony of modelling

[14] This explanation is not generally accepted. Other explanations claim that *interpreted* patterns are imaged differently from abstract patterns (see e.g., Slezak, 1991; Logie, 1995). The difference may be related to the relative difficulty of disengaging and re-engaging attention (e.g., Kovordányi, 1996). However, it is difficult to decide this issue given the evidence available so far.

Experiments by Denis, Gonçalvez & Memmi (1995) have demonstrated an inexactness of mental images when these do not have to be transformed (rotated), but inspected (scanned). The reaction time patterns that Denis and his colleagues obtained led them to propose and model that positions in a mental image are represented metrically, but within an uncertainty region around the constructed value. This inexactness could be explained by current theories of mental imagery, which involve a continous re-generation of images (e.g., Kosslyn, 1980, 1994; Logie, 1995).

Inexactness may make it impossible to remember certain details in perceived images and/or to operate on them, which is unavoidable. However, what about images in whose construction people have a certain freedom? We assume that often, imagers use that freedom in a way which takes advantage of the capabilities of the imagery system and which is minimally affected by its limitations — in short, that imagers use strategies to make the most of the resource imagery system.

A straightforward way of dealing with inexactness is to avoid constructing images with the properties that lead to problems, i.e. images in which fine discriminations would be necessary. In other words, image elements should be sufficiently different in localisation to allow the necessary discriminations. This includes an avoidance of unnecessary equalities in image elements (points). We call this the regularization strategy. It will be discussed in more detail in the section on ordinal and metrical positioning strategies below.

So an adequate metrical model should ideally consist of the 'easiest' model plus a modification which generates the right order effect (to account for the data) and generates regularized images (to be in accord with the background theory about inexactness and strategies of dealing with it). Of course, it should also generate correct Allen inferences to account for the data. This was formulated as a model containing:

• *distance parameters* specifying the length of the separation ($<$, $>$), the overlap (o, oi), or the offset (s, si, f, fi, d, di) of the relations. (m and mi must be separated by a distance of 0.) We use 2 such parameters: Δ_n (normal) and Δ_l (large). They are associated with relations depending on whether these are 'shifts' or 'deformations' and they prescribe 'movements' to construct the new interval's starting- and end points (see fig. 7).

• a *correction term* $\varepsilon_{no\text{-}of\text{-}steps}$. This is associated with relations depending on how many relations have been processed before. It leads to slight, progressive adjustments in the movements' lengths. ε_1 is the adjustment made for the first relation, and ε_2 is the adjustment made for the second relation. $\varepsilon_{no\text{-}of\text{-}steps}$ can be defined as determined by only one parameter, ε, and the number of steps taken, *no-of-steps*.

These adjustments generate the order effect, because Allen relations receive a different metrical interpretation depending on when they are processed, i.e. depending on whether they hold between X and Y or between Y and Z. The adjustments also guarantee regularization, because newly generated starting points and end points cannot be equal to existing starting points and end points unless this is specified by relations (*s, si, f, fi, m, mi*). As an example consider fig. 6 again: If X *fi* Y and Y *d* Z, and we moved X's starting point to the right to construct Y and then moved Y's starting point to the left *by the same amount* when we construct Z, we would obtain a singular image with X's Z. By moving left a bit more than we have moved right, we obtain the regular, and empirically preferred, X *d* Z.

It is not clear how to decide on psychological grounds whether movements should be shortened or lengthened. We shall therefore motivate the decision to lengthen them with a computational argument: lengthening leads to an algorithm satisfying the specification given by the data best.

Δ_n, Δ_l, and the $\varepsilon_{no\text{-}of\text{-}steps}$. ($\varepsilon$) are defined relative to the standard interval length, i.e. we assume a scale-invariant imagery process.

The following algorithm and diagram show how the three parameters control the construction.

Process:

insert the first interval as the current-interval at
  standard length into the image at the standard first
  position
no-of-steps := 0
for each premise take
  increment *no-of-steps* by 1
  if the premise relation R marks a shift
   (i.e. if $r \in \{<,m,o,oi,mi,>\}$) then
    $\Delta := \Delta_l$
  else $\Delta := \Delta_n$
  adjust and place a copy of the current-interval
   according to r and Δ, using ε and *no-of-steps*
  insert the obtained interval into the image as the
   next-interval
  current-interval := next-interval
return the Allen relation obtained from reading the
  starting- and end points of the first an the last interval

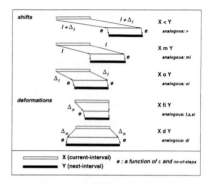

Figure 7: Constructing a new interval: computing starting points and end points from the previous interval, the Allen relation, and the three parameters, lengthening movement.

This theory explains the data well: only 9 empirical model preferences out of 60 multiple-model cases are not explained. As in the ordinal model, compositions of inverses were not considered. Fig. 8. shows the results in detail. The table should be read as follows: If $X\, r_1\, Y$ (r_1 at left end of row i) and $Y\, r_2\, Z$ (r_2 at top of column j), then $X\, r_3\, Z$ (r_3 in cell ij). Cells are empty on the secondary diagonal because compositions of inverses were not considered (like the ordinal model, the metrical model does generate a correct solution however). Other cells are empty if and only if the corresponding compositions have only a single model. Like the ordinal model, the metrical model does generate a correct solution however. For these compositions, the empirically preferred mental models and the preferences generated by the two computational models are all equal and equal to the logically correct single model. The remaining cells correspond to compositions with multiple models. If cells have one entry in fig. 8., this entry is the preferred mental model and at the same time the preference generated by both the ordinal and the metrical computational models. If they have two entries separated by a comma, these are the two models which empirically were approximately equally preferred; and both computational models generate one of these empirical preferences. If cells are subdivided into three entries, the top entry is the empirical preference, the bottom left entry is the preference generated by the ordinal model, and the bottom right entry is the preference generated by the metrical model.

	<	m	o	fi	s	d	di	si	f	oi	mi	>
<						<,d			o / o | <	o	o	
m						o			o	o		oi / > | oi
o			<	< / < | o		o	m / o | o	o	o,d	oi	>	
fi						d				oi	oi	>
s		o	o			fi / o | di				oi		
d		o	o					oi		oi		
di	<	o	o		o			oi	oi	oi	>	
si	<	o	o			d						
f			o				di,oi	oi		oi		
oi	<	o		oi	d / oi | oi	oi	mi / oi | oi	mi / oi | oi	>			
mi	< / < | o		oi		oi	oi						
>		oi	oi		oi / oi | >	>						

Figure 8: Composition tale for preferred models in Allen inferences: If $X\,r_1\,Y\,(r_1$ at left end of row i) and $Y\,r_2\,Z\,(r_2$ at top of column j), then $X\,r_3\,Z\,(r_3$ in cell ij). Table shows compositions with non-unique solutions only, and no compositions of inverses.

We performed a *sensitivity analysis* of the results with respect to variations in the 3 parameters of the algorithm. We defined $errors(\Delta_n,\Delta_l,e_1,e_2)$ to be the number of empirical model preferences not explained by the algorithm for a given choice of distance parameters and correction terms. By specifying the correction term as a function of the parameter e, this can be simplified to a function $errors(\Delta_n,\Delta_l,\varepsilon)$.[15] *errors* yields "--" if for a given choice of parameters non-models are produced, i.e. incorrect solutions.

First, the relevant ranges for the parameters were determined.[16] A simulation was run, and the results were plotted. A composition table can be described which contains the results of

---

[15] The specific functional form is not critical, since it is only a first step to find out parameter ranges, which are then described analytically as depending on e_1 and e_2.

[16] It is straightforward to determine absolute upper and lower bounds for the Δs to ensure that adding/subtracting them from starting- and end points generates the prescribed Allen relations. ε was only examined systematically in the range $(-0.1, 0.1)$ because it is supposed to mark a 'slight adjustment'.

applying the parameter values with the smallest number of errors. This composition table defines a set of inequalities. From these inequalities constraints delimiting the area of best fit were determined analytically. These constraints turned out to be interpretable qualitatively:

$e_2 > e_1 > 0$: Any value below 0 leads to a marked decrease in fit (up to 12 errors more). (A value of exactly 0 for both e_1 and e_2 leads to singular images, which increases the number of errors dramatically.) In other words, computational reasons suggest that the movements get progressively 'slightly lenghtened'; it is not just *any* deviation from singular results that happens.

There are two constraints to guarantee no non-models: $\Delta_l \leq [1 - 2e_1 - e_2] - 2\Delta_n$, and $\Delta_n < [0.25 - 0.5e_1 - 0.5e_2]$. This could be interpreted as an upper bound of 1/4 for Δ_n. There is a further constraint to guarantee not more than 9 errors: $\Delta_l \geq 0.5 - 0.5e_1 - 0.5e_2$. This could be interpreted as a lower bound of 1/2 for Δ_l. Together, these constraints imply that Δ_l should really be 'large' compared to Δ_n.

The metrical computational model has been implemented in COGENT, a graphical modelling environment for the development of cognitive models proposed by Cooper, Fox, Yule and Sutton (this volume).

Mental models and mental images

A replication study (Strube et al., 1997) of the Knauff et al. (1995) experiment provides further evidence for the two models: There are fewer differences in model preferences between either of the computational models and either of the two experimental data sets than there are between the two data sets.

As mentioned above, there are 6 differences between the ordinal model and the data of Knauff et al. (1995) and 9 differences between the metrical model and these data. There are 9 differences between the ordinal model and the data of Strube et al. (1997) and 7 differences between the metrical model and these data. There are 6 differences between the two models, but there are 13 differences between the two data sets.

Still, both computational models were formulated on a relatively small empirical basis. So predictions made by them extrapolate rather strongly. A more cautious extrapolation can be placed relative to one another in such a way that the generated model is useful for the reasoner, assisting him in whatever task he is trying to accomplish. This means that properties of and relations between elements that are relevant for the task are represented adequately, and that construction, transformation and inspection operations that are relevant for the task are supported and simplified. Once positioning strategies are formulated, it can be tested whether an empirical validation is possible at this abstract level.[17] Based on these arguments, further experiments can be proposed and further empirical data can be gathered to try to validate the models.

The positioning strategies which motivate the construction processes of the two computational models of Allen inferences stress different aspects of usefulness. Both aspects are important, and they do not exclude one another. Therefore, it is likely that both strategies play a role in the construction of mental models. Below we will propose a cognitive architecture which takes this into account by letting the two strategies and the two corresponding representations assist one another.

Ordinal and metrical positioning strategies

This section describes the linearization strategy formulated for ordinal mental models and the regularization strategy formulated for metrical mental models. The latter has already been mentioned in the description of the metrical computational model; it is the abstraction of the idea that motivated the search for the metrical computational model. In the following, both strategies will be described, and it will be shown in which sense they increase the usefulness of mental models. Both strategies stipulate that, if possible, mental models should be constructed — in all sorts of tasks — that have certain geometrical properties which are desirable from a representational or processing point of view.

The *linearization strategy* is an ordinal positioning strategy. It focusses on the efficiency of inspection. A configuration of n intervals C is *linearized with respect to the interval* $[s_i\ e_i]$ if $s_i < s_j \Leftrightarrow e_i < e_j$ for $j \in \{1, ..., n\}$ and $s_j < s_j \Leftrightarrow e_j < e_i$ for $j \in \{1, ..., n\}$. A configuration of intervals is *linearized* if it is linearized with respect to each of its intervals. The *linearization strategy*

---

[17] The abstract strategies do not describe unique solutions to most single tasks, but constrain the set of solutions (see below). An empirical validation at the more abstract level would test whether solutions are from this set.

states that whenever among the models of an n-term series task there are linearized interval configurations, then the preferred model will be a linearized one.

What computational reasons are there to prefer linearized models? A linearized configuration can be compactly encoded as an ordering at the interval level. We may interpret this as a kind of chunking strategy which helps to reduce working memory load. Even more important from an algorithmic point of view is the fact that the representation at interval level permits a hierarchical search. A model inspection process that exploits this fact would search at the interval level and only go down to the point level where necessary. Similar hierarchical representations are known to play an important role in other areas of spatial cognition (e.g. cognitive maps, see for example McNamara, 1991).

Figure 9: The linearization principle

Consider the example given in fig. 5 . Fig. 5 describes the insertion of the end point of the interval Z in the three-term series task ($X\ oi\ Y,\ Y\ m\ Z$) with the preferred mental model $X\ o\ Z$. The three different models which could be constructed are shown in fig. 9. It turns out that the scanning process which inserts the end point of Z runs through all three solutions and stops only at the last of them. One might expect that a model construction process determined by scanning would try to minimise scanning distance, but obviously the model construction process does not follow such a strategy. A closer look at the point orderings of the three models reveals that the model $X\ o\ Z$ is the only model for which the intervals can be brought into a linear ordering compatible with the point ordering. The ordering $Y < X < Z$ is compatible with $s_Y < s_X < e_Y = s_Z < e_X < e_Z$ in the sense that it reflects the ordering of the intervals' starting points as well as that of the intervals' end points. Neither the first nor the second model in fig. 9 allows such a compact encoding of the point ordering at the interval level. X o Z is also the empirically preferred mental model.

The *regularization strategy* is a metrical positioning strategy.[18] It focuses on the usefulness of representation. More exactly, it focusses on the usefulness of representation if the relevant relations are order relations: Not only should the right order relations be represented, they should also be represented in a way that whatever information is extracted from inspection of the image is stable over time.

A configuration of n intervals $C = \{[s_1\ e_1] \ldots [s_n\ e_n]\}$ is called *regularized* if no two points of the $2n$ interval starting points and end points in it are equal, unless they are forced to be equal by a premise relation. (E.g. when a premise is $X\ fi\ Y$, the end points of these two intervals are forced to be equal.) The *regularization strategy* states that whenever, among the models of an n-term series task, there are regularized interval configurations, then the preferred model will be a regularized one.

What representational advantages cause the preference for regularized models? Loosely speaking, if two points are constructed as equal, but image inspection yields inexact values (i.e. possibly a little lower, possibly a little higher than the constructed values), the mental model relation extracted from the image will be unstable in the sense that different inspections can give three different order relations between the two points constructed as equal, relations which are then interpreted as three different Allen relations. If however the two points are constructed as unequal, small divergences from the constructed values will not affect the order relations of the two points, so the interpretation as an Allen relation, i.e. the mental model, will be stable.

Consider the example of fig. 9 again. As an example of the possible distribution of values, assume that inspected values can lie in a region around the constructed value. The premises of

---

[18] These equalities may also be called *singularities* as opposed to *regularities*, which gives the strategy its name.

the task are X oi Y and Y m Z. If the end point of Z is constructed as equal to the end point of X, but inspection values can differ from constructed values, the mental model is unstable: At any inspection, the end point of Z can be equal to the end point of X (yielding the mental model intended by the construction, X fi Z), but it can also be smaller (yielding X di Z) or larger (yielding X o Z). If the starting point of Z is constructed as larger than the starting point of X, all[19] inspected values will be larger, so the mental model is stable: X o Z. This is also the empirically preferred mental model. Another regular mental model of the same premises is X di Z (not shown in the figure).

A formal and more detailed analysis of this problem is given by Berendt (1996b). It is shown that regularization maximizes the expected utility of mental images. The formal derivation of regularization as the best solution to a decision problem is based on the following assumptions: (1) Reasoners try to maximize expected utility and this takes place under conditions of bounded rationality. Expected utility is defined via the stability of mental models, i.e. it decreases with the probability of making inspection errors. (2) Inexactness means that inspected values can be described by a random variable whose mean is equal to the constructed value (cf. Denis et al., 1995); (3) Concerning the mental models to be constructed, it is assumed that these generally have a higher proportion of necessarily unequal points than of necessarily equal points.

Berendt (1996b) also shows that to obtain maximally stable mental models, regularization must be supplemented by an interpretation of the image at a coarser level of granularity ('sketch interpretation': very small metrical divergences must be ignored).

---

[19] or most, depending on the distribution model of inexactness

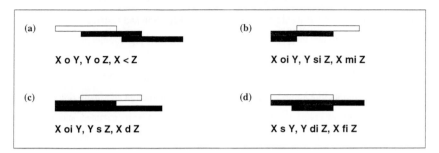

Figure 10: Examples of empirically preferred mental models that are (a) linearized and regularized, (b) linearized, but not regularized, (c) regularized, but not linearized, and (d) neither.

It can easily be verified that, where possible, nearly all the empirical model preferences found for the three-term series task are linearized and regularized. There are of course some compositions where one or both of the principles cannot be applied, because the task has no linearized model, or because its regularized model does not differ from the non-regularized one. Fig. 10 shows examples of empirically preferred mental models that obey two, one, or none of these principles.

So the Allen inferences task described in this paper is an example of the application of both strategies. The positioning strategies also apply to different sorts of mental models tasks, and the descriptions could easily be generalised. But an ordinal model need not be regularized, and a metrical model need not be linearized. So maybe both kinds of representations are involved. But how do they interact? To answer these questions we will propose a minimal working memory architecture.

A proposal for a minimal architecture

The two computational models have different ways of associating representations of the mental model with processes. Mental images can play a role in both models. The question is what role these play in processing.

The ordinal computational model assumes that model construction operates on an ordinal model. It is possible that from this ordinal model, a metrical model or image is generated and regenerated, and that inspection to find the conclusion of the composition task operates on this image. A strong epiphenomalist view could dispute the assumption that the image is causal for anything, i.e. it would assume that both construction and inspection operate on the ordinal model, that the image is just (re)generated as an epiphenomenon (see Schlieder (1996b) for a discussion of these two possibilities).

The metrical computational model assumes that model construction and inspection operate on the metrical model or image. But here, too, the image needs to be regenerated, and it has been assumed that regeneration creates inspected values distributed around a mean which is the constructed value.

The regeneration process therefore needs an underlying representation on which regeneration is based. This underlying representation could be the ordinal model, augmented by metrical parameters for the distances between the points. These parameters would specify the constructed values. Altogether, the process could operate as follows: Construction and inspection operate on the metrical model, on the ordinal model, or on both. The metrical model is a "mental image". The ordinal model is what is classically called a "mental model". Image information is encoded in the ordinal model. From this, the image is regenerated using metrical parameter values. This minimal architecture is shown in fig. 11.

In it, the regularization positioning strategy is important because the image is inexact, but the mental models obtained from inspecting the image should be stable. The linearization strategy is important because this may economise on storage, and also because regeneration, based on hierarchical search, may be simpler.

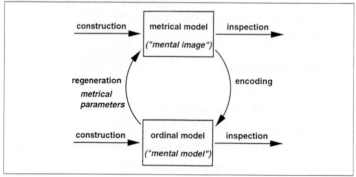

Figure 11: A minimal architecture involving an ordinal and a metrical model stabilising each other.

Therefore, the architecture proposes that two working memory systems are involved in reasoning with *visual mental models*. These can be interpreted in Kosslyn's (1994) model of the imagery system. The ordinal model is held in the activated part of associative memory, and the metrical model is held in the visual buffer. It is assumed that these are neuroanatomically separated systems. This separation is not a mere duplication, but plays an important role in the functioning of working memory: The possibility of feedback or 'rehearsal' between the two systems stabilises the representation.[20] This could imply that the advantages of constructing a mental model of a task in visuo-spatial working memory are not so much that it is easier to represent the configuration in a visuo-spatial format, but that memory processes improve the maintenance of the (visual) mental model . In other words, the "mental model" (or visual mental model) used in reasoning is a functional abstraction of the whole loop and not just the classical ordinal "mental model".

Summary, open questions and directions for further work

This paper has described an experiment on spatial mental models based on the system of Allen interval relations. The inferences are viewed in the framework of mental models in problem solving: a set of premises may have one or multiple models (in the logical sense). Questions that may be asked include: Which models are generated at all? Which models are generated preferentially? What differences are found between premises with a single model versus premises with multiple models? In the experiment reported here interest focusses on the question which models are generated preferentially? Subjects were asked to provide one answer to each of 144 Allen inference questions. Evidence was found of preferred mental models: In tasks with multiple models, a great majority of subjects chose the same solution.

Two computational models of the empirically found preferred mental models were proposed. One is based on ordinal information only, modelling the mental model as an ordering of points. The other is based on metrical information, modelling the mental model as a mental image. Both explain the data well.

---

[20] That the feedback loop stabilises the representation is a proposal suggested by Rita Kovordányi (personal communication). Kovordányi is working on a computer simulation to investigate how the parameters of the feedback loop influence image fading.

The concrete construction rules in each of the two computational models are derived from two more abstract positioning strategies, linearization and regularization. These describe properties of a mental representation which are advantageous for representation and/or processing and require construction rules to be such that representations with these properties are generated. It is argued that these positioning strategies are applicable to a wider range of tasks. Also, the positioning strategies and therefore the two representations, the ordinal model and the metrical model, complement each other. Therefore, a minimal working memory architecture is proposed which involves the ordinal *and* the metrical model. It is argued that the feedback or rehearsal loop between the two representations constitutes the gain of this 'duplication' by stabilising the mental model.

The computational models can be used to make predictions for further experiments involving Allen relations. The data on Allen relations' four-term series by Rauh and Schlieder (1997) can be analysed from this perspective. More importantly, the abstract positioning strategies can be used to make predictions for different spatial mental models tasks. These should be comparable to the Allen inferences task in being defined in pictorial space.

Spatial tasks in large-scale space may be affected by other information associated with the entities reasoned about (e.g. functional properties of landmarks along a route). Nevertheless, it should be investigated whether principles are transferable. The transfer of another general structural property of both models should be investigated: the interaction of a general representation of a relation and a modification of this relation specified by when entities in that relation are inserted into the mental model. In the metrical computational model, the first aspect is modelled by the distance parameters, and the second is modelled by the correction term and its development across the stages of construction. A similar idea has been successfully used in the modelling of distance estimation tasks in large-scale space (Berendt & Jansen-Osmann, 1997).

Acknowledgements

We wish to thank the participants of the First European Workshop on Cognitive Modelling, in particular Pete Yule and Rita Kovordányi, for discussions and comments.

References

Allen, J. (1983). Maintaining knowledge about temporal intervals. *Communications of the ACM, 26,* 832-843.

Anderson, J. (1978). Arguments concerning representations for mental imagery. *Psychological Review, 85,* 249-277.

Berendt, B. (1996a). Explaining preferred mental models in Allen inferences with a metrical model of imagery. In: *Proceedings of the Eighteenth Annual Conference of the Cognitive Science Society (COGSCI-96).* San Diego. 489-494.

Berendt, B. (1996b). The utility of mental images: How to create stable mental models in an unstable image medium. In: *Proceedings of the First European Workshops on Cognitive Modelling. Berlin. Technische Universität Berlin, Fachbereich Informatik, Report No. 96-39.* 97-103.

Berendt, B. & Jansen-Osmann, P. (1997). Feature accumulation and route structuring in distance estimations - an interdisciplinary approach. In S. Hirtle and A. Frank (Eds.) *Spatial Information Theory: A Theoretical Basis for GIS.* (pp.279-295). Berlin: Springer.

Byrne, R., & Johnson-Laird, P. (1989). Spatial reasoning. *Journal of Memory and Language, 28,* 564-575.

Cooper, R., Fox, J., Yule, P. & Sutton, D. (this volume). COGENT: An Environment for the Development of Cognitive Models.

Denis, M., Gonçalves, M.-R. & Memmi, D. (1995). Mental scanning of visual images generated from verbal descriptions: towards a model of image accuracy. *Neuropsychologia, 33,* 1511-1530.

Evans, J., Newstead, S., & Byrne, R. (1993). *Human Reasoning. The Psychology of Deduction.* Hillsdale, NJ: Lawrence Erlbaum.

Finke, R. A. & Kosslyn, S.M. (1980). Mental imagery acuity in the peripheral visual field. *Journal of Experimental Psychology: Human Perception and Performance, 6,* 244-264.

Güsgen, H. (1989). *Spatial Reasoning Based on Allen's Temporal Logic* (Technical Report ISCI TR-89-049). Berkeley, CA: International Computer Science Institute.

Hernández, D. (1994). *Qualitative Representation of Spatial Knowledge.* Berlin: Springer.

Hunter, I. (1957). The solving of three-term series problems. *British Journal of Psychology, 48,* 286-298.

Huttenlocher, J. (1968). Constructing spatial images: a strategy in reasoning. *Psychological Review, 75,* 550-560.

Johnson-Laird, P.N. (1972). The three-term series problem. *Cognition, 1,* 58-82.

Johnson-Laird, P. & Byrne, R. (1991). *Deduction.* Hillsdale, NJ: Lawrence Erlbaum.

Johnson-Laird, P., Byrne, R. & Schaeken, W. (1992). Propositional reasoning by model. *Psychological Review, 99,* 418-439.

Knauff, M., Rauh, R. & Schlieder, C. (1995). Preferred mental models in qualitative spatial reasoning: A cognitive assessment of Allen's Calculus. In *Proceedings of the Seventeenth Annual Conference of the Cognitive Science Society.* 200-205

Kosslyn, S.M. (1980). *Image and Mind.* Cambridge, MA: MIT Press.

Kosslyn, S.M. (1994). *Image and Brain.* Cambridge, MA: MIT Press.

Kovordànyi, R. (1996). Towards a cognitive model of creative reinterpretation of mental images. *Proceedings SAIS'96.*

Ligozat, G. (1990). Weak representation of interval algebras. *Proc. AAAI-90,* 715-720

Logie, R.H. (1995). *Visuo-Spatial Working Memory.* Hillsdale, NJ: Lawrence Erlbaum.

McNamara, T.P. (1991). Memory's view of space. In G.H. Bower (Ed.), *The Psychology of Learning and Motivation: Advances in Research and Theory* (Vol. 27, pp. 147--186). New York: Academic Press.

Mukerjee, A., & Joe, G. (1990). A qualitative model for space. *Proc. AAAI-90,* 721-727.

Rauh, R., & Schlieder, C. (1997). Symmetries of model construction in spatial relational inference. *Proceedings of the Nineteenth Annual Conference of the Cognitive Science Society,* Stanford University, August 7-10, 1997.

Reisberg, D. & Chambers, D. (1991). Neither pictures nor propositions: What can we learn from a mental image? *Canadian Journal of Psychology, 45,* 288-302.

Rips, L. (1994). *The Psychology of Proof: Deductive Reasoning in Human Thinking.* Massachusetts, CA: MIT Press.

Schlieder, C. (1995*). The Construction of Preferred Mental Models in Reasoning with Allen's Relations.* IIG-Report 5/95, Freiburg: Universität Freiburg. To appear in C. Habel (Ed.). Mental models in discourse comprehension and reasoning.

Schlieder, C. (1996a). Qualitative shape representation. In P. Burrough & A. Frank (Eds., *Geographic Objects with Indeterminate Boundaries,* London: Taylor & Francis.

Schlieder, C. (1996b). Diagrammatic Reasoning about Allen's Interval Relations. *AAAI 1996 Spring Symposium Series: Reasoning with Diagrammatic Representations.* Stanford University. 83-91.

Strube, G., Knauff, M., Kuß, T., Rauh, R. & Schlieder, C. (1997). Spatial mental models: Reasoning with Allen's relations. *Proc. European Conference on Cognitive Science ECCS '97.* (pp. 8-13). Manchester: University of Manchester.

Slezak, P. (1991). Can Images Be Rotated and Inspected? A Test of the Pictorial Medium Theory. In *Proceedings of the Thirteenth Annual Conference of the Cognitive Science Society.* 55-60.

2.2 Three empirically-based experiences in modelling diagnostic reasoning processes: Features and Issues

Laurence Alpay, Eileen Scanlon, Rose Dieng & Alain Giboin

Abstract

This chapter reports three experiences in the modelling of diagnostic reasoning processes: 1) modelling of medical problem solving, 2) modelling of physics problem solving, and 3) modelling of road accident analysis. In a first part, the main features of each study are described, and a synthesis is proposed. In a second part, a number of cognitive modelling issues arisen from the experiences are discussed: i) modelling from protocols to rules, ii) using the think-aloud methodology, iii) modelling different levels of expertise, iv) using different modelling tools and languages, v) re-using models, tools or languages, and vi) using generic models.

Introduction

Reasoning is an important and central activity in human intelligence (e.g. Anderson 1980). Over the past decades, papers from the disciplines of cognitive psychology, artificial intelligence, and cognitive sciences have been published reporting empirical findings in the field, and theoretical approaches that propose to account for these findings. People can reason in various ways: for example they construct proofs using propositional logic (formal rule theory, e.g. Evans et al 1993). They also construct models that represent states of the world in which premises are true, the conclusions being constructed by generating a description of their models (mental models theory, Johnson-Laird 1983). Furthermore, human beings can reason in real world domains by retrieving and applying domain-specific rules or context sensitive schemas. In addition to rule-based reasoning, the reasoner may perform case-based reasoning, by relying on previous cases he/she processed in the past (successes or failures). People also have cognitive biases that stem from the reliance on judgmental heuristics (heuristics and biases theory, Kahneman et al 1982) .

Diagnosis can be viewed as the task of identifying the cause of a fault or an error that manifests itself through some observed behaviour. In a diagnostic problem solving task people reason using various approaches including domain rules and heuristics, for example for technical diagnosis and medical diagnosis. Substantial work was carried out in CommonKADS (Breuker & Van de Velde, 1994) in order to integrate these various approaches into a unified framework for diagnostic reasoning. In this paper, we focus on reasoning processes people use in performing a diagnostic task. As will be detailed in the next sections, the aspects of human reasoning investigated here mainly relate to the use of domain-specific rules and to a certain extent to heuristics.

By studying cognitive processes such as diagnostic reasoning, one is interested in constructing or testing a process model. We report here on three empirically-based approaches to cognitive modelling for diagnostic reasoning, in different domains (medicine, physics and road accident analysis). The approaches to cognitive modelling chosen included SOAR, Prolog and Conceptual Graphs as modelling tools. Reasoning processes of subjects at various levels of expertise - from novices to experts were modelled.

Although the cognitive modelling activity in each domain has its own specificity, and the process of comparing these studies has proved to be difficult, we can report on a number of aspects which have emerged, related to contextual features and re-usability. As expressed in Rademakers and Vanwelkenhuysen (1992), there is a need for empirical indication that can justify the study of generic models in the process of modelling problem solving behaviour. This paper does not aim at providing a generic model from these three studies; it offers some empirical evidence for discussion of generic modelling of the diagnostic task.

The first section presents diagnostic problem solving in the three domains, and details the modelling aspects of diagnostic reasoning in each domain. The second section examines a number of issues for cognitive modelling arisen from the empirical studies.

The Three Cognitive Modelling Experiences and their Features

This section presents the diagnostic task in three different domains: physics, medical and road accident analysis. For each study, this section also details the modelling of the diagnostic task, with specific regard to reasoning processes. Modelling diagnosis in the three example domains embed several expertise dimensions. We have focused on novice vs. expert in the medical problem solving study, experts from different specialities in the accidentology study, and multiple representations of knowledge for a student in the physics problem solving study.

Experience 1: Diagnosis in Physics Problem Solving

The Domain

In modelling physics problem solving behaviour, the task is to distinguish between different types of declarative and procedural knowledge available to the problem-solver e.g. a student. Typically students need to move from a qualitative analysis of the problem set to a route to finding a solution which involves the recall, selection and manipulation of physics knowledge in the form of an equation or graphical representation.

Diagnosis in physics problem solving can therefore involve the recognition of a particular example, as one of a type of problem which the subject (e.g. a student in our educational context) has previously solved, or in the case of less familiar examples, recognising which features in the problem description are salient. For example, a student may focus on a particular term such as acceleration in the problem statement and assume that Newtonian laws will be relevant (Scanlon and O'Shea, 1988).

Goals of the Study: Modelling Diagnosis Using Switches of Representations

Many theoretical models have been constructed to simulate the processes of problem solving in physics. They are of two types: psychological models which attempt to simulate human cognitive processing and artificial intelligence models which mimic aspects of human behaviour. Interest in modelling physics problem solving arises from various different communities. Physics educators are concerned about improving the effectiveness of physics teaching. Cognitive scientists are interested in studying physics problem solving so that they can understand better how learning occurs in a domain which is sufficiently constrained by a series of laws which can be expressed mathematically, but sufficiently 'real world' in nature so that students will bring their own set of beliefs about how the world works. Both the physics education and the cognitive science communities have different perspectives on what makes a physics problem interesting, but they have a shared interest in looking at the subject areas of kinematics and dynamics. These two perspectives also influenced our choice of the type of problem examined within the subject areas, namely a recall problem, an equation manipulation problem and a graphing task.

The following sections discuss the analysis of the verbal protocols, the actual modelling task, and the evaluation of the models. An example of protocols is also included.

Analysis of Verbal Protocols

In our study of physics problem solving, the data sources consist of think aloud protocols of two hundred and fifty nine solutions to a variety of kinematics and dynamics problems. These protocols, the work of thirty five subjects with varying amounts of familiarity and expertise in problem solving working individually and in pairs were analysed. The protocols were examined for a number of features which are hypothesised to play a role in a subject's success or failure in solving a particular problem. The problem solving behaviour is described in (Scanlon, 1993). The graphing task was designed to prompt students to use both an algebraic and an iconic representation of the problem and to prompt the expression of the interrelationship of these in their paper and pencil working, so the modelling had to contend with the interesting issue in the protocols of how such switches of representation were accomplished.

The models were constructed by a process of iteration between protocol analysis and model construction. They capture several features of the behaviour observed in the protocols, i.e. problem interpretation; equation solving; reading and focus of attention; and transfer between equations and graphical representations for problems. The model of student behaviour on the first problem concentrates on equation solving, the model of the second on features of reading and problem interpretation, and the third on graph drawing and interpretation. The models on the graph drawing and interpretation task were most developed (Scanlon and O'Shea, 1988).

Modelling of errors was achieved by omission or combination of production rules. In order to account for behaviour on the graph problem, we found we needed to distinguish between different types of declarative and procedural knowledge available to the student. They are (i) recall of a variety of equations (EK-Equation Knowledge), (ii) general common sense knowledge about time, distance, velocity, and acceleration (BPK - Basic Physical Knowledge), (iii) knowledge about the type and difficulty of problems set in school textbooks (SPK- School Problem Knowledge), (iv) equation manipulation skills (EMS) and (v) graph interpretation skills (GIS). These different types of procedural and declarative knowledge are brought to bear by the student as they solve the problem. A parsimonious account using production rules generated the behaviour of the original group of students solving the problem. This account was compared with the remaining protocol data to test the explanatory power of the model, and the format of the production system compared with Young and O'Shea's (1981) evaluation criteria.

Modelling Switches of Representations

A general framework for the solution process was constructed first. This is summarised in Table 1. Firstly, the students use their knowledge of school text books to interpret the problem. Then they recall an equation. The students generally draw on one of two sources of declarative knowledge namely BPK (Basic Physical Knowledge) or SPK (School Problem Knowledge), usually SPK. In fact, in the production rule account these sources of declarative knowledge have been combined In addition some students also use GIS (Graph Interpretation Skills) but no student used both GIS and another knowledge source to produce an answer. Then according to the skill applied they either roughly check their answer against the other variables in the equations or they check the answer approximately against the graph. It proved possible to break each of the protocols into the four phases described above and shown in Table 1. By carefully looking at the utterances it was possible to identify where the different knowledge sources were brought to bear. The analysis was tightened by devising a framework based on production rules to use in the construction of nine specific models to describe the various problem solving behaviours.

INTERPRET		read problem
		use GIS to draw graph
RECALL		use GIS,BPK or SPK to recall equations from EK
SOLVE	use EMS to substitute values in equation	use GIS to substitute values in equation
CHECK	use size of answer to check	use rough size checking against graph

Table 1: General framework

The physics production rule models presented can be thought of as summaries of a number of subjects' behaviour on a particular problem. Errors can be generated by rule omission, by the deletion of some of the conditions on a particular rule or by the combinations of left hand conditions with right hand actions. The models therefore provide a principled account of sources of error behaviour in the protocols, and highlight some of the important elements of physics problem solving behaviour which are sometimes overlooked.

Modelling the successful and unsuccessful problem solving behaviour of students on this graph problem led to the observation that novices solving a physics problem can more easily achieve success when they restrict themselves to using only one representation of the problem. One important component of expertise in problem solving or learning is the ability to control and hence minimise shifts from one type of knowledge representation or problem solving technique to another. As novices acquire this type of expertise, their efficiency as problem solvers or learners increases. According to this view, experts try to be as economical as possible in the number of transitions from rule set to rule set. On the other hand, novices often behave in a spendthrift way and flip from one rule set to another. For example a novice may go from reading the problem to solving it, from problem solving to using expectations about school work, from using graphs to using equations and so on. The uneconomical path of least resistance leads the novice to change representations rather than back track when stuck.

Protocol

An extract from one of the protocols studied illustrates this opportunistic unhelpful switching. While looking at a velocity-time graph the subject switches to the incorrect use of an equation of motion: "Just a minute, average velocity...oh well average velocity is top velocity minus bottom velocity divided by the time taken".

Evaluation of Models

The construction of the models was used as a technique for examining the fine structure of such protocol data.

The models were constructed by a process of iteration between protocol analysis and model construction for half of the protocols collected. The extent to which the models capture several features of the behaviour observed in the protocols (e.g. problem interpretation, equation solving, reading and focus of attention and transfer between equations and graphical representations for problems) was evaluated by comparing the remaining protocols with the models' behaviour in terms of sequence of events and medium (graph or equation) used.

Nine distinct prototype models were created from a rule set of 27 production rules and implemented using production systems (see later section "Modelling from Protocols to Rules").

This modelling exercise revealed the potential importance for problem solvers of self awareness. The novice problem solvers found that switching representations from graphical to algebraic or vice versa when reasoning about a problem was in general an unproductive reasoning strategy.

Experience 2: Diagnosis in Medical Problem Solving

The Domain

In medical problem solving, the patient case contains the initial complaint of the patient. The physician handles observations (also called findings) i.e. medical facts about a patient which can be viewed as the direct evidence from which hypotheses about possible diagnoses are generated and tested. This evidence can be either a sign, a symptom or a test result. A sign is defined as objective and observable by the physician, whereas a symptom is a subjective sensation reported by the patient or any observation that the patient gives to the physician.

The physician generates hypotheses as part of his/her medical problem solving task, that is, the presence of a disease or a more general disease category or any pathological problem. Any problem that the physician thinks is the cause of the patient's pain e.g. inflammatory problem can be considered as an hypothesis (see Elstein et al., 1978).

Goals of the Study: Modelling Diagnosis from a Developmental View

Medical problem solving has been studied from different approaches. One approach has been on the development of expertise (e.g. Lesgold, 1984. Our research work (Alpay, 1992) has investigated further this developmental perspective i.e. from novices to experts, in the context of intelligent tutoring systems in medicine. Our focus has been on modelling reasoning strategies used in the task of medical diagnosis.

The following sections discuss the reasoning strategies used in this study, give an example of encoding protocols, and briefly describe the models of interactions of strategies which have been built.

Reasoning Strategies in Medical Problem-Solving

In the context of medical problem solving, a reasoning strategy is used to refine the details of the patient's case and to generate one or more hypotheses which correspond to a diagnosis. A medical reasoning strategy is related to how one makes inferences between findings (e.g. signs, test results) and diseases. In using a medical reasoning strategy, the physician makes a decision about what move to make in the current state. This decision describes a choice between two or more actions and the move is based on the physician's knowledge.

It should be noted that we make a distinction between reasoning processes such as forward or backward reasoning and reasoning strategies such as generalisation or hypothesis generation. Forward and backward reasoning are concerned with the direction (either top down or bottom) upon which to conduct the problem search through the space, in this case of the domain of back problems. Patel and Groen (1986) have studied the reasoning processes of expert cardiologists in terms of forward and backward reasoning. Their results showed that experts making accurate diagnoses used bottom-up forward reasoning whereas experts making inaccurate diagnoses used at least some top-down backward chaining.

In contrast to forward and backward reasoning, reasoning strategies result in a search space (e.g. possible hypotheses for a back pain problem) and reflect the degree of specificity of the solution i.e. choice of a hypothesis for medical diagnosis. As Clancey pointed out (1986), a strategy "reasons" about operators and problem solving methods. Physicians do not use strategies randomly. There is some logic behind each choice (i.e. the strategy applied) which describes a line of reasoning in diagnosing the patient case. In our study, concepts such as questions to the patient, clinical and laboratory tests correspond to the operators, and problem solving involves applying some strategy for manipulating these concepts.

From the medical problem solving literature, we identified a set of reasoning strategies, and we refined them. These strategies are domain generic and based on generalisation, specialisation, confirmation, elimination, problem refinement and hypothesis generation.

An empirical study was carried out to examine the development of these strategies. Ten protocols of physicians at various levels of expertise (medical student, house officer, registrar, general practitioner, expert consultant) were collected and analysed. Subjects participated in a consultation with a simulated patient. This was followed by a post interview session between the subject and the experimenter.

<u>Coding Verbal Protocols:</u>

Three basic units of encoding were defined for the interactions between the patient and the doctor and for the doctor's verbalisations during the think aloud and the post interview sessions. Protocols were first coded using low level categories (such as hypotheses, symptoms, signs). Two "non medical" categories were added to the low level coding - a planning category and a consultation category, to take into account the planning approach subjects took during the consultation and thus being goal oriented. A set of glossaries containing the encoding vocabulary for the low level categories was created. These glossaries were enriched by reading about back pain problems and through the analysis of the protocols of the pilot study. An example of the schematic representation of a doctor/patient interaction in the think aloud session and a portion of an actual protocol is shown in Figure 1.

Schematic representation:

doctor <category> <utterance-1>.......<utterance-n>

patient<utterance-1> <category>.......<utterance-n>

Example of low level coding:

4th year student: <u>When did the pain start ?</u>

                category #3 (onset of the pain)

Patient: <u>It started this morning</u>   category #3 (onset of

the pain)

Figure 1: An example of the schematic representation of a doctor/patient interaction in the think aloud session and a portion of an actual protocol.

High level categories i.e. the reasoning strategies were defined in terms of these low level categories. A notation of the form $R(x,y,..)$ where R's are relations and the x,y, etc arguments was used to formalise the strategies (Ericsson and Simon 1984). In the formalisation of the strategies, the arguments represented the low level categories, and the predicates corresponded to strategies.

Here is an example of the formalisation and encoding for the hypothesis generation strategy: HGN(observation, hypothesis, goal, phase). The hypothesis is being generated from the observation which is also the evidence for the hypothesis. An example of encoding of an excerpt of actual protocols for the hypothesis generation strategy is shown in Figure 2.

The first 5th year student asked about radiation of the pain because of the possibility of sciatica.

Protocol	**Categories**
Replay of a question in the think aloud session	
First 5th year student: <u>and is the pain just in your back or</u> <u>do you get any in the leg at all ?</u>	#3
Patient: No, just in the back, just in the area I showed you.	
Student's explanation in the post interview session:	
First 5th year student: I was asking about <u>sciatica</u>	#10

Encoding

HGN(observation: no radiation of the pain, hypothesis: sciatica, goal: check radiation of the pain, phase: history)

Figure 2: Encoding of an excerpt of actual protocols for the hypothesis generation strategy.

Underlying some of the strategies (such as generalisation, specialisation, problem refinement and hypothesis generation) is a causal reasoning, linking together various medical knowledge such as findings and diseases. The reasoning strategies extracted from these verbal protocols can be translated into domain specific rules (in this study specific to back pain problems). For example, we have rules such as:

For hypothesis generation:

If radiation of the pain in the leg Then possibility of a sciatica.

If pain in the lower back Then possibility of a prolapsed intervertebral disc

For generalisation of hypotheses (diseases):

If prolapsed intervertebral disc Then mechanical causes

Models Of Interactions Of Strategies

In the study there was no evidence of monotonic development of the strategies. Instead, it was found that strategies were combined with one another in meaningful ways. It was found that these interactions of strategies reflected a development from one level of expertise to another and were not random combinations of strategies.

Models of interactions of strategies at different levels of expertise were built by splitting the data collected into two equivalent halves. The first half of the protocols were used to construct a developmental user model which describes explicitly models of changes of reasoning strategies from novice to expert. The other half of the protocols were used to evaluate the prototype developmental user model.

The modelling of the development of strategies consists of building not *one* model but a number of models that show how medical diagnosis varies at different levels of expertise. The process of building these models was incremental, that is, each model was built as extension of the model at the level below. By doing so, the changes that have occurred from one level of expertise to another were made explicit. Each model contains strategies applied at that level of expertise and the interactions between these strategies.

The prototype system diagnosed a subject's reasoning strategies, determined the level of expertise and produced a plan corresponding to the application of these strategies. Planning in artificial intelligence was used as a means of decomposing medical problem solving into a set of goals; the goals being associated with the strategies. The developmental user model was implemented in LPA Prolog on a Macintosh (see section "Using Different Modelling Tools and Languages").

Experience 3: Diagnosis in Accidentology

The Domain

The road accident analysis (accidentology) is defined as the analysis of the malfunctioning of the system conductor/vehicle/infrastructure (CVI) in the framework of a particular accident. The aims of this analysis are 1) to understand the sequencing of the accident, 2) to explain the origins of the malfunctioning of the CVI system, and 3) to foresee actions to be taken in order to prevent similar accidents in the future (Fleury et al., 1991; Ferrandez et al, 1995).

The analysis of an accident requires a diversity of knowledge coming from various disciplines such as, for example, psychology, engineering of the vehicle and of the infrastructure, mathematics (kinematics). Experts from INRETS (Institut National de REcherche sur les Transports et leur Sécurité) are of three types: 1) psychologists (specialists in driver behaviour), 2) vehicle engineerands, 3) road infrastructure engineers. During the analysis of the accident, all the experts share a common focus: 1) understand how the accident happened, and 2) identify the accident factors. However, each specialist has specific sub-tasks (corresponding to his/her speciality) in order to bring his contribution to the common goal. Thus, for example, the psychologist will be interested in understanding the behaviour of the driver, the vehicle engineer will be concerned with a possible malfunctioning of the car while the road infrastructure engineer will be interested in diagnosing the dangers due to the road infrastructure.

The diagnostic task in accidentology consists of determining the nature and causes of the malfunctioning within the three components of the CVI system: the conductor or driver, the vehicle and the infrastructure. Depending on the speciality of the expert (e.g. psychologist, vehicle engineer), the links between the three components and their interpretations vary in nature and importance. For example, the expert psychologist may tend to focus on the component "driver", and the vehicle engineer on the component "vehicle". Experts have at their disposal data from the brief (e.g. the accident happened at night), some of which will be viewed as clues. The goal is to generate possible explanations (or mechanisms / hypotheses) to identify the causes of the accident.

Mechanisms of detection, construction and evaluation of analogies (as cited in Klix & Bachmann 1998) were found with the experts from INRETS. For example, experts detect analogies between a given accident they analyse and the accidents that they have examined in the past (analogies between specific scenarios). Furthermore, the experts also built generic analogies, that is, generic scenarios which are a synthesis of analogous accidents. These scenarios are then used to detect analogies of the type specific scenario/generic scenario. When an expert analyses a new specific accident, he may make analogies with other accidents he studied in the past e.g. accidents that occurred on an infrastructure with a similar configuration, or concerning the same profile of driver or a given type of vehicle. For example, from his studies on accidents related to old drivers, to cross-road accidents and to accidents involving small fast cars of GTI Type, the psychologist 2 (we refered to as psy 2) built generic scenarios for such kinds of accidents. And exploitation of such generic scenarios during analysis of a new accident case is typically an analogy-based reasoning (even more a case-based reasoning when the expert appeals to a particular past case, similar to the new one).

The experts evaluate the proposed analogies, in particular they accept or reject those analogies depending on their relevance. When an analogy is rejected, the experts usually try to resolve this conflict co-operatively, that is, by looking for an acceptable compromise resulting from each other's view (as discussed in Tack, 1998). An example of co-operation occurs when an expert appeals to a vehicle engineer (specialist in kinematics reconstitution) in order to confirm or invalidate some hypotheses on the speed or trajectories of the vehicles. By the same way, a contradiction between the speeds claimed by the two drivers involved in the accident can sometimes be solved thanks to the results of the kinematics reconstitution. Therefore a psychologist or an infrastructure engineer will naturally cooperate with a vehicle engineer in order to choose more plausible hypotheses.

Another kind of co-operation takes place when an expert is known as being specialist of a type of accident thanks to his thematic studies on a given type of accident - such as GTI vehicle accidents for psy 2. Other experts may then appeal to him in order to evaluate concurrent hypotheses. Last, the experts can also consult the investigators that made the dossier of the accident to be analysed, in order to have more information on the context of the accident (as everything is not necessarily written in the accident dossier).

Goals of the Study: Modelling Diagnosis from a Multiple Expertise View

Accidentology is studied in the context of knowledge acquisition from and modelling of multiple experts (Alpay et al., 1996b) using the CommonKADS methodology (Breuker and Van de Velde, 1994) in the ACACIA (Acquisition des Connaissances pour l'Assistance à la Conception par Interaction entre Agents) project (Dieng et al., 1994) at the INRIA research centre in France.

We report here on one particular cognitive modelling activity grounded on our previous work in medical problem solving (Alpay, 1996a) presented in the previous section. The work reported here focused on a specific aspect of the accident analysis, namely, the search for clues/signs: the activity of searching for clues is an important aspect in the analysis of the accident, and is shared by the various kinds of experts. Furthermore, the task of searching for clues is related to the generation and testing of hypotheses, and as such is closely linked to the diagnostic task in which we are interested.

The following sections discuss the analysis of the verbal protocols, give an example of coding protocols analysis, and representing the reasoning strategies into conceptual graphs. The models of reasoning strategies built are also briefly examined.

Analysis of Verbal Protocols

A set of protocols of seven experts were collected by the ACACIA team. For the modelling task reported here, we used analyses of verbal protocols, in particular related to the activity of searching for clues. Protocols analysis of the experts were used in particular: i) from a free-conversation interview with psychologist 1 (referred to as PSY1), ii) from a free-conversation session as well as on the specific case studies with psychologist 2 (referred to as PSY2), and iii) from a free-conversation session with the infrastructure engineer 1 (referred to as INFRA1).

Below is an example of protocol analysis extracted from a collective discussion on a case between PSY1, a vehicle engineer VEH-ENG1 and an infrastructure engineer INFRA1:

"INFRA1 : That's why, this angle of the Car 1, it is a minimum. So, it confirms he can come only from the right side. There cannot be such an angle at the crash, we are sure that the crash occurred there, there are clear tracks. We are sure that, at the crash, the Car 1 does not come from the central lane.

PSY1 : It is sure there has been no preselection at the central level with the intention to turn to the left later on. There is a kind of manoeuvre in the continuity, with effectively as VEH-ENG1 says, a rather brief taking of information on the back, perception of headlights far away and attention focalisation on what occurs in front, with vehicles arriving and so search of a gap in order to pass at any price because the priority goal of this guy is to reach at any price this oil station, and at that moment certainly...

INFRA1 : Yes, but if the manoeuvre is sudden, the search of a gap is performed when he is on the right lane..."

Coding of Protocol Analyses

The generic strategies investigated in the medical problem solving study were re-used. Each strategy re-used for the accidentology study was defined in a way similar to those found in medical problem solving (see section "Experience 2: Diagnosis in Medical Problem Solving"). The strategies were grouped as follows: for searching an hypothesis (hypothesis generation), for filtering an hypothesis (generalisation, specialisation), for testing an hypothesis (confirmation, elimination). The non hypothesis-oriented reasoning strategy is problem refinement. We coded some parts of protocol analyses, re-using low level coding categories for medical problem solving (e.g. hypothesis, clue) and added new ones specific to the accidentology (e.g. factor or mechanism).

As in the case of medical problem solving, the reasoning strategies extracted from the protocol analyses are in a large part domain specific rules. An example of a rule of expertise of hypothesis generation for PSY1 generating the hypothesis "problem of hidden visibility" from the clue "road bump" is: If road bump Then problem of hidden visibility.

Formalising Reasoning Strategies with Conceptual Graphs

The reasoning strategies were represented with the Conceptual Graphs (CG) formalism (Sowa, 1984), and we used the tool GCKAT (Conceptual Graph Knowledge Acquisition Tool) developed in ACACIA (Martin, 1995; Martin, 1996) to support this knowledge acquisition activity. The representation of conceptual graphs provides good expressiveness; it aims to express meaning in a form that is logically precise, humanly readable and computationally tractable. A graph is made of concepts and relations e.g. [Concept1] -> (Relation) -> [Concept2].

The steps to use conceptual graphs to formalise reasoning strategies used in accidentology included building a typology of concepts for the three experts and a typology of conceptual relations for the reasoning strategies, specifying the bases of CG's (e.g. base of hypotheses, base of strategies), and constructing the typologies and the graphs using the CGKAT tool.

Figure 3 shows the corresponding conceptual graph for the rule of expertise of hypothesis generation given above: "Road bump" is considered by the expert as a clue of the type hidden visibility, and "problem of hidden visibility" as an hypothesis of the type infrastructure.

```
[ReasoningStrategy:
        [Interpretation:
        [RoadBump]->(ROLE) ->[Clue_HiddenVisibility]]
        ->(Relation_Hypothesis_Generation)->
        [Hypothesis:
        [HiddenVisibilityProblem]->(ROLE)
>[HypothesisInfrastructure]]].
```

Figure 3: Conceptual graph for a domain rule of expertise for hypothesis generation.

Models of reasoning strategies

Based on the protocol analysis of experts done in the ACACIA project and with those reasoning strategies in hand, we have constructed for the three given experts models of reasoning strategies focusing on the experts' activity of searching for clues. The models were validated by the expert themselves. The models of reasoning strategies are in fact models of inferences for a specific context within accidentology. Moreover, the models are at present static as they do not describe the dynamics of those strategies.

A Synthesis of the Features of the Three Experiences

Contextual Features of the Domain

One element of the context for the diagnostic task includes the dependencies of the domain. The diagnostic task is by nature linked to the domain in which it is performed e.g. medicine or physics, and to dependencies within the domain (e.g. back pain problems, or the relationships of laws in Newtonian mechanics).

From the studies we carried out we can draw some points of comparison between these three domains. In medicine diagnosis, the starting point is the patient's complaint, the patient's signs and symptoms, whereas in accidentology, it is the accident and some data in the accident (e.g. data in the brief). In physics it is the problem statement and the initial values of the relevant variables. The three diagnostic tasks rely upon knowledge, either physics, medicine or accidentology knowledge based on the CVI system as well as strategic/reasoning knowledge. The physician will search for diseases or pathologies explaining the patient's condition, and the expert in accidentology will look for mechanisms, clues and factors which account for the accident. The physician will select hypotheses which he/she has generated as part of his/her differential diagnosis, while the expert in accidentology will select hypotheses of mechanisms and of possible factors as part of the overall scenario of the accident.

Summaries

Table 2 summarises the purpose and the context of the modelling in the three example domains. Table 3 summarises the methodologies used across the three domains (techniques of elicitation, representation and validation). It is interesting to note that even though the field of application and the cognitive processes modelled differ across the studies, similar methodologies are found to carry out the cognitive modelling activities.

Domain	Area	Cognitive processes studied	Level of expertise
Physics	problem solving	Switches of representations	Novice
Medicine (back pains)	problem solving	Development of expertise	novice/expert
Accidentology	knowledge acquisition	Multiple expertise	Expert

Table 2: Purpose and context of modelling in the three example domains

Domain	Think aloud	Rule based	Tools & Languages	Evaluation Techniques
Physics	–	–	OPS5 SOAR	split-half testing
Medicine (back pains)	–	–	Prolog	split-half testing
Accidentolog y	–	–	CG Common-KADS	Validation by experts

Table 3: Methodologies in the three cognitive modelling activities

The popular method of think-aloud is useful for both physics and medical problem solving as well as for knowledge acquisition in accidentology. Likewise across the three domains, the traditional rule-based approach was chosen to express rules of expertise. There are various different languages that can be used for task analysis and cognitive modelling, as the choices in the three example domains show. In both medical and physics problem solving studies, the cognitive models built were evaluated using the remaining half of the protocols. In the accidentology, the models were directly validated by the human experts.

Issues of Cognitive Modelling Arising from the Experiences

The first part of this chapter has reported on three empirically based experiences of modelling diagnostic reasoning. This second part discusses a number of issues relevant to the cognitive modelling activities carried out in the three empirical studies:

• Modelling from protocols to rules,

• Using the think-aloud methodology,

• Modelling different levels of expertise,

• Using different modelling tools and languages,

• Re-using models, tools or language,

• Using generic models.

Modelling from Protocols to Rules

The type of verbal protocols from which cognitive models will be developed is an important contextual feature in the modelling activity. Protocols can be consultations between a patient and physician (as in medical problem solving), free-conversation or case-based interviews (as in accidentology), or pairs of subjects working on problems (as in physics problem solving) using think aloud instructions.

In accidentology, we can notice differences. For instance, in the free-conversation based protocol, the strategies are applied on generic elements such as clues, factors and hypotheses. Examples drawn from the protocols are probably typical ones that the experts refer to at first. In the case-based accident protocol, the expert used a mixture of elements from the specific accident as well as from his knowledge of generic ones.

Furthermore, in analysing the protocols, one needs to be aware of differentiating a diagnosis (generated by the subject) which stems from his/her actual problem solving task, from a diagnosis generated from a "performance task" (i.e. the expert shows what he knows). This is a distinction that was found in interviewing physicians during their medical problem solving task.

In the examples reported here, verbal protocols were used as a source for building models. However, as Anderson (1993) points out one should not constrain cognitive models to correspond exactly to verbal protocols. To abstract away from the verbalisations to some representation that is easier to simulate is a more flexible strategy, but is however one to be used with caution as it can be a license to ignore problematic portions of protocols.

Models developed from the protocols can be expressed using production rules as illustrated in the physics example (see section "Experience 1: Diagnosis in Physics Problem Solving"). Two distinct views of the role of production system models are available. Neches, Langley and Klahr (1987) said:

> The first framework treats production systems as a formal notation for expressing models. Viewed in this way it is the content of the models rather than the form of their expression or interpretation scheme that is the object of interest.

> The second view treats the interpreter of a production system as a highly specific theory about the architecture of the human information processing system. In its strongest form this view asserts that humans actually employ the functional equivalent of productions in reasoning, understanding, language and other intelligent behaviour. (p. 2)

We subscribe to the first view. The role of production rule modelling used in the physics example was that of a data analysis technique. The value of this technique is that attention is focused on the detail of the problem solving behaviour evident in the protocols.

In general, in order to account for error behaviour on protocols, it is necessary to develop an explicit representation of the processes concerned. This model can be cast in the form of a set of production rules. This set of rules can be a number of things: it can be a model of any particular subject's solution to a physics problem, it can be a general model of physics problem solving. It can be a pool from which rules are drawn to model a given subject's particular problem protocol. The rule set for each subject would then be a performance model of the subject's behaviour on the problem. So given a problem it should predict the subject's answer. A competence model would generate a range of possible answers to a given problem. The implementation of production rule systems is discussed in a further section "Using Different Modelling Tools and Languages".

In the other two example domain reported here, different approaches to formalise rules from protocols were taken. In the accidentology example, rules of expertise were formalised using the conceptual graphs formalism (see section "Experience 3: Diagnosis in Accidentology"). In the medical example, domain specific rules were embedded in the definition of the reasoning strategies (see section "Experience 1: Diagnosis in Medical Problem Solving").

Using the Think-Aloud Methodology

A general definition of a protocol is the detailed record of a subject's performance on a task, although a wide variety of different types of records are described as protocols of which verbal data is only one example. This verbal data can be collected in a variety of ways. The protocols here were collected using explicit think aloud instructions. One form of this is concurrent probing where subjects are asked questions as they perform the task e.g. what are you thinking now? What hypotheses are you using now? Ericsson and Simon (1984) review the status of such techniques and reject such claims as Nisbett and Wilson (1977) that such data is suspect, and provide recommendations for good practice as follows: use more than one set of data, use concurrent verbalisation rather than retrospective accounts, and avoid overspecific or overgeneral probes.

For example, in the medical problem solving study physicians were asked during the consultation with the patient to think aloud through their reasoning processes and verbalise what they were doing. Retrospection was used during the post-interview session with the subject. In the accidentology study, experts were asked to verbalise their analysis of the accident case given to them. In the physics problem solving study, pairs of subjects were asked to think aloud in their solving of physics problems, and dynamic records of their written problem attempts also collected.

Modelling Different Levels of Expertise

Research in the area of expertise has been studied in terms of three directions: expert behaviour, novice behaviour and the differences between experts and novices, in various domains such as physics and programming. The research on expertise makes it clear that experts and novices differ in fundamental ways. These differences extend to a variety of behavioural responses such as problem solving performance, perception, preferences and social attitudes.

In the empirical studies reported here different aspects of expertise have been modelled i.e. differences between novices and experts in physics problem solving, development of expertise from novice to expert in medical problem solving, specialities within the domain of expertise of accidentology.

In the studies of physics and medical problem solving and accidentology, the context linked to the instantiations of the reasoning processes is an important factor as this describes or reflects aspects of what makes up the expertise (as a level of expertise or as a speciality).

Some of the criteria related to the context which we found in the three studies include the following:

Categorisation of data: In physics problem solving experts and novices categorise problems differently, the novices often relying on superficial problem features. In medical problem solving, an expert physician will tend to categorise symptoms, signs and hypotheses.

In accidentology, experts from the different specialities will refer to categories such as clues, factors, mechanisms or hypotheses. Furthermore, in accidentology, we found that an expert psychologist will tend to classify data into reliable and unreliable ones, and an infrastructure engineer looks at data as objective (e.g. speed limits) or furtive (i.e data related to the day of the accident such as a trunk unloading soil on the ground). There is an overlap of categorisation from one domain to the other one e.g. hypothesis, or signs and symptoms.

Focus: In physics problem solving, expert subjects focus on consistency and real world checking. In medical problem solving, the physician may focus on phases of the consultation e.g. the patient's past history or the physical examination. In accidentology, the focus is linked to the reference (or the non reference) to one of the components of the CVI system. For example, regarding the classification of the clues, one of the psychologists will focus on clues of the conductor and of the infrastructure, whereas one of the infrastructure engineers will also strongly take into consideration the vehicle component.

Level of detail: In medical problem solving, according to the level of expertise, the physician will ask more detailed and tailored questions during a consultation, or will generate more specific hypotheses. In accidentology, the level of details refers to the contents of each component on the CVI system (e.g. not surprisingly, the infrastructure engineer provides detailed clues for the road network which is not of prime concern for the psychologists).

Using Different Modelling Tools and Languages

Production rule system are often used in cognitive modelling. For example, in the study of physics problem solving, models of subject behaviour were represented as production rules. Some of the models were implemented using MACLISP in POPSI (Packet Oriented Production System Interpreter) (Evertsz, 1993) designed for use as a research tool for cognitive modelling, Other models were implemented using another production rules system OPS 5 (Brownston et al., 1985). Another system based on production system is SOAR, a cognitive architecture built around multiple spaces for representing knowledge and implemented as a production system. In the study of physics problem solving, a set of models were re-represented in SOAR (Laird, 1986) as it appeared the ability to define separate problem spaces for the graph and equation working might produce some benefits. However, the consequent loss of inspectable conflict resolution strategies was unhelpful (O'Shea and Scanlon 1989).

Cognitive models can also be implemented using programming languages used in Artificial Intelligence. For example, in the study of medical problem solving, the developmental model of reasoning strategies was implemented using PROLOG.

Other approaches are chosen. For example, in accidentology, the reasoning strategies were first represented using the conceptual graph formalism, and then implemented using the conceptual graph dedicated tool CGKAT.

It is clear that more and more, cognitive models are not only formulated on paper but are also implemented. As Van Someren (1994) points out, there are important advantages of implementing simulation programs such as clear interpretations of what the model does, the visibility of gaps and redundant branches. Furthermore, running a simulation program using different conditions or problems sometimes show unexpected behaviour.

Developing cognitive models of diagnostic reasoning can be achieved using various tools and languages as illustrated with the three studies here. Recently, a general cognitive modelling environment has been developed (Cooper et al., 1998). COGENT is a non domain specific cognitive modelling package which allows to build computational models using a graphical programming languages. Extent use of COGENT has already included the implementation of production rule models. A re-implementation for example of the production rule system for physics problem solving and the developmental models of reasoning strategies in medical problem solving would allow us to investigate how beneficial such software systems would be in our modelling activities for diagnostic reasoning.

Re-using Models, Tools or Languages

Two aspects of re-use are discussed here , that of reasoning strategies, and of methodologies. Our approach to re-usability can be characterised as bottom-up in that we start from instantiation and customisation of modelling diagnostic problem solving, working towards examining what aspects can be generalised.

Re-use of reasoning strategies:

The study reported here in modelling reasoning strategies in accidentology has shown that the re-use of reasoning strategies for diagnostic problem solving in medical problem solving to another domain (i.e. accidentology) can be feasible. Results are encouraging; we have found a number of examples for which those strategies can be applied in accidentology. The hypothesis generation is the strategy which is the most applied. This is expected as the hypothesis generation is part of the diagnostic activity. Interestingly, this strategy is divided into two domain-dependent sub-processes: a) an explicitation (generation) of mechanism and an explicitation (generation) of factors. This finding highlights the closeness between re-usability and context.

In the physics problem solving protocols, there was a surprising tendency to over generalisation by students i.e. the application of reasoning strategies in inappropriate situations. Over generalisation was also found in medical problem solving, in the protocols of novices i.e. medical students.

Re-use of methodology:

In the study of medical problem solving presented here, the reasoning strategies were extracted from the experts' protocols, using a set of coding categories (e.g. hypotheses, symptoms, signs, diagnosis). We have also re-used coding categories for the accidentology to model the reasoning strategies. The re-use of coding categories includes the categories hypothesis, sign and symptom (the last two closely relate to the accidentology categories datum and clue), whereas additional categories specific to the accidentology include factor and mechanism. This issue is linked to the categorisation of data mentioned in the previous section.

The studies of physics and medical problem solving shared a commitment to evaluation of the modelling work in terms of detailed sequences from the protocol data. They also shared an innovative approach to conducting this evaluation based on splitting each corpus of data in half, one half to be used in model construction, the other in evaluation.

Modelling cognitive processes such as diagnostic reasoning can be achieved using various methods as illustrated with the three studies here. As Cooper et al (1996) point out the development and testing of computational models of cognition is typically ad hoc, and there are few generally agreed methodological principles to guide this activity. They argue for a systematic methodology for cognitive modelling to address this problem.

Role of re-usability

Achieving re-usability is important (e.g. Geldof, 1994). As Ritter and Baxter (1998) argue for cognitive models to succeed, models must become not only more easy to understand and to extend but also to re-use, with for example displays and packaging utilities programs. In the previous sections, the explicit and successful re-use of reasoning strategies from medical problem solving to accidentology was discussed. Based on the examples we have in medical problem solving, a re-use of such strategies in physics problem solving seems promising. Re-usability can be achieved by using generic models (see next section on "Using Generic Models").

Using Generic Models

Generic models have been recognised as an important aid in the process of modelling problem solving behaviour. In diagnostic reasoning, one might speak generally in terms of rule-out strategies, setting-up a differential and so on. However, using generic models in the process of modelling problem solving has its drawbacks such as for instance the fact that generic models can often be too general to give useful support and guidance (Rademakers & Vanwelkenhuysen 1992). There are various approaches to high level descriptions of models of problem solving (for details see Karbach et al., 1990) including KADS (Wielinga et al, 1992), a principled approach to knowledge-based system development. In this section, we focus on the generic model for diagnosis developed in CommonKADS[1], a subsequent version to KADS .

In the CommonKADS methodology, a model of expertise (for example for diagnosis) is built by describing three layers. The domain layer represents static knowledge of the expert and includes the concepts of the domain, their structures, and relations between these concepts. The inference layer is described by inference structures, that is, by networks which link knowledge sources and their roles and show which inferences can be made in this domain. The task layer describes the structures of the task and their decomposition in order to control the inferences of the inference layer.

In the work reported here on modelling reasoning strategies in accidentology, we have modelled expertise knowledge at the domain level of CommonKADS expertise model. We view the models of reasoning strategies we built at the inference level of CommonKADS expertise model. The instantiations of the reasoning strategies are done at the domain level. We have not dealt with the task level where we foresee the interactions of the reasoning strategies.

The CommonKADS expertise model for diagnosis by "generation and discrimination of hypotheses" provides a basis within which we can view some of the reasoning strategies found in medical problem solving (and re-used in accidentology). From our view point, the knowledge source "generate-hypothesis" is similar to our hypothesis generation strategy (from an observation to an hypothesis), whereas the knowledge source "discriminate-hypothesis" can be in fact subdivided into the strategies of confirmation and elimination of hypotheses. We see the strategies of specialisation and generalisation of hypotheses as an additional step between "generate hypothesis" and "discriminate hypothesis". The CommonKADS model is hypothesis oriented, and thus the problem refinement strategy which we identified in medical diagnosis does not seem to suit within this particular model.

In Benjamins (1994), the diagnostic task is decomposed into three sub tasks which can be realised using problem solving methods: 1) symptom detection, 2) hypothesis generation, and 3) hypothesis discrimination. This decomposition is called the prime diagnostic method. The author defines the following; A task (i.e. what needs to be achieved) is realised by problem solving methods (i.e. how the goal of a task can be achieved). A method consists of primitive inferences (i.e. an inference that can be carried out using domain knowledge to achieve a goal). A strategy is constituted by a particular configuration of inferences and control knowledge.

This definition of a strategy is more complex than the one we used in physics or medical problem solving and accidentology. Following this above terminology, we view our reasoning strategies as primitive inferences. The input and output roles of such inferences are related to our coding categories (e.g. clue, hypothesis, factor). We have not specified the tasks which reflect the contexts in which reasoning strategies are applied (e.g. analyse the conductor's interview, analyse the infrastructure checklist). A set of tasks for the accidentology has been defined in (Alpay et al., 1996b) and could be used to put our reasoning strategies in context. The interactions of reasoning strategies (not addressed here) would represent part of the control knowledge over those strategies. The physics tasks do contain a reasonably wide description of context, but more work needs to be done to develop the relationships between such features as student expectations of particular types of problem solving tasks.

While the CommonKADS generic model for diagnosis stems from an analysis of diagnostic problem solving by experts or expert systems in various areas such as medical diagnosis and diagnosis in engineering, our approach rather has relied more on an empirical study of diagnosis in different domains. We have not aimed to provide a generic model from the three cognitive modelling activities reported here but rather to examine aspects of comparison and re-usability. We need further evidence and support to carry out such a task. We have become aware that to consider satisfactorily the issue of what are successful generic approaches to modelling and reasoning strategies we need to consider a wider definition of task and strategy.

Conclusions

The work reported here on modelling diagnostic reasoning in physics problem solving was carried out independently, whereas the modelling tasks in medical problem solving and accidentology are closely linked as some aspects of the work for modelling medical diagnostic reasoning was purposely applied to another domain.

A number of relevant issues arisen from the three empirically based experiences were discussed in details. Certain aspects emerged in relation to contextual features and re-usability. We have distinguished between the contextual features of the domain, (focusing on its dependencies), and the contextual features of diagnostic modelling e.g. taking into account the types of protocols upon which the modelling is based. Furthermore, we highlighted criteria linked to these contextual features, such as the categorisation of data, the focus in the diagnosis and the level of detail.

From the examination of these three studies in which empirical data on diagnosis in different application domains was modelled, we have established the groundwork for some future investigations. These will include for example looking at other subject areas within our chosen target domains, as well as exploring the use of general cognitive modelling environment like COGENT to review the modelling work carried out in these three studies.

References

Alpay, L. (1996a). *Modelling of reasoning strategies, and representation through conceptual graphs: application to accidentology.* ACACIA Project, INRIA Research Report n.2810, Sophia-Antipolis, France.

Alpay, L., Amerge, C., Corby, O., Dieng, R., Giboin, A., Labidi, S., Lapalut, S., Despr/s, S., Ferrandez, F., Fleury, D., Girard, Y., Jourdan, J-L., Lechner, D., Michel, J-E., & Van Elslande, P. (1996b). *Acquisition et modélisation des connaissances d'experts en situation de coopération: application à un système d'aide àl'analyse des accidents de la route.* Rapport Final de Recherche DRAST no. 93.033 (MT R070), ACACIA Project, INRIA, Sophia-Antipolis, France.

Alpay, L. (1992). Alternate approaches to medical reasoning and diagnosis. In R. Moyse & M.T. Elsom-Cook (Eds.), *Knowledge Negotiation.* London: Academic Press Limited,

Anderson, J. (1993). *Rules of mind.* Hillsdale: Lawrence Erlbaum.

Anderson, J. (1980). *Cognitive Psychology and its implications.* Freeman.

Benjamins, R. (1994). On a role of problem solving methods in knowledge acquisition - Experiments with diagnostic strategies. In L. Steels, G. Schreiber, & W. Van Velde (Eds.), *Proceedings of 8th European Knowledge Acquisition Workshop* (pp. 137-157). Springer-Verlag.

Breuker J., & Van de Velde, W. (1994). *CommonKADS library for expertise modelling, Reusable Problem-Solving Components.* IOS Press.

Brownston, L., Farrell, R., Kant, E. & Martin, N. (1985). *Programming expert systems in OPS5: an introduction to rule-based programming.* Massachusetts: Addison-Wesley.

Clancey, W.J. (1986). From GUIDON to NEOMYCIN and HERACLES in twenty short lessons: ORN final report 1979-1985. *AI Magazine,* 40-60.

Cooper, R., Fox, J., Yule, P., & Sutton, D. (1997). COGENT: An environment for the development of cognitive models. *Chapter in this book.*

Cooper, R., Fox, J., Farringdon, J., & Shallice, T. (1996). A Systematic Methodology for Cognitive Modelling. *Artificial Intelligence,* 85, 3-44.

Dieng, R., Corby, O., Labidi, S. (1994). Expertise Conflicts in Knowledge Acquisition. In B.R. Gaines & M. Musen (Eds.), *Proceedings of the 8th Banff Knowledge Acquisition for Knowledge Based Systems Workshop, Banff, Canada,* Vol. 2.

Ericsson, K., & Simon, H. (1984). *Protocol analysis: verbal reports as data.* Boston, Mass.: MIT Press.

Elstein, A.S., Shulman, L.S., & Sprafka S.A. (1978). *Medical Problem Solving: An Analysis of Clinical Reasoning.* Cambridge, Mass: Harvard University Press.

Evans J., Newstead S.E., & Byrne R.M.J. (1993). *Human Reasoning: The psychology of deduction*. Hillsdale: Lawrence Erlbaum.

Evertsz, R. (1993). *The POPSI manual*. Technical Report, IET, The Open University, Milton Keynes, UK.

Ferrandez, F., Brenac, T., Girard, Y., Jourdan, J.-L., Lechner, D. Michel, J. E., Nachtergaele, C. (1995). *L'étude détaillée d'accidents orientée vers la sécurité primaire : Méthodologie de recueil et de pré-analyse*. INRETS, Presses de l'E.N.P.C.

Fleury, D., Fline, C., & Peytavin J.F. (1991). *Le diagnostic local de sécurité, outils et méthodes. Guide méthodologique*. Editions du Service d'Etudes Techniques des Routes et de Autoroutes (SETRA). Collection Etudes de Sécurité.

Geldof, S. (1994). Towards more flexibility in Reuse. *Proceedings of the 14th International Avignon Conference on Expert Systems, Paris, France*.

Johnson-Laird, P.N. (1983). *Mental Models*. Cambridge: Cambridge University Press.

Kahneman, D., Slovic, P., & Tversky, A. (1982). *Judgement under uncertainty: Heuristics and biases*. Cambridge: Cambridge University Press.

Karbach, W., Linster, M., & Voss, A. (1990). Models, methods, roles and tasks: many labels-one idea? *Knowledge Acquisition*, 2, 279-299.

Klix, F., & Bachmann, Th. (1998). Analogy recognition - Analogy construction. *Chapter in this book*.

Laird, J.E. (1986). *SOAR users manual:Version 4*. Intelligent Systems Laboratory, Xerox Palo Alto Research Centre, Palo Alto, California.

Lesgold, A.M. (1984). Acquiring expertise. In J.R. Anderson & S.M. Kosslyn (Eds), *Tutorials in Learning and Memory* (pp.31-60). New York: W.H. Freeman.

Martin, P. (1996). Exploitation de graphes conceptuels et de documents structurés et hypertextes pour l'acquisition de connaissances et la recherche d'informations. *Unpublished doctoral dissertation, Université de Nice - Sophia-Antipolis, France*.

Martin, P. (1995). Knowledge acquisition using documents, conceptual graphs and a semantically structured dictionary. *Proceedings of the 9th International Workshop on Acquisition Knowledge for Knowledge-Based Systems, Banff, Canada*, 9.1 - 9.19.

Neches, R., Langley, P., & Klahr, D. (1987). *Production system models of learning and development*. Cambridge: M.I.T. Press.

Nisbett, R., & Wilson, T. (1977). Telling more than we can know: verbal reports or mental processes. *Psychological Review*, 84, 231-259.

O'Shea, T. & Scanlon, E. (1989). *Recreating in SOAR an OPS model of physics problem solving*. Paper presented at the Second EUROSOAR meeting, Nottingham, UK.

Patel, V.L., & Groen, G.J. (1986). Knowledge based solution strategies in medical reasoning. *Cognitive Science,* 10, 91-116.

Rademakers, P., & Vanwelkenhuysen, J. (1992). Generic Models and their Support in Modelling Problem Solving Behaviour. In J-M. David, R. Simmons, & J-P. Krivine (Eds.). *Second Generation Experts Systems.* Heidelberg: Springer Verlag.

Ritter, F., R. M. Jones & Baxter, F. (1998). Reusable Models and Grafical Interfaces: Realising the potential of a unified theory of cognition. *Chapter in this book.*

Scanlon, E. (1993). Solving the problem of physics problem solving. *International Journal of Mathematics for Science and Technology,* 24 (3), 349-358.

Scanlon, E., & O'Shea, T. (1988). Cognitive economy in physics reasoning. In H. Mandl, & A. Lesgold (Eds.), *Learning Issues for Intelligent Tutoring Systems* (pp. 258-277).New York:Springer-Verlag.

Sowa, J. (1994). *Conceptual Structures: Information Processing in Mind and Machines.* Reading, MA: Addison-Wesley Publishing.

Tack, W.H. (1988). New approaches in research on cooperative conflict resolution by group decisions. *Acta Psychologica,* 68, 113-136.

Van Someren, M., Barnard, Y., & Sanberg, J. (1994). *The Think Aloud Method: a practical guilde to modelling cognitive processes.* London: Aademic Press.

Wielenga, B., Schreiber, Th., and Breuker J. (1992). KADS; a modelling approach to knwoledge engineering. *Knowledge Acquisition,* 4, 5-53.

Young, Y., & O'Shea, T. (1981). Errors in children's subtraction. *Cognitive Science,* 5, 153-177.

Acknowledgements

The authors wish to thank Pat Fung from the Open University for her comments on earlier versions of this paper.

Footnote

[1]Although the CommonKADS methodology was not used in the specific study reported for the accidentology domain, it was exploited in ACACIA for knowledge acquisition and modelling of multiple expertise (Alpay et al., 1996b).

2.3 A Computational Model for Creative Planning

Luís Macedo, Francisco C. Pereira, Carlos Grilo
& Amílcar Cardoso

Abstract

This paper describes a computational case-based model for creative planning. We explain a view of the creative process and also enumerate the properties of a creative product. Our approach is inspired in Wallas' model for the creative process in that he considers that creativity involves a sequence of four stages: preparation, incubation, illumination and verification. Preparation includes problem acquisition and background knowledge assimilation, which is represented by documented past experiences (cases). These cases are structured networks of hierarchically and temporally related case pieces. With the aim of achieving a flexible knowledge, these case pieces can be considered individually, providing the ability to recombine them in the incubation stage, and thus increasing the creative potential of the system. We sustain that illumination may comprise recursive calls of the sequence of the first three stages. This computational model is implemented in the system INSPIRER/SICOM. We show how a musical composition task may be cognitively modelled and treated as a planning task. A short example illustrating how INSPIRER/SICOM generates music is presented.

Introduction

Attempting to model the creative abilities of the human mind with computers is a hard task. This is because, first of all, human creativity is still an unclear issue, that keeps challenging many cognitive science researchers. Nevertheless, some progress has been achieved in this field, although leading to many opposite and non-complete theories.

Creativity may be present in four main types of acts: creation, invention, discovery and production (Cabezas, 1993; for more details about discovery see Grasshoff & May, 1998).

Although there are four main perspectives to creativity (the creative person, the creative environment, the creative product, or creative act, and the creative process), the creative process and the creative product perspectives are the most addressed in the literature (Brown, 1989). This may mean that these two are also the most important of the four perspectives.

The literature refers to two main concepts as related to the act of creation: bringing into existence something original and novel which did not exist before; giving an original manner of existence to something that already exists. However, everybody seems to agree that one cannot generate new things out of nothing. Besides originality, appropriateness is also referred to by the authors as an important characteristic of a creative product (Ibáñez, 1991). Cabezas (1993), for instance, states that creativity results from the combination of previous ideas, experiences, elements, phenomena, images, realities, etc., in a new, original and useful way.

Although there are several explanation models for the creative process, we are interested in those entailed in problem-solving (also called cognitive models). From the main initial problem-solving models, Good Problem Solving, Creative Production, and Invention, proposed by J. Dewey, Wallas and Rossman, respectively (as cited in Brown, 1989), Wallas' model has won much acceptance in the cognitive research community. He proposed that creativity involves four sequential steps: preparation, incubation, illumination (or insight, Knoblich & Ohlsson, 1998) and verification.

Spiro (as cited in Armbruster, 1989) defended that flexible knowledge is a prerequisite for knowledge restructuring and hence for creativity. He sustains that flexible knowledge representation is that in which fragments of knowledge are represented in a way that allows them to be reassembled into new knowledge structures. Knowledge-based retrieval systems (Koton, 1989) are a consequence of combining nearest neighbour and knowledge-guided techniques. These systems are characterised by the use of domain knowledge for the construction of explanations as to why a problem had a particular solution in the past.

Case-Based Reasoning (CBR) systems represent this domain knowledge by cases (Kolodner, 1993). They are particularly appropriate for domains where a strong theory does not exist but past experience is accessible.

The products of creation may be plans, designs, etc. A plan is a specific sequence of steps (or actions) with the aim of goal achievement. Case-Based Planning (CBP) systems (Veloso, 1992) re-use past sequences of actions from past plans to construct new ones.

Linda Wills and Janet Kolodner (1994) proposed a model for creative design based on three steps: enumeration of several alternative solutions; re-description and elaboration of problem specifications; and evaluation of proposed solutions.

In this paper we will focus on a computational case-based model for the creative planning process. Our approach to creativity is based on the Wallas' model, although we adopt a non-linear, recursive execution of the four sequential stages. We think that the potential solution for the problem obtained at the illumination stage may be comprised of other problems and each one of them may recursively lead to a sequence of three stages: preparation, incubation and illumination. The global validation of the entire solution is made at the verification stage. Our approach to creativity is presented in the next section. In section 3 we introduce our computational model for creative planning, subdivided in four phases. Section 4 presents an application in the musical composition domain. We also explain how the musical composition process may be cognitively modelled and treated as a planning task. A short example illustrating how music is generated by INSPIRER/SICOM is presented in section 5. Finally, some conclusions about our work are presented in section 6.

Our approach to creativity modelling

In broad words, we feel that creativity is characterised by linking, combining, associating or integrating different (and possibly contrary) things in the same product (the creative product) directly or using metaphoric and analogical techniques (Klix & Bachmann, 1998). In this sense, we'll now expose our perspectives on the creative product and the creative process.

On the creative product point of view, there is a general consensus that it must be original and appropriate (Cabezas, 1993).

An original product is characterised by being:

1. Novel, i.e., not common, not conventional and not frequent. E.g., Copernicus's theory was a new scientific product, which no one had proposed before.

2. Singular, i.e., it must be unique, idiosyncratic, peculiar and personal. E.g., every musician or writer has a particular style, which is preserved in his/her products.

3. Somehow unpredictable, i.e., the creative activity uses and changes in an unpredictable way what already exists. This means these products are not totally or perfectly explained. They are a consequence of some inspiration. E.g., it is not possible to explain why J. S. Bach created *The Art of Fugue* in that way and not in another.

An appropriate product is:

1. Useful by satisfying a need, i.e., it must be something that provides a better existence to someone (solving a problem), or causing him/her particular emotions.

2. Coherent, i.e., without incompatibilities between its parts and executable.

As a consequence of these characteristics, a creative product is surprising, i.e., it causes a psychological and unexpected astonishment.

We based our explanation model for the creative process on Wallas' work. Its adequate (in our opinion) explanation of the creative process, judging by the reports of creative persons about their creative experiences, has weighted on our choice. Being a general approach we think it may be adapted specifically to creative planning. Thus we consider that a creative product (plan, design, etc.) is obtained trough performing the following steps:

1. Preparation. This phase includes: (i) a formulation of the problem in the sense of knowing what is to be solved; (ii) an accumulation or assimilation of knowledge, to which we call background knowledge necessary to create something.

2. Incubation. This phase corresponds to the generation and formulation of possible solutions. This process can be unconscious or partially conscious. During this phase, the problem is being pursued, and the flexibly organised background knowledge, acquired during the previous phase, is being restructured into new schemata, i.e., new mental structures are created by re-combinations and re-orderings of the original knowledge (Armbruster, 1989). Concurrently to this knowledge restructuring, new knowledge may be acquired which may lead to new re-combinations or may fill some lacking piece of knowledge, and then the solution may be completed conducing to the illumination stage, or at least augmented, just like putting a missing piece in an incomplete puzzle, and the incubation proceeds. This kind of knowledge is called opportunistic knowledge and the process, opportunistic reasoning (Hammond, 1988).

This is particularly clear in situations where illumination or insight comes when mental work is not pursuing the problem, but suddenly receives news experiences that directly or by analogical reasoning constitute or are conducive to the solution of the problem.

3. Illumination. In this stage the solution is consciously proposed. This solution may imply the decomposition of the problem into sub-problems, which will be recursively pursued through the first phases of the creative process.

4. Verification. In this stage the creative properties (novelty, usefulness, etc.) of the solution are tested and some revisions and adaptations are made if necessary. If the solution is still considered as a non-creative product, then it may be rejected and the whole sequence may be repeated from the beginning, trying to find a new solution.

A computational model for the creative planning process

In this section we describe our creative planning process from a computational point of view.

Preparation

Background knowledge

As was said above, the creative process is based on previous knowledge which we represent by cases. Since we deal with creative planning, cases are plans.

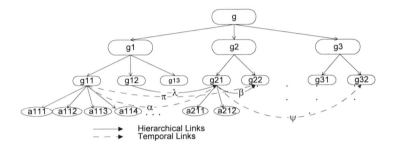

Figure 1: Case structure as a tree-like network of hierarchically and temporally related case pieces.

Within our approach a case plan is a set of goals and actions organised in a hierarchical way (Figure 1): a main goal (the main problem) is refined into sub-goals (the sub-problems), and so on, until reaching the actions (the leaf nodes of the tree) that satisfy the goals.

It is worth noting that although the actions are represented by the leaf nodes, some of their properties (attributes) are inherited from the attributes of their hierarchical ascendants.

In our model each node of the hierarchical structure corresponds to a case piece. To complete the case structure there are links between case pieces, representing causal justifications, or explanations. Some of these links maintain the hierarchical case structure, others reflect causal temporal relations between case pieces. Thus, the existence of a case piece in a plan case is causally explained by several case pieces of the same case plan.

Considering the hierarchical links only (represented in Figure 1 by continuous arrows), the inherent meaning of the represented structure is: g, the main goal of the plan (or the main problem), is achieved by sequentially achieving sub-goals (sub-problems) *g1, g2* and *g3*. Each one of these sub-goals is also broken up into other sub-goals.

For example, $g1$ is broken up into $g11$, $g12$ and $g13$, and $g2$ into $g21$ and $g22$. To achieve the goal $g11$, the actions $a111$, $a112$, $a113$ and $a114$ must be sequentially executed by this temporal order.

Besides being explained by the goal-refinement process, through hierarchical links, a case piece may also be explained through temporal links (represented in Figure 1 by discontinuous arrows). For example, $g21$ (sub-goal of $g2$) is a consequence of case pieces $g11$ and $g12$, which is represented by the temporal links labelled α and λ, respectively.

A case piece has seven types of information describing its relevant aspects: a name that uniquely identifies the case piece, the name of the case to which the case piece belongs, the case piece address, the constraints, a set of attribute/value pairs, the antecedents and the consequents.

The address of a case piece represents its hierarchical (level) and temporal position on the case (for more details see Pereira, Grilo, Macedo & Cardoso, 1997).

Further information in a case piece is a set of attribute/value pairs describing several properties which characterise the case piece.

The constraints are also attribute/value pairs. The semantics of a set of constraints $C = \{a_1 = vc_1, a_2 = vc_2, ...,a_n = vc_n\}$ of a case piece $\underline{p}$ is: if $\underline{p}$ ascendants have any of the attributes $a_1,a_2, ...,a_n$, then its values must not be different from, respectively, vc_1, vc_2, ...,vc_n; otherwise, $\underline{p}$ is incoherent with its ascendants. Thus constraints play the role of determining whether or not the case piece is a candidate occupying a missing piece (see below) in a solution, depending on whether or not they are coherent with the attributes of the missing piece's hierarchical ascendants.

Antecedents and consequents are causal links that follow, respectively, from and to other case pieces. Antecedent links show how a case piece is explained by the existence of other case pieces (e.g. in Figure 1, $g21$ is explained by $g11$ and $g12$ through the links labelled α and λ, respectively, and by $g2$ through a father link). Consequent links show how a case piece explains the existence of other case pieces (e.g., in Figure 1, $g21$ partially explains $g22$ and $g32$ through links β and ψ, respectively, and $a211$ and $a212$ through father links).

Each antecedent or consequent link is classified according to two main kinds of links: hierarchical and temporal ones (described above).

Sometimes the type of relation between antecedent fact(s) and the consequent one may be unknown. This lack of a complete theory is common in CBR (Bento, Macedo & Costa, 1994).

This idea leads to another classification of the links between case pieces: we say that a link between the case pieces *a* and *b* is explicit if we know it well and so we are able to represent it. Otherwise we name it implicit. In Figure 1, *g13* implicitly explains *g21*. There is not an actual link between them, but it is coherent to assume that the existence of *g21* is partially due to the previous occurrence of *g13*. We may also say that g implicitly explains *g21*, although there is not a well known relation between them.

We call the *case piece context* to the set of case pieces that surround it. We distinguish eight types of contexts according to the kind of link existing between the case piece considered and the surrounding ones. Thus, each one of these surrounding case pieces is included in one of the contexts of the set C = {antecedent-hierarchical-implicit context, antecedent-hierarchical-explicit context, antecedent-temporal-implicit context, antecedent-temporal-explicit context, consequent-hierarchical-implicit context, consequent-hierarchical-explicit context, consequent-temporal-implicit context or consequent-temporal-explicit context}. Notice that the name of the context reflects the classification of the link to the case piece. For example, in Figure 1, the antecedent-temporal-explicit context of *g21* is{*g11, g12*}(for more details see Pereira, Grilo, Macedo & Cardoso, 1997).

Problem

A new problem to be solved by the system may comprise a set of linked case pieces. At least the main goal (the root case piece) must be included, with its name, address, constraints and attributes of information instantiated.

The meaning associated to a problem description composed by the main goal is the following: the system must find a structured plan solution to achieve the goal; the solution must satisfy the goal's constraints.

If the problem also includes sub-goals or actions with the same instantiated information types, then the meaning of the problem description is augmented by the following: the system must find a structured plan solution to achieve the goal; the solution must satisfy the goal's constraints and must achieve the specified sub-goals and perform the specified actions. Thus a problem may be a partial structured solution given by the user. The system just has to coherently complete it.

Incubation

At this stage, the main goal is solved by re-combining sub-goals or actions of previous cases. Since the complete information about this goal is not already known (for example, the number of sub-goals that are necessary to achieve it or the links that follow from it may be unknown at this point), the main goal that best matches the considered one is retrieved from a case in memory. The next step is retrieving the main goal's sons from memory, starting by the oldest, assuming its context (currently, the retrieved main goal) and its address as indexes.

The process of retrieving a case piece from memory is the following: Consider that π is the structured solution currently being constructed, and π_j a place in solution π in which a case piece is missing. The retrieval of a case piece to be placed in π_j involves the following steps:

1. Construction of the set of candidate case pieces by selecting those which belong to the same level of π_j.

2. Application of a constraint-based filter to the case pieces selected in 1., eliminating those whose constraints are incompatible with the attributes of the π_j's ascendants. This step is performed as follows: Given a case piece p presented in memory, candidate to fill π_j, and given the set of constraints $L_c = \{c_1 = vc_1, c_2 = vc_2, ..., c_n = vc_n\}$ of case piece p, and the union of the sets of attribute-value pairs $L_a = \{a_1 = va_1, a_2 = va_2, ..., a_m = va_m\}$ of the hierarchical ascendants of π_j, then p is not filtered from the set of candidate case pieces to fill π_j if and only if: $\forall i \in \{1,2,...,n\}$, $\forall j \in \{1,2,...,m\}$, $\forall a_j = va_j \in L_a$, $\sim\exists c_i = vc_i \in L_c : c_i = a_j \wedge vc_i \neq va_j$.

3. Application of a similarity metric value (Macedo et al., 1997) to each candidate case piece, taking into account the similarity between the context, the attributes and the address of π_j and the context, the attributes and the address of the candidate case piece p.

4. Ranking of the candidate case pieces by their similarity metric value.

5. Selection of the case piece according to the criterion established by the user to the current hierarchical level (each level has selection criterion. For example, in level 1 the selected case piece may be the one with the greater similarity metric value, but in level 4, it may be the one with the lesser similarity metric value).

6. Validation of placing the selected case piece on π_j. This step comprises the verification of link incompatibilities between the selected case piece and the partially constructed solution

for the given problem. Performing one of the following options solves these incompatibilities: (i) relaxing incompatibilities; (ii) selecting another case piece.

The similarity metric value for a case piece is expressed in percentage. Thus, when a case piece has a similarity value equal to x%, this means that its context, attributes and address is x% similar to the context, attributes and address of the free position. Selection of a case piece involves the computation of a similarity metric value for it and the consideration of the selection criterion. This means that first the candidate case pieces are ranked by their similarity metric value, and then the established criterion for that level determines which case piece is selected. This criterion reflects the degree of originality needed in that level. For example, the user may want no originality at all at level 1 , because at this level new solutions are usually similar to old ones. However, he/she may also want solutions with a maximum of 50% of originality in level 5. Therefore, at this level, the candidate case pieces with a similarity value less than 50% are not considered for selection. The first one tried for selection is the one with a similarity value equal or higher than 50%. This means that the re-combination of case pieces is not made by chance, but instead considering the needed originality. It is worthy of notice, that we are not proposing a definite measure of originality. Instead, we are assuming the simplist and highly arguable view that "the more differeht, the more original".

After a case piece is selected, it is submitted to a validation process consisting of the verification of incompatibilities between the selected case piece and the partially constructed solution for the given problem. At this point there may be links that follow from earlier case pieces, pointing to the free position.

We call them suggestions, as they correspond to proposed but not definitive links.

If an incompatibility exists between a suggestion and an antecedent link of the selected case piece there are two choices: (i) try to adapt it, relaxing the validation by ignoring the less important of the incompatible links (e.g., if the suggestion is strong and the antecedent link of the selected case piece is weak, the validation step substitutes the second link by the former one in the selected case piece, and then this case piece is added to the new case); (ii) if it was not possible to adapt it, select another one (taking into account the criterion for that level) and apply the validation step to it.

Illumination

At this stage the solution constructed in the incubation stage is proposed. However, as we said, the solution may include problems. Each one of these problems initiates another sequence of three stages (preparation, incubation, illumination) until its solution is found. This solution may also be composed of other problems, and so on.

Verification

The entire solution is submitted to a validation and test concerning its originality and appropriateness. At the current stage of the development of INSPIRER/SICOM, verification is performed by the user.

An application in the Musical Composition Domain

As studied by Lerdahl and Jackendoff (1983), Balaban (1992) and Honning (1993), music is a domain in which structure, hierarchy and time are more than occasional keywords. Music is indeed a highly structured and organised world. As stated by Balaban, any music can be represented by a hierarchy of temporal objects (an object associated with a temporal duration), in such a way that each one has, as descendants, a sequence of sub-objects that starts and ends at the same starting and end point as the object's. Figure 2 shows an example.

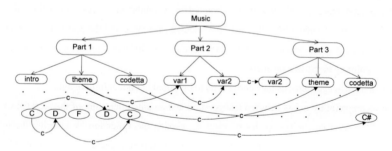

Figure 2: A case in the musical domain showing the tree-like structure of a piece of music.

There are important relations in music, since many musical objects may be causally explained by a transformation (like *repetition, variation, inversion, transposition*, etc.) of some other object. These causal relations are represented through temporal links (*c* links in Figure 2) which correspond to the associated transformations (e.g. the temporal link between *theme* of *part1* and *var1* of *part2* may represent a *variation* transformation which, when applied to *theme* originates *var1*).

The goal of our application is to use music analysis as a foundation for a generative process of composition, providing a structured and constrained way of composing creative pieces, but nevertheless keeping the essential traits of the composer's style. We use analysis of music pieces by a seventeenth century portuguese composer (Carlos Seixas).

Since a music piece is a temporal sequence of actions (for example sequences of musical notes) we may consider it as a plan, and therefore the act of composing as a planning task.

The use of four stages to perform a musical creation is corroborated by musicians' experiences.

In fact, they start by considering the main problem (e.g., a sonata), which is solved by a sequence of another set of problems (e.g., Part1, Part2 and Part3). These problems are also solved analogously, and so on, until reaching the deepest level. After this, the entire music is validated and , if necessary, some revisions are made.

An example

In this section we briefly illustrate the musical generation process used by INSPIRER/SICOM.

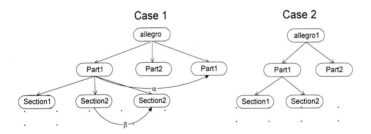

Figure 3: Cases initially presented in memory.

Preparation

The system was seeded with two musical cases partially represented in Figure 3. The problem given to the system (represented by the PROLOG fact *case_node(new_case, allegro, 0, [],* *[ton='I',comp=2/4],_,_))* is to come up with a music sonata characterised by having binary measure and tonality 'I'.

Incubation

First, a case piece with more similarities than the one represented in the problem is retrieved from a case in memory.

For the current problem, and considering that INSPIRER/SICOM has case 1 and case 2 in memory, the system retrieved the main goal of case 1, since it is the one with more similarities to the goal proposed as problem. At this point, the solution is the one presented in Figure 4 - (i).

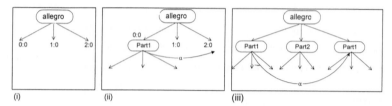

(i)   (ii)   (iii)

Figure 4: Sequence of some steps in the generation of a new case.

The next step is finding a sequence of three nodes which will jointly form a solution to the problem. The first free position to be filled is the one with address 0:0. The system found in memory the following set of candidate pieces, which are ranked by similarity of metric value with the new case's free position of address 0:0: *Part1* from case 1, *Part1* from case 2 would be, *Part2* from case 1, *Part2* from case 2. The selection of one of these pieces depends on the used criterion. In this level the criterion is to select the most similar. Therefore *Part1* from case 1 is selected. However, if the criterion was to select the less similar, then *Part1* from case 2 would be selected. But, before its addition to the solution, this piece is submitted to a compatibility test. Since it does not have any incompatibilities with other pieces of the current solution, it is added to it (Figure 4 - (ii)).

The next step is retrieving a node for the free position with address 1:0, and then to the free position with address 2:0. The system chooses *Part2* from case1 and *Part1* also from case 1, respectively (Figure 4 - (iii)). Thus the solution is reached.

Illumination

The solution is the temporal sequence of *Part1, Part2* and *Part1 (repetition)*.

However, these pieces are also unsolved problems. Consequently, each one is included in a new preparation stage. The system starts by *Part1* to which it finds the following solution:

Section1 from case 1, *Section2* from case 1, and *Section2* from case 1 *(repetition)*. Then it takes *Part2* as a problem and in a similar way achieves a solution to it.

These solutions also include problems and the process is recursively repeated until reaching the actions (in this application, the actions are the music notes).

Verification

The entire solution presented to the user by the system is validated by an expert.

Conclusions

We have presented an approach to a computational model for creative planning, taking as source cases of past plans. With the aim of dealing with flexible knowledge, cases are split into pieces, providing a wide variety of re-combinations of these pieces. These re-combinations, rather than made by chance, are guided by the similarities between the context (defined by the links), the attributes and the address of the case pieces in memory and of the free position on the *under construction* solution.

As stated by Wallas, the creative process involves four stages. However, we defend that the potential solution proposed in the illumination stage may comprise a problem decomposition.

As shown, the musical composition process may be considered as a planning task and is an appropriate domain to our creative approach, judging by the reports of musicians about their creative experiences. However, other domains like story or screenplay generation are also possible applications for INSPIRER.

References

Armbruster, B. (1989). Metacognition in Creativity. In J. Gloves, R. Ronning, & C. Reynolds (Eds.), *Handbook of Creativity* (pp.177-182). New York: Plenum Press.

Balaban, M. (1992). Musical Structures: Interleaving the Temporal and Hierarchical Aspects in Music. In M. Balaban, K. Ebcioglu, & O. Laske (Eds.), *Understanding Music with AI: Perspectives in Music Cognition* (pp. 110-138). Cambridge, England: AAAI Press/MIT Press.

Bento, C., Macedo, L., & Costa, E. (1994). RECIDE - Reasoning with Cases Imperfectly Described and Explained. In M. Keane, J. Halton, & M. Manago (Eds.), *Proceedings of the Second European Workshop on Case-Based Reasoning* (pp. 263-272). Paris: Springer Verlag.

Brown, R. (1989). Creativity: What are we to measure?. In J. Gloves, R. Ronning, & C. Reynolds (Eds.), *Handbook of Creativity* (pp.3-31). New York: Plenum Press.

Cabezas, J. (1993). *La Creatividad. Teoría básica e implicaciones pedagógicas* [Creativity. Basic Theory and Pedagogical Implications]. Salamanca, Spain: Libreria Cervantes.

Grasshoff, G., & May, M. (1997). Cognitive Modelling of Scientific Discovery Processes. In *Proceedings of the First European Workshop on Cognitive Modelling.*

Hammond, K. (1988). Opportunistic Memory: Storing and recalling suspended goals. In J. Kolodner (Ed.), *Proceedings: Workshop on Case-Based Reasoning* (pp. 154-168). San Mateo, CA: MorganKaufmann.

Honning (1993). Issues in the representations of time and structure in music. *Contemporary Music Review, 9,* 221-239.

Ibáñez, R. M., (1991). Definicion de la creatividad. In R. Marin, & S. De La Torre (Eds.), *Manual de la Creatividad* [Handbook of Creativity], Barcelona: Vicens Vive.

Klix, F., & Bachmann, T. (1998). Analogy Recognition - Analogy Construction. In U. Schmid, J. F. Krems, & F. Wysotzki (Eds.), *Mind Modelling: A Cognitive Science Approach to Reasoning, Learning and Discovery*. Lengerich: Pabst Science Publishers.

Kolodner, J. (1993). *Case-Based Reasoning*, San Mateo, CA: Morgan-Kaufmann.

Koton, P., (1989). Using Experience in Learning and Problem Solving (Doctoral dissertation, Massachusets Institute of Technology, Laboratory of Computer Science). MIT/LCS/TR-441.

Knoblich, G., & Ohlsson, S. (1997). Computational Modelling of Insight. In *Proceedings of the First European Workshop on Cognitive Modelling.*

Lerdahl, F., & Jackendoff, R. (1983). *A Generative Theory of Tonal Music*. Cambridge, England: MIT Press.

Macedo, L., Pereira, F. C., Grilo, C., & Cardoso, A. (1997). Experimental Study of a Similarity Metric for Retrieving Pieces from Structured Plan Cases: its Role in the Originality of Case Solutions. In D. Leake, & E. Plaza (Eds.), *Proceedings of the Second International Conference on Case-Based Reasoning*, New York: Springer Verlag.

Pereira, F.C., Grilo, C., Macedo, L. & Cardoso, A. (1997). A Structured Framework for Representing Time in a Generative Composing System. *Proceedings of the International Workshop on Temporal Reasoning.*Florida, USA

Veloso, M. (1992). Learning by Analogical Reasoning in General Problem Solving (Doctoral dissertation, School of Computer Science, Carnegie Mellon University).

Wills, L., & Kolodner, J. (1994). Towards More Creative Case-Based Design Systems. *Proceedings of the Twelfth National Conference (AAAI-94)*. Seatle: AAAI Press.

Author's Note

Luís Macedo, Instituto Superior de Engenharia de Coimbra and Centro de Informática e Sistemas de Coimbra, Coimbra, Portugal; Francisco C. Pereira, Carlos Grilo and Amílcar Cardoso, Centro de Informática e Sistemas da Universidade de Coimbra, Portugal.

The computational modelling of creative planning is an ongoing study conducted at the Center for Computer Studies and Systems of the University of Coimbra, in collaboration with the Coimbra School of Music. We would like to thank Anabela Simões and António Andrade, teachers at the Coimbra School of Music for their valuable contribution, and Ofélia Libório for her comments on psychological issues.

This work was partially founded by a grant ref. Praxis XXI BD 9611/96 attibuted to Francisco C. Pereira.

Correspondence concerning this article should be addressed to Luís Macedo, Instituto Superior de Engenharia de Coimbra, Quinta da Nora, 3030 Coimbra, Portugal, or to Amílcar Cardoso, Departamento de Engenharia Informática da Universidade de Coimbra, Polo II, 3030 Coimbra Portugal. Electronic mail may be sent to macedo@eden.dei.uc.pt or to amilcar@eden.dei.uc.pt

2.4 Analogy Detection - Analogy Construction

(An Approach to Similarity in Higher Order Reasoning)

FRIEDHART KLIX & THOMAS BACHMANN

Introduction

Analogical reasoning is a curious kind of mental activity. It is neither reducible to inductive nor to deductive reasoning, and it is not an example for abduction (see Krems in this volume). It relies on a specific kind of correspondence between different knowledge domains. The correspondence itself seems to be controlled by specific identification of similarities. The example: MONTGOMERY WAS THE WELLINGTON OF EL ALAMAIN means that battles in World War II remind one of Waterloo. Both are characterized by a specific resemblance: the similar role of two outstanding historical figures. Another example is given by the analogy: THE SHARK IS THE WOLF OF THE OCEAN. This example refers to similarities in the behavior of two different predators in two different habitats. In both cases there are similar and dissimilar components between the respective knowledge areas. Another kind of example arises by comparisons of properties of different concepts: SHARK : FISH :: TREE : PLANT. In this example one concept is superordinated to another.

All three examples show similarities between the respective concepts, but they show dissimilarities as well. This reminds one of the statement of Gentner & Markman (1993) "Similarity is like analogy". They are obviously right in the sense that similarities play a major role in detecting and understanding analogies. However, analogies seem to be more than similarities. The crucial point is that analogical reasoning sometimes opens doors to new knowledge and surprising insights. The comparison between different kinds of comparable knowledge reveal more information than each of the analogy components contains for itself (see Tourangeau & Rips, 1991).

Analogical reasoning is a process of cognition. Obviously the process of analogy-detection and analogical mapping includes different inductive and deductive components. For that reason it is difficult with a kind of creative thinking to produce analogies and much easier to understand a given analogy by the mutual mapping of information contents (see Michalski, 1989). However it is not reducible to these components of human reasoning at all.

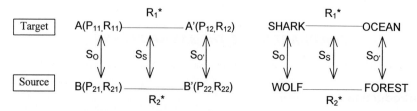

Figure 1: A commutative diagram describing the conceptual structure of analogies: A source-area B - B' is mapped onto a target-area A - A'. The concepts (A, B) are defined by property sets (P_{ij}) and relations (R_{ij}) to other concepts. The analogy is due to the common relations R_1* and R_2*. S describes the similarity between both conceptual areas (S_o - Similarity of object-concepts, S_S -Structural similarity of the relations).

To point out the invariant structure of the examples we use a commutative diagram (Fig. 1). A and A′ represent a target knowledge domain (i.e. concepts with properties (P_{1j}) and possible relations (R_{1j}) to other concepts) and higher order relations (R_1*) between them. B and B' denote another concept area, the source, with different properties (P_{2j}) and possible relations (R_{2j}) and higher order relations R_2* between them. In the case of SHARK : FISH (A - A′) and TREE : PLANT (B - B') each pair has properties in common $P_{i1} \cap P_{i2} > \varnothing$ ($\varnothing$ is the empty set) and others in which they differ ($P_{i1} \cap P_{i2} \neq \varnothing$). A crucial point in order to understand the heart of an analogy is the R_i* relations. It connects the two concepts by a higher order relation. If there is a relation so that $P_{11} \subset P_{12}$ then R_i* indicates that there is a sub-super-concept relation (like TREE : PLANT). If the same relation holds between P_{21} and P_{22} then R_1* $\approx R_2$* and the two pairs are analogous to each other.

The WELLINGTON-MONTGOMERY or the SHARK-WOLF analogy are more difficult. Concerning the latter, it is obvious that the location of both is one common relation R_1* $\approx R_2$*, another one could be the similar predator-prey behavior.

In view of our everyday acquaintance with analogies we have to distinguish between two kinds of mental procedures: (1) to recognize that there is an analogy in the defined sense and (2) to produce or construct such a cognitive structure. The first case is widely investigated. A huge literature exists on analogy recognition (see Gentner, 1983, 1989; Gick & Holyoak, 1980; Rumelhart, 1989; Sternberg, 1977, Klix 1992b). It is generally accepted that the acceptation procedure is based on two mechanisms: on the detection of similarities (identical vs. different components in the respective level) and on mapping procedures between the two areas which leads to a decision as to whether R_1^* and R_2^* are sufficiently similar or not.

The process of analogy construction is more complex and difficult than the process of analogy recognition. Hence, at the beginning only one knowledge structure is given, say A - A′, and it is open as to whether a similar knowledge area B - B' exists at all (in general there is not only one similar area in memory, but more). The crucial point is how such an analogous area of knowledge can be found in memory and what are the steps during the analogy-construction process.

A very specific and significant case is given if there are not only simple concepts in the A - A′ area (like OAK and TREE and COLLIE and DOG) but more conceptual connections (like SLAUGTHER and SELL) or event-sequences (like TRAVEL and ARRIVE). In these cases we have to assume a construction process beginning in the A $\xrightarrow{sim}$ B comparison and properly pursue step by step constructing an appropriate A' $\xrightarrow{sim}$ B' level which contains $R_1^* \approx R_2^*$ between A and A' and B and B' respectively ($\approx$ means a sufficient correspondence, i.e. similarity degree between sim and sim '). It may also happen that the relational connections between the events A - A' are new and unknown, and it may be therefore relevant to derive an explanation of these A - $R_1^*(?)$ - A' connections, and it may also be the case that a corresponding (or sufficiently similar) B - B' level involves an (hypothetical) explanation for what is going on in the A - A' domain as an event sequence. An example may be given by the phenomenon of lightning and the following thunder. The connection of the two was unknown for naive people in the past. The old Teutons gave an explanation with an analogy: They found the similar event in a forge. They explained: The god of the forge drives during a thunderstorm across heaven, swinging his hammer and producing the lightning like the blacksmith in his forge. Here we have a typical analogical inference: unknown visible connections are explained by similar properties in a known knowledge area.

It makes sense that the visible but unexplainable relation in area A - $R_1^*(?)$ - A′ is defined as the target area and the possibly explaining background B - R_2^* - B' as the source area. Finding an explaining source area often resembles some types of problem solving processes. The process of analogy finding may often be some kind of intelligent behavior.[21]

---

[21] It is interesting to note that well known intelligence tests like the Raven test use analogy terms. However the process which underlies an intelligent solution is widely unknown and remains unconsidered.

To sum up this introduction one can say that analogical reasoning involves three different kinds of cognitive achievements: (1) to detect similarities by comparison procedures, (2) to induce or generate similarities by search processes, and (3) to resolve an open or unknown connection by identifying similar phenomena of behavior in another knowledge domain. In short: to explain the A - R_1*(?) - A' connection by a B - R_2* - B' substitution. The key is to find a source domain which is suitable to explain the phenomena in the A - A' domain. Obviously similarities between different knowledge areas play a major role in the reasoning process. We will focus on this point in the next section.

First, we define different components of our conceptual knowledge: concepts of different complexity and possible components of their similarities. Second, we introduce two experiments concerning similarity judgments among event-related conceptual knowledge. Third, we outline an experiment which we carried out to analyze different strategies during analogy finding (which is really analogy construction). Finally, the results will be discussed and a model for knowledge representation and analogy construction will be proposed.

Simple and complex similarities depending on concept types

Sufficient reasons are given that an exact definition of similarities between concepts might be a suitable approach to tackle the analogical reasoning process - at least so far as it depends on similarities between concepts. However concepts are very different.

In our research group at Humboldt University (see Klix 1992b; van der Meer 1987; Preuß, 1985; Schmieschek, 1988) we have shown that it is necessary to distinguish different types of concepts and different types of relations between them. This is important because they are of different complexity and they involve different components which influence the overall impression of similarity.

The first type are (simple) *object-concepts* such as TREE, APPLE or BIRD or more abstract concepts such as GUILT, HONOUR, or AUTHORITY. They are defined by sets of properties and relations (P_{ij} and R_{ij} in Figure 1). Similarity between them is determined by their common and different properties (see Tversky, 1977). *Property-determined relations* are e.g. sub- super- ordination, coordination, synonymity, antonymity, and attribute-relation.

The second type are *event-concepts*. They classify every-day life situations such as TEACH, BUY or SELL. They are structurally defined by a semantic core (usually a verb) and a specific set of semantic *event-relations* to object-concepts: The concept TEACH demands an ACTor (TEACHER) teaching has a RECipient (STUDENT) an OBJect (BIOLOGY) with an INStrument (VIDEO), at a specific LOCation (SCHOOL), a specific goal or purpose (the

ACTor-Purpose-Connection (A-P) e.g. TO ACQUIRE KNOWLEDGE). Other concept types refer to TRANSFormations of the properties of the recipients or the objects (SLAUGTHER, SAW) or of TRANSITions in space or time (GIVE, OVERTAKE).

Finally, there are concepts which are defined by sequences of events. Characteristic concepts are HOLIDAYS, MARRIAGE or the famous RESTAURANT VISIT. These events are connected by higher order relations such as CAUSALITY, CONDITION or TEMPORAL ORDERS.

Figure 2 shows a possible representation of a complex event-sequence consisting of three types of concepts and three types of semantic relations between them.

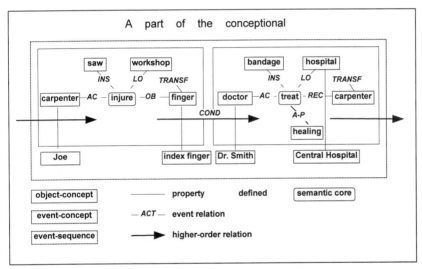

Figure 2: A representational model for a complex knowledge domain. The event-sequence (INJURE-TREAT) consists of two event-concepts with associated object-concepts defined by a property set. All concept types induce different types of semantic relations (higher-order relations, event-relations and property-determined relations). Different cognitive procedures allow the horizontal or vertical access to concepts or to other knowledge areas.

How can we apply these assumptions in order to describe the role of similarity in the process of analogy detection or construction? To illustrate this question let us turn back to the example: THE SHARK IS THE WOLF OF THE OCEAN. What are the correspondences between the two knowledge domains? Is it the similarity between SHARK and WOLF or is it the relation 'lives in...'?, or just the predatory behavior? Applying our model of conceptual representation the analogy has the following relational and conceptual structure (Figure 3).

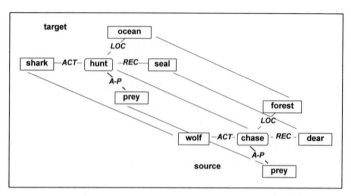

Figure 3: The full relational structure of an analogy with event-concepts. The doted lines indicate the corresponding object-concepts and the possible points for similarity comparisons. Note that in this example both semantic cores (HUNT and CHASE) have the same relational structure.

We cannot suppose that only the property-determined similarity between SHARK and WOLF controls the construction of this analogy. If all these several components (concepts and relations) influence the similarity impression, the property similarity models (e. g. Tversky, 1977) are probably not sufficient in this case. The approach should become generalized in the sense that relational connections between the concepts are included. This generalized measure demands the detailed description of the relational structure of event-concepts.

We have shown in many experiments that the number and kind of event-relations within an event-concept is well defined (for more see Klix, 1992a, 1992b). However they vary between different event-concepts. For example in the concept SHOPPING the relations ACTor, RECipient, OBJect, LOCation, and TRANSITion are relevant. In the concept WALKING the relations ACTor, LOCation, and TRANSITion are relevant. Hence, a possible way to measure the similarity between event-concepts could be an extension of the Tversky-Measure, computing the common and the different semantic relations like object-properties. We will call this representation the *dichotomous model*, because it describes whether a semantic relation exists for a specific event-concept or not.

However the problem is more complex. Concerning any semantic core (e. g. the verb FIGHT), its meaning depends on the context. Fighting is possible as a purpose for or against (A-P-Relation) something which refers to an Object (OBJ) or for or against a person (REC). Whole or partial transitions (TRANSIT) or transformations (TRANSF) of objects or persons can happen, sometimes an instrument is needed (INS), sometimes not. The examples demonstrate that there might be a second source variability which can be used in order to determine the relational similarity, the degree of shaping of the specific semantic relations of an event-concept on specific relational dimensions. This will be called the *dimensional model*. In the following experiment we investigated the semantic structure of typical event-concepts in order to attain the test concepts for the following analyses of similarities between analogous event-concepts.

Experiment 1

The first experiment concerns the description of the relational structure of typical event-concepts by our sample of event-relations. We assume that if words for event-concepts are presented to subjects, each subject has a conceptual memory representation of that event, specified by the subject's own experience (we call that the individual dimensional model).

Method

Subjects. 20 undergraduate students of the Institute of Psychology at Humboldt-University Berlin, Germany took part in the experiment

Stimuli and Design. Using the Celex-Database (Baayen, Piepenbrock & van Rijn, 1993) all German verbs with a frequency above 100 were selected. A judging group of four persons had to classify the verbs into semantically homogenous groups. We obtained 13 groups of verbs. The seven verbs with the highest word frequency of each group were selected as experimental material.

Subjects received the verb groups on a sheet of paper. First, the subjects had to select the most typical word for each of the 13 groups. Then they were instructed to imagine a typical situation for the selected verb and to answer yes/no questions for each kind of a semantic relation (e.g. "Is the action directed to a person?", "Is the action directed to a thing?", "Is an instrument used in this situation?", "Is there a purpose in the action (A-P)" etc.).

Results

The number of yes-answers were counted for each of the 13 verb-groups. The most typical verb was selected for each group. For illustrating the dimensional model the relative frequencies for each relation were computed. The common relations for all subjects were determined with the Binomial-Test. These results are shown in figure 4. The bold letters show which semantic relations for each verb were affirmed by all subjects. This presents the dichotomous model where we had assumed that the similarity can be computed by the common and different semantic relations (like the properties in the Tversky-Model).

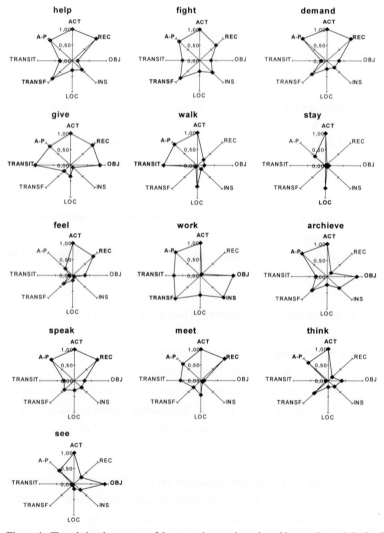

Figure 4: The relational structures of the semantic cores investigated in experiment 1. In the diagrams the relative frequencies of the assumed relations are shown (0-1). The bold letters indicate the significant relations for the dichotomous model.

Looking at these structures one can see specific characteristics for each verb. For example the semantic core of the verb STAY has the structure ACT - *STAY* - LOC for most of the subjects. These are the relations covered by the dichotomous model. However about 50 % of the subject answered the purpose-question (A-P) with "YES". That means STAY sometimes happens with a specific purpose (e. g. waiting for something) and sometimes without a specific purpose. This variability is covered by the dimensional model. Another example is the semantic core of GIVE. The subjects decided that it has the structure ACT - *GIVE* - REC - OBJ - TRANSIT - A-P, but no instrument is needed and no specific location is of relevance. A last illustration is given with the verb THINK. Subjects produced the structure ACT - *THINK* - A-P. That means the event THINK needs no object-concepts except the concept of the actor. In contrast the dimensional model shows a lot of variability: About 60% of the subjects assume the object- or recipient-relation as the pointer to the substantial object or the person, that we can think of. And 60% assumed a transformation which means that thinking can change something in the mind.

The results show that the dimensional model describes the relational structure of event-concepts with greater differentiation than the dichotomous model. With the next experiment we will show how to determine the similarity between those concepts.

Experiment 2

Because of the different types of object-concepts and semantic relations the similarity between event-concepts seems to be a result of multiple comparisons. Gentner (1989) in her *Structure Mapping Theory* (SMT) argued that the relational correspondence is specifically relevant in analogies. Isolated relations, attributes or features of objects could be neglected. In Gentner's view, the similarity between source and target is based on their relational correspondence. Hence, our structural similarity, determined by the dichotomous or the dimensional model for semantic relations, should be a more reliable predictor of the event-concept similarity. This approach refers to the event-concept as a structure because it only considers the event-relations in their appearance or form. However event-concepts also include specific object-concepts defined by their properties. The results of the first experiment show a high variability in the structures of the investigated event-concepts. The reason might be the individual event-experience. Each of the subjects has filled the relational slots of the semantic cores with individually specific object-concepts. Hence, we assume the mean object-concept similarity as the second main predictor of event-concept similarity. However this component needs to be more differentiated. As we shall see, it is probably not the case in analogy detection or construction that subjects instantaneously perform an overall match by evaluating all object-concept similarities. It is more likely that there are only a few corresponding and highly similar object-concepts which determine the event-concept similarity. We may call this part of the analogous structure the similarity focus.

A third component for similarity prediction is the aim or purpose of a specific action represented by an event-concept. Sometimes it can be described by the A-P-Relation. The aim and purpose are often controlling problem solving and analogy detection (see Duncker, 1935; Hesse, 1991; Kedar-Cabelli, 1985). It is a component that describes the needs and motives of the actor.

Considering the different components of event-concepts for the description of their similarity, we can distinguish different influential factors which contribute to the overall similarity:

1. The structural similarity defined by the dichotomous model (S_{S-DIC}). It is the proportion of identical vs. different semantic relations.

2. The structural similarity defined by the dimensional model (S_{S-DIM}). It is the relative frequency in which the concepts are explained by their respective semantic relations.

3. The property-determined similarity between the corresponding object-concepts using the mean object-concept similarity (S_O).

4. The property-determined similarity between the two most similar object-concepts, which we call the focus of similarity (S_{max}).

5. We assume that even the purpose of an action, the A-P-Relation, has a specific influence on the similarity judgments.

All these components can play their role in similarity estimations of those different semantic structures which we have in the mind.

Method

Subjects. Four groups ($n_1=25$, $n_2=22$, $n_3=16$, $n_4=15$) of undergraduate students of the Institute of Psychology at the Humboldt-University, Berlin took part in this experiment.

Stimuli and Design. 26 complete event-concepts were used. Each event-concept consisted of a verb (SC) and four object-concepts. A group of three trained persons constructed the experimental material and was instructed to watch carefully for clearness and typicality. The material consisted of three relational basic types with the following structures: ACT-SC-REC-INS-LOC (DOCTOR-TREAT-PATIENT-INJECTION-HOSPITAL); ACT-SC-REC-OBJ-LOC (SALESMAN-SELL-COSTUMER-BOOK-STORE) and ACT-SC-OBJ-INS-LOC (MECHANIC-REPAIR-CAR-WRENCH-GARAGE).

Procedure. The relational structure was determined as in the first experiment with subject Group 1. Group 2 had to classify all object-concepts separately for each type by similarity. Group 3 had to classify all complete event-concepts by similarity and Group 4 by similarity of the purposes of each action within an event-concept (the A-P relation). The concepts were presented simultaneously on a computer monitor in randomized order and separately for each subject-group. Subjects sorted the concepts by mouse-clicks into seven list-fields. The following instructions were given: to classify all concepts, to use all list-fields and to put at least three concepts in each list-field. After the classification task, the frequencies of common classification for every pair of concepts were counted. In this way we acquired a complete similarity matrix for each concept type. The structural similarity for the dichotomous model was computed by using the Jaccard-Tanimoto-Coefficient, for the dimensional model the Euclidean-Similarity was computed.

Results

In order to predict the event-concept similarity we used multiple regression analysis. All analyses were performed with LISREL 8 using the WLS-method for non-normal continuous variables (Jöreskog & Sörbom, 1989). The sample for these analyses were the full sub-diagonal similarity matrixes for the complete event-concept comparisons ($n*(n-1)/2 = 325$).

Table 1a shows the regression of the dimensional structural similarity (S_{S-DIM}) and the mean object-concept similarity (S_O) on the event-concept similarity (S_E).

a) Dimensional Model and Mean Object Similarity on Event-Concept Similarity			b) Dimensional Model and Similarity Focus on Event-Concept Similarity		
Regression on S_E	S_O	S_{S-Dim}	Regression on S_E	S_{max}	S_{S-Dim}
γ	0,32	0,40	γ	0,31	0,38
t-value	5,89**	7,18**	t-value	5,58**	6,76**
SE	0,06	0,05	SE	0,06	0,06
R^2	0,33 F(322) = 79,30; p<0,01		R^2	0,32 F(322) = 75,76; p<0,01	

c) Dichotomous Model and Mean Object Similarity on Event-Concept Similarity			d) Dimensional Model and Mean Object Similarity on Event-Concept Similarity (A-P)		
Regression on S_E	S_O	S_{S-Dic}	Regression on $S_{E_{A-P}}$	S_O	S_{S-Dim}
γ	0,32	0,30	γ	0,44	0,36
t-value	5,45**	4,98**	t-value	6,85**	6,30**
SE	0,06	0,06	SE	0,06	0,06
R^2	0,26 F(322) = 56,57; p<0,01		R^2	0,41 F(322) = 117,8; p<0,01	

e) Correlations	S_{ACT}	S_{REC}	S_{OBJ}	S_{INS}	S_{LOC}	S_{S-Dim}	S_{S-Dic}	S_O	S_{max}
S_E	0,35	0,40	0,28	0,38	0,23	0,49	0,42	0,43	0,44
$S_{E_{A-P}}$	0,48*	0,37	0,27	0,32	0,29	0,48	0,44	0,54*	0,52

Table 1: Results of the multiple regression for the similarity prediction of event-concepts (details are explained in the text, the important values are in the gray fields).

The results show that there is a high influence of both predictors on the event-concept similarity and a explanation of variance of 33%. Replacing the dimensional structural similarity (S_{S-DIM}) by the dichotomous structural similarity (S_{S-DIC}) decreases the explanation of variance to 26% (Table 1c). The more differentiated representation of the variability with the dimensional model shows a significantly better fit to the empirical similarity data for the event-concepts. In the third analysis the mean object-concept similarity (S_O) was replaced by the similarity of the two most similar corresponding object-concepts (similarity focus - S_{max}). This leads to nearly the same results (Table 1b).

In Table 1d the regression results of the structural similarity with the dimensional model and the mean object-concept similarity on the event-concept similarity under the purpose-instruction are shown. (Purpose means in this connection the goal of an actor, in German termed as Finalitaet.) The amount of explained variance increases up to 41%. The correlation table (table 1e) shows that the coefficients for the object-concept similarity decreases, except the correlation between actor and event-concept similarity. It significantly increases together with the mean object-concept similarity. The correlation of the two structural similarities are nearly constant.

Discussion

The main result of the second experiment was the similarity prediction of event-concepts by the structural similarity of the semantic relations. Both models, the dichotomous and the dimensional one, show a good fit to the data. However, the dimensional model fits slightly better. In the sense of the SMT the similarity of two knowledge domains is a function of their structural correspondence. However we can show additionally a significant influence of the object-concept similarity on the overall event-concept similarity. We conclude that some salient properties of the object-concepts influence and sometimes even determine the similarity classification. These properties can be understood as a kind of cue stimulus for analogy detection and construction, which are effective when the structural similarity between the domains is non-sufficient.

The second main result is the effect of the purpose-instruction on the data. The overall explanation of variance increased. The effect is due to the similarity of the actor-concepts. However the similarity matrixes of the event-concepts (simple similarity instruction vs. A-P-instruction) are not very different. This shows the high relevance of object-concepts in analogical reasoning.

Experiment 3

In the third experiment we investigate the analogy construction process. We try to find out the relevance of different semantic relations over the course of the construction process. The results of the last experiments lead to the assumption that the actor-concept contains a lot of relevant information for analogical reasoning. The actor is strongly associated with a specific event (e. g. WOLF - CHASE etc.) and gives information about the A-P-Relation. It is possible that the construction process begins with the selection of a potential actor. On the other hand it is probable that also the semantic core is an important feature at the beginning of the analogy construction. The semantic core activates the relational information which is needed to find a corresponding structure. Pinker (1994) points out that the basic structure for events is the triad „WHO did WHAT to WHOM". He explains a lot of syntactic invariances in different languages with this construct. It can be seen as a basis for 'The Language Instinct'. If we map this onto the analogy construction process the triad ACT - SC - REC/OBJ should appear. Another open point is the role of the mean similarity of the object-concepts.

Method

Subjects. A group of 16 undergraduate students of the Institute of Psychology at Humboldt-University took part in this experiment

Stimuli and Design. 42 complete event-concepts were used in this experiment. Each event-concept was given as a verb (SC) with four attached object-concepts. The group of three trained persons extended the experimental material from Experiment 2 in the same manner. The material consisted of three relational basic types with the following structures: ACT-SC-REC-INS-LOC; ACT-SC-REC-OBJ-LOC and ACT-SC-OBJ-INS-LOC.

Procedure. The experimental task was to construct a new analogous event-concept with references to a given one. After an instruction and training phase 15 event-concepts appeared on the left side of a computer screen (see figure 5). The order of the concept types on the screen was randomized. The subjects could select corresponding concepts from alphabetical word lists for each concept-type by a mouse-click on the words of the given event-concept. The selection of the words generates a structural analogy on the right side of the screen. In case none of the offered words fitted the intention of the subjects, they had the possibility to type one or two words of their own choice into the empty fields. When the analogy construction was finished, subjects were asked to explain the analogy. The sequence of the concept selection and the similarity of the concepts was recorded for each trail.

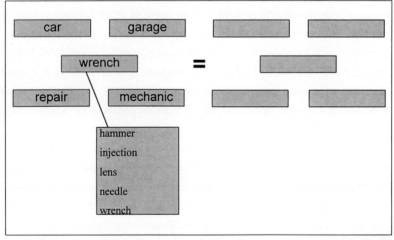

Figure 5: The experimental design for experiment 3. The task was to construct on the left side of the computer-screen an analogous event-concept to the given concept on the right side by selecting corresponding concepts out of the word lists. The similarity of the selected concepts and the selection order was recorded.

Results

Figure 6 shows the percentages of selecting a specific concept for each position in the analogy construction task. Subjects choose the actor with more than 56% of the analogies at first, followed by the semantic core (19%). The result supports our assumption. However, the process is more complex. In a second analyses the choice-data were transformed into ranks and scaled with a two-dimensional model. Figure 7 shows stable solutions for the three relational types with stress-coefficients between 0.04 and 0.06. The solutions show two different construction strategies. The horizontal axis represents a more property-determined strategy. The subjects started the construction with an actor, followed by the semantic core and than the recipient or the object. At the fourth and fifth position the instrument, other object-concepts and the location were selected. The vertical axis represents the more structural approach on analogy construction. In this case the subject started with the semantic core, determining the relational structure of the event-concept, followed by the actor, the recipient or the object. At the end the other concepts were selected. There were no individual preferences or learning effects in the data. This means the subjects decided to use the different strategies from trial to trial, depending on the concrete event-concept.

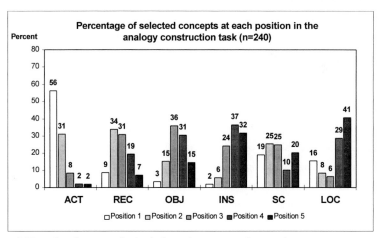

Figure 6: The order of concept selection in the analogy-construction experiment.

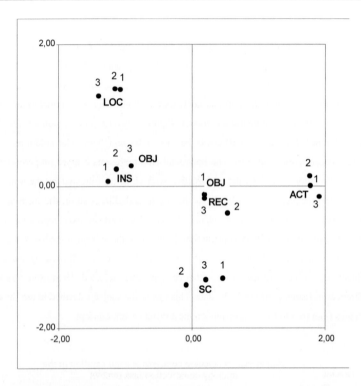

Figure 7: Multidimensional scaling of the order of concept selection in experiment 3. The solution shows two different construction strategies: (1) to start with the actor using the property similarity and the information about the aim and purpose; (2) to start with the semantic core focusing on structural alignment.

However, what about the object-concept similarity? The distribution in figure 8 shows a preference for selecting similar concepts (Mean = 0.55; SD= 0.17; N=121). However, there are only a few analogies with very low or very high object-concept similarity. Most of the analogies constructed by the subjects had a mean similarity between the corresponding object-concepts. All constructed analogies were of good structural alignment.

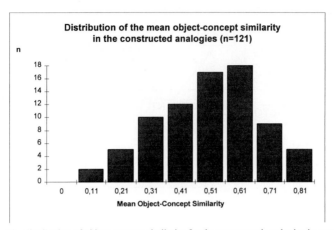

Figure 8: The distribution of object-concept similarity for the constructed analogies in experiment 3. The distribution shows that the subjects choose concepts of a slightly shifted mean similarity to perform the analogy construction.

Discussion

The results of the third experiment lead to modifications of the event-concept representation (Figure 9). We propose to divide the event-concept model into two different parts. The central part is the semantic core with its specific substructure of semantic relations. The actor-concept as the starting point of the action (containing information about the purpose) is connected by the semantic core with the recipient or the object as the target of the action. We call this partial structure the *event-core*. In an evolutionary view these three core constituents (ACT-SC-REC/OBJ) can be seen as a structure which contains the most relevant information of an event. Additionally, it is very efficient to use this substructure for a primary evaluation of the intention of the actor and the target and consequences of the action. One may say that this order results from a syntactic effect (S-P-O) on the construction process. However, we cannot decide whether the construction order is influenced by the syntax or whether both phenomena have a common cause, a conceptual representation which reflects characteristic environmental interactions of subjects. An argument against the syntactical influence is the second construction dimension where the subjects started the process with the semantic core, because no German speaker starts a sentence with the verb.

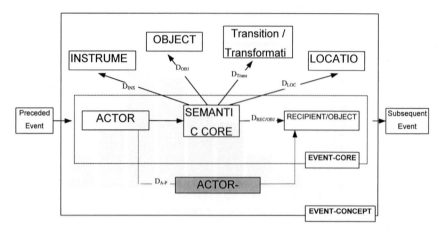

Figure 9: A model of the representation of event-concepts consisting of the event-core (ACT-SC-REC/OBJ) as a part of the whole event-concept with the other semantic relations. The semantic relations are shaped on dimensions which show the degree of belonging to a specific representation.

The second part of our conceptual event-representation are the other semantic relations with the linked object-concepts. These relations are very variable in their semantic significance. Together with the specific object-concepts the meaning of the event-concept becomes more differentiated (and vice versa). An example may be the concept GAME: it selects together with LAWN a specific subclass such as SOCCER, GOLF etc.; together with BOARD another subclass like CHESS etc.; with instruments like CARDS selects another group etc.

Finally, we could identify different strategies in analogy construction. The first strategy is to start the construction process by selecting an actor-concept. In this case the subjects focus on the properties of the actor and the A-P-Relation of the event-concept. They map this relation type onto the second conceptual structure. The second strategy is to use a more structural approach by starting the process with the selection of an appropriate semantic core and to compare the object-concepts step by step. Both strategies seem to be fairly independent from each other. In order to explain the process of analogy detection the different strategies show that both relations as well as properties are used to find a potential source-area. The object-concept similarity in the construction task seems to be controlled by an general rule: to select concepts with a mean similarity to the target-area. The reason may be as follows: if the concepts are very similar, the analogy could became trivial; if there is no property similarity, the analogy is dissatisfactory and difficult to understand (see also Bachmann, 1994).

Conclusion and comment

We had the hypothesis that there is data in the human memory which enables the derivation similarity judgments between knowledge areas. For that reason concepts were taken as anchor points of human knowledge.

By investigating the role of similarity in analogical reasoning we pursued two main goals: (1) to find an appropriate description of the semantic components of an event-concept (defined by properties and semantic relations) in order to predict the similarity estimations of subjects; (2) to investigate the role of specific semantic components during the process of analogy construction.

Among conceptual knowledge areas the event-concepts play an outstanding role. They constitute a mean level of complexity. Concepts such as BUY and STEAL, WIN and OVERCOME, RENOUNCE or LOOSE have common as well as different semantic components. We have argued that such commonalties as well as differences influence the similarity impressions within or between knowledge areas. We distinguished semantic cores (mainly verbs) which point to specific object-concepts (mainly nouns). The pointers themselves are defined as semantic relations. The linked object-concepts are defined by properties, surrounding a specified set of objects.

Different models for measuring complex similarities have been derived. Their application reveals that different components of such concepts influence the overall similarity judgments. A model which takes into account the real distribution of semantic relations (the so-called dimensional model) leads to a suitable prediction of the event-concept similarity. It is slightly better than the dichotomous model where the relations are assumed as dichotomous structural components. Furthermore, we could show that the object-concept resemblance is a second similarity predictor and that the purpose of an action is (together with the actor) a traceable influential factor in similarity judgments. The final overall similarity depends additionally on prevailing properties and on characteristic semantic relations.

The role of *similarity in analogy construction* was central to our approach. To produce analogies by thinking is a testimony of creative capability. Its source is the comparative interaction between different knowledge areas, and this means mainly conceptual knowledge. An experimental approach was designed what allows crucial steps in the construction procedure to be pursued. Concerning the three different strategies one can say that the actor and the semantic core are dominant components. An important outcome was that there exist a trade off between novelty and similarity: Completely strange concepts without any similarity produce nonsensical impressions with no information content; extremely similar concepts produce trivialities. The suggestive pool, containing of course creative analogies, lies in between. However there is a noticeable tendency in the role of similarity: if the concept pairs make at all sense, then the creative impression is higher, the more different the knowledge areas are. There seems to be a threshold. Beyond it the expressivity of an analogy drops down, and far beneath it it becomes senseless.

The two strategies are outlined in a way which opens up (we hope) the possibility of simulating the process of analogy generation. This would mean no less the chance to simulate components of creative thinking. It might happen that in the future the generalization of such methods enables the attachment of computer intelligence to human inventive activities - maybe even for the construction of creative computer programs.

References

Bachmann, Th. (1994). *Aspekte der Analogiebildung.* Unveröff. Diplomarbeit, Humboldt-Universität zu Berlin.

Duncker, K. (1935). *Zur Psychologie des produktiven Denkens.* Berlin: Verlag von Julius Springer.

Gentner, D. (1983). Structure-mapping: A theoretical framework for analogy. *Cognitive Science, 7,* 155-170.

Gentner, D. (1989). The mechanisms of analogical reasoning. In S. Vosniadou & A. Ortony, (Eds.), *Similarity and analogical reasoning* (pp. 199-241). Cambridge, MA: Cambridge University Press.

Gentner, D. & Markman, A. B. (1993). Similarity is like analogy. In C. Cacciari (Ed.), *Proceeding of the workshop on similarity at the University of San Marino.* Milano, Italien: Bompiani.

Gick, M. & Holyoak, K. J. (1980). Analogical problem solving. *Cognitve Psychology, 12,* 306-355.

Hesse, F. W. (1991). Search and acceptance in analogical problem solving. *Zeitschrift für Psychologie, 199,* 235-242.

Jöreskog, K. & Sörbom, D. (1989). *LISREL 8.* Chicago: Scientific Software International.

Kedar-Cabelli, S. (1985). Purpose-directed analogy. *Proceeding of the Seventh Annual Conference of the Cognitve Science Society,* (pp. 150-159), Irvine, CA. Hillsdale, NJ: Erlbaum.

Klix, F. (1992a). Higher order learning mechanisms in knowledge domain. *Zeitschrift für Psychologie, 200,* 91-103

Klix, F. (1992b). *Die Natur des Verstandes.* Göttingen: Hogrefe.

Michalski, R. S. (1989). Two-tiered concept meaning, inferential matching, and conceptual cohesiveness. In S. Vosniadou & A. Ortony (Eds.), *Similarity and analogical reasoning* (pp. 332-345). Cambridge, MA: Cambridge University Press.

Pinker, S. (1995). *The Language Instinct.* New York, NY: HarperPerennial.

Preuß, M. (1985). *Experimente über Relationserkennungen im menschlichen Gedächtnis.* Unpublished dissertation, Berlin: Humboldt-University.

Rumelhart, D. E. (1989). Towards a mircostructural account to human reasoning. In S. Vosniadou & A. Ortony (Eds.), *Similarity and analogical reasoning* (pp. 298-312). Cambridge MA: Cambridge University Press.

Schmieschek, M. (1988). *Strukturbeschreibung von ereignisbestimmtem Wissensbesitz im menschlichen Langzeitgedächtnis.* Unpublished dissertation, Berlin: Humboldt-Universität.

Sternberg, R. J. (1977). Component processes in analogical reasoning. *Psychological Review,* 84, 353-378.

Tversky, A. (1977). Features of similarity. *Psychological Review* 85, 327-352.

van der Meer, E. (1987). Zur Kennzeichnung von ereignisbestimmtem Wissen. *Wissenschaftliche Zeitschrift der Humboldt-Universität zu Berlin,* 36 (5), 398-406.

Section III

Learning

3.1 Explicit Learning in ACT-R

Niels A.Taatgen

Abstract

A popular distinction in the learning literature is the distinction between implicit and explicit learning. Although many studies elaborate on the nature of implicit learning, little attention is left for explicit learning. The unintentional aspect of implicit learning corresponds well to the mechanistic view of learning employed in architectures of cognition. But how to account for deliberate, intentional, explicit learning? This chapter argues that explicit learning can be explained by strategies that exploit implicit learning mechanisms. This idea is explored and modelled using the ACT-R theory (Anderson, 1993). An explicit strategy for learning facts in ACT-R's declarative memory is rehearsal, a strategy that uses ACT-R's activation learning mechanisms to gain deliberate control over what is learned. In the same sense, strategies for explicit procedural learning are proposed. Procedural learning in ACT-R involves generalisation of examples. Explicit learning rules can create and manipulate these examples. An example of these explicit rules will be discussed. These rules are general enough to be able to model the learning of three different tasks. Furthermore, the last of these models can explain the difference between adults and children in the discrimination-shift task.

Introduction

One of the basic assumptions all architectures of cognition share is that all learning can be described with a fixed set of mechanisms. The term 'mechanism' refers to the fact that learning is unintentional and is always at work. The term 'fixed' refers to the fact that learning never changes, and is the same for each person, regardless of age or intelligence. This view of intelligence seems to be at odds with the general view of learning in psychology. The hallmark of learning is adaptation, the capacity of the organism to change its behaviour to suit a particular environment. This does not necessarily imply that learning itself is susceptible to adaptation. But work from developmental psychology clearly suggests that learning changes with age. One classical experiment that shows that the way children learn differs from adults is discrimination-shift learning (Kendler & Kendler, 1959). We will discuss this experiment in more detail later on. A second counter-intuitive aspect of learning mechanisms is the fact that learning is unintentional. Although we have no complete control over learning, the idea that we have no control at all seems to be too strong.

The distinction between implicit and explicit learning is centred around this issue. Implicit learning is unconscious and unintentional, so is consistent with the mechanistic and fixed view of learning in architectures of cognition. In explicit learning, on the other hand, goals and intentions determine what is learned. Moreover, many studies suggest that explicit learning is much more powerful than implicit learning (for an overview see Shanks & John, 1994). Some things can't be learned by implicit learning, but can be learned by explicit learning. Finally, things that can be learned implicitly can often be learned faster explicitly. Another aspect of learning that seems to be at odds with mechanistic learning is learning through insight. Many learning mechanisms model gradual learning. Learning in the PDP neural network tradition is gradual (Rumelhart & McClelland, 1986), and chunking in SOAR is inspired by, and can explain the power law of practice (Newell & Rosenbloom, 1981). A property of insight learning is a sudden qualitative shift. Take for example match stick algebra (MSA), as discussed in Knoblich and Ohlsson (1996). In MSA, subjects have to correct equations of Roman numbers made out of the match sticks by moving a single match stick. Initially, subjects only try moves that leave individual symbols intact, for example by changing I + II = I into I + II = II. This corresponds well to what is normally allowed in algebra. It takes a lot of time and effort for subjects to discover that symbols can be broken up, for example that an X can be changed into a V by moving a single match stick, so that X + I = VI can be changed into V + I = VI. Once a subject has discovered this, he can apply this immediately in later problems. In other words, the subject has learned something about a certain constraint in the context of MSA. This type of learning is not gradual, but step wise. So the central question of this chapter is how learning mechanisms in architectures of cognition can be made consistent with an adaptive view of learning that allows for flashes of insight. Or, stated in another way, we need a theory of explicit learning. We will concentrate the discussion on the ACT-R architecture (Anderson, 1993), but some aspects may apply to other architectures as well.

Since mechanisms in architectures are fixed, we have to seek for other ways of explaining adaptation in learning. The only thing that changes over time in an architecture is the knowledge in its memory. An explanation of changes in learning has to be an explanation in terms of changes in the content of memory. As a consequence, the learning capabilities of an individual can be divided into two classes, the implicit learning mechanisms of the architecture and explicit learning strategies in its memory. What is the nature of these explicit learning strategies? There are two possibilities. The first possibility is, that an explicit strategy can directly effect memory. In that case, we might have a rule in procedural memory that can directly change other rules by adding conditions, changing weights, etc. This, however, doesn't seems to be a good option. One of the essential properties of procedural memory is, that it cannot access its contents directly. To be able to intentionally change a rule we need such a direct access. Moreover, it would violate one of the basic assumptions of an architecture of cognition, that the learning mechanisms in the architecture are sufficient. So we have to focus on a second, more likely possibility, that explicit learning is built on top of implicit learning in the sense that it learns by using implicit learning mechanisms.

A relatively simple example might explain this point. It is a well-known fact that people aren't very good at remembering facts that cannot easily be related to other knowledge they have. The whole tradition of theories about short-term memory that started with Miller's magical number seven is based on this fact (Miller, 1956). Atkinson and Shiffrin (1968) introduced the mechanism of rehearsal, to account for the fact that some facts in short-term memory do get stored in long-term memory, and others do not. Closer scrutiny however shows, that rehearsal isn't really a mechanism in the sense discussed earlier. Rehearsal isn't always at work, most of the time it isn't. People only rehearse if they have consciously decided to do so. So rehearsal isn't mechanistic, it is tied to intentions. Neither is rehearsal fixed. It is apparent that small children do not use rehearsal at all, so it must either be a dormant strategy that surfaces at some point, or a strategy that children acquire at some point during development. So rehearsal is a typical example of learning that is not part of the architecture, but rather a strategy represented in memory. We will return to this issue after a brief introduction of learning in the ACT-R architecture.

Learning in ACT-R

The ACT-R architecture has two memory systems, a declarative memory and a procedural memory. Associated to each of these memory systems is a number of learning mechanisms that add and maintain the knowledge in them. ACT-R is based on the theory of rational analysis (Anderson, 1990), and the learning mechanisms of ACT-R are no exception to this. According to rational analysis, the cognitive system is optimised to its environment. Therefore a careful examination of the environment can shed as much light on the system as studying the cognitive system itself.

Implicit learning in declarative memory

A first example of the role of rational analysis in ACT-R is declarative memory. Elements in declarative memory, called chunks, closely resemble nodes in a semantic network. Each chunk has an activation value. This value represents the odds that the chunk will be needed in the current context. To be able to estimate this value, the learning mechanisms have to keep a close track of the environment. The activation value of a chunk has two parts, the base-level activation and activation through associations with other chunks. The latter is context-dependent: once a certain chunk is part of ACT-R's current context, all chunks with an association to this chunk gain activation temporarily, since the presence of an associated chunk increases their chance of being needed. The base-level activation of a chunk is based on its past use. Two factors play a role: how many times a chunk was needed in the past, and how long ago this was. The learning rule used in ACT-R is derived from Bayesian statistics. Anderson shows that this rule both reflects regularities in the environment and empirical data from memory experiments. Association strengths are learned using similar rules. ACT-R uses activation values of chunks to order the chunks in the matching process, because the activation value determines the time it takes to retrieve the chunk.

Implicit learning in procedural memory

As the name implies, knowledge in production memory is represented by production rules. Associated with each rule are a number of parameters. The strength parameter is used to reflect past use of a rule, and is governed by the same laws as the base-level activation of chunks. The a, b, q and r parameters of a rule reflect its past cost-benefit characteristics. The a and b parameters represent the current and future cost of a rule, and the q and r parameters the chance of succeeding and reaching the goal. Bayesian statistics are again used to estimate these parameters. The cost-benefit parameters are used in conflict resolution. For each rule that is allowed to match, an expected outcome is calculated using the equation:

$$\text{expected outcome} = PG-C$$

In this equation P is the estimated chance of success, calculated from q and r, G the estimated value of the goal and C the estimated cost of reaching the goal, calculated from a and b.

New rules are learned by the production compilation mechanism. This involves generalisation of examples in declarative memory.

The examples are stored in specialised chunks, dependency chunks, that contain all the information needed: an example goal, an example solution, chunks (called constraints) that must be retrieved from declarative memory in order to create a solution, and sometimes additional sub-goals that must be satisfied before the main goal can be reached.

```
dependency 2+3                          (p addition-problem production 1
        isa dependency                  =example-goal-variable>
        goal example-goal 1                     isa addition-problem
        modified example-solution 1             arg 1 =two-variable
        constraints fact 2+3                    arg 2 =three-variable
example-goal 1                                  answer nil
        isa addition-problem            =fact 2+3-variable>
        arg 1 two                               isa addition-fact
        arg 2 three                             addend 1 =two-variable
        answer nil                              addend 2 =three-variable
example-solution 1                              sum = five-variable
        isa addition-problem            ==>
        arg 1 two                       =example-goal-variable>
        arg 2 tree                              answer =five-variable)
        answer five
fact 2+3
        isa addition-fact
        addend 1 two
        addend 2 three
        sum five
```

Figure1: Example of ACT-R's production compilation. The left column shows contents of declarative memory, the right column shows the learned production rule.

Figure 1 shows an example of deriving a rule for doing a simple addition. The chunk dependency 2+3 points to example-goal 1 in which the addition 2+3 must still be calculated. In example-solution1 the answer is supplied in the answer slot. The additional fact needed to derive the rule is the fact that 2+3 equals 5. When the dependency chunk is added to declarative memory, the rule production-problem-production 1 will be derived and added to production memory. Note that all identifiers starting with an =-sign are variables and can be matched with arbitrary chunks in declarative memory.

How can ACT-R's learning mechanisms, which are clearly implicit in nature, give rise to explicit, intentional learning? The next section will explore this question.

Explicit learning in ACT-R

Explicit learning in declarative memory

The implicit mechanisms to calculate the activation of a chunk in declarative memory provide a good estimate of the chance the chunk will be needed. But sometimes it is not enough to rely on the environment to cue the right facts the right number of times. As has already been observed in the introduction, rehearsal can provide a strategy that can help us memorise facts. Since base-level activation is calculated from the number of times a certain fact is retrieved, rehearsal can emulate extra uses of a certain fact. In other words, rehearsal tricks the base-level-learning mechanism into increasing the activation of a certain chunk.

Craik and Lockhart (1972) have observed that the effectiveness of rehearsal depends on the level of processing. Simple maintenance rehearsal turns out to be much less effective than elaborate rehearsal, in which subjects try to associate the new fact with existing facts. This distinction can be easily explained in ACT-R, since elaborate rehearsal not only increases the base-level activation, but also increases associations with other chunks.

In a previous study I have shown how rehearsal can be modelled in ACT-R (Taatgen, 1996). Rehearsal is implemented by a set of production rules that create sub-goals to do the rehearsal. The basic rehearsal productions can be enhanced by task-specific rules that can do elaborate rehearsal. The model was able to reproduce the data from classical free-recall experiments, and provide explanations for the primacy and recency effect. Rehearsal is clearly intentional in this model: it only occurs if ACT-R decides to push a rehearsal goal.

Explicit learning in procedural memory

The production compilation mechanism creates rules from dependency chunks in declarative memory. The architecture, however, does not specify how dependencies are created. This is not necessary, since dependencies are just chunks in declarative memory. Dependencies may be picked up from the environment, or may be supplied by a parent or teacher. On the other hand, chunks may be created and manipulated by production rules. So an explicit theory of learning procedural rules involves dependency-manipulating rules in production memory. These rules create dependencies that are compiled into new rules by the production compilation mechanism (figure 2). Again, strategies in procedural memory manipulate the implicit mechanisms: instead of slowly gathering and generalising regularities from the environment, intentionally created rules are learned.

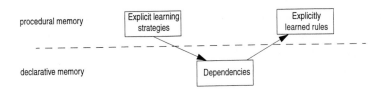

Figure 2: The process of explicit learning for procedural memory

The process described here is closely related to the concept of mental models (Johnson-Laird, 1983). A mental model is a mental construct that helps us, predicting properties and events in the outside world. A dependency created by explicit learning strategies is a kind of mental model.

How to decide whether to implement explicit learning?

Since explicit learning is intentional, a decision has to be made at some point to start a learning attempt. We'll concentrate the discussion on explicit strategies for procedural knowledge, but similar points may be made on the decision to implement rehearsal.

The easiest case that indicates an explicit strategy is needed, is when we get a certain outcome which turns out to be different from our expectations, an expectation-failure, in terms of Schank (1986). Often, however, indications aren't as clear. At some point we have to make a decision that our current approach isn't working and something else is needed.

Decisions in ACT-R are based on a cost-benefit analysis of the available options. So suppose we present a new task to a subject. We have supplied some information to the subject about the task. The subject has several options. Should he just start an attempt in accomplishing the task using the information he has? Should he ask for advice, or go to the library to find more information? Or should he first reflect on the task, to come up with some new strategies? Suppose we restrict our analysis to two possible strategies: search and reflection. If the subject chooses search, he attempts to accomplish the task given his current knowledge about the task. If he chooses reflection on the other hand, he will try explicit learning strategies to come up with new rules.

In Taatgen (1997), I describe a model that calculates the expected outcome of either strategy over time. I will briefly summarise the results here. The expected outcome has three components, as mentioned before, P, the chance of reaching the goal using the strategy, G, the estimated value of the goal, and C, the estimated cost of a strategy. Since G is not related to a strategy, we will concentrate on P and C. For search the cost is relatively constant, and typically low. The chance of success of search, however, decreases over time if the goal is not reached, reflecting the fact that repeated failure is a strong indication that the current knowledge is false or insufficient. An assumption of reflection is, that it needs existing knowledge to work with. You can't get something out of nothing. This knowledge can have several sources, as we will see later on. For now we will assume that the only source of knowledge is implicit knowledge gained through search. So if we have little implicit knowledge to work with, the cost of reflection is high, since it is difficult to come up with something useful. As our explicit knowledge increases, the cost to come up with something new increases as well.

A final assumption of the model is, that search increases implicit knowledge, reflection increases explicit knowledge, and explicit knowledge is more powerful. This enables us to describe the increase of knowledge over time, related to the conflict resolution mechanism that selects the strategy with the highest expected outcome. Figure 3 shows an example of the results of the model. Figure 3a shows the growth of knowledge about a specific problem, and figure 3b shows the expected outcome of search and reflection. The discontinuities in both graphs indicate a change of strategy.

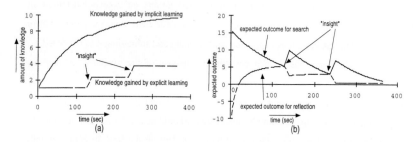

Figure 3: Results of a model. (a) shows growth of knowledge over time, and (b) shows the conflict resolution process.

A pleasing aspect of this model is, that it can give a rational account of the explore-impasse-insight-execute stages often identified in problem solving that requires insight. In the explore stage, the subject still thinks his existing knowledge is the best way to reach the goal, in the impasse stage he decides that the existing knowledge is insufficient, and in the insight stage reflection starts in an attempt to gain new explicit knowledge. Finally, in the execute stage the search process continues using the newly gained knowledge.

An ACT-R model of a simple explicit strategy

The model discussed above is just a mathematical model and only represents the amounts of several types of knowledge with their cost-benefit characteristics. To see if the approach discussed here really works, we have to make a detailed ACT-R model in which actual learning occurs. The main parts of interest in such a model are the dependency-creating rules, since these rules form the explicit learning part of the model. These rules have to be quite general, since they must be applicable to a wide range of problems. So general rules are in principle context-independent. To be able to work, though, they operate on context-dependent knowledge in declarative memory. Possible sources of knowledge are:

- Task instructions and examples
- Relevant facts and biases in declarative memory
- Feedback
- Old goals and old dependencies for the same problem

The beam task

The task we will start with is a beam task. The assumption is, that the model initially has no task-specific rules about beam-problems. So the only procedural knowledge the model has is a number of general rules. Later on, we will use the same general rules for other tasks. The problem is relatively easy: a beam is given with weights on the left and the right arm. Attached to the arms of the beam are labels, each with a number on it. The task is to predict whether the beam will go left, right, or remains in balance. The number on the labels have no influence on the outcome. Figure 4 shows an example of a beam. Although the task is easy if we know something about weights and beams, it is much more difficult if we know nothing at all.

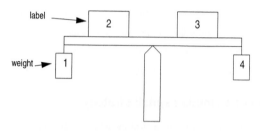

Figure 4: Example of the beam task

The general rules used to learn this task are the following:

Property-retrieval

If there is a task that has a number of objects, create a dependency that contains an example of retrieving a certain property of each of the objects. In the case of the beam task, the objects are the arms of the beam, and weight and label are possible properties. So this rule creates a rule that directs attention to a certain aspect of the task.

Find-fact-on-feedback

If feedback indicates that the answer is incorrect, and also contains the correct answer, set up a dependency that uses the goal and the answer as examples. Also, retrieve some fact that serves as a constraint on the dependency. To be able to generate correct rules for the beam task, we need to retrieve the fact that a certain number is greater than another number, in order to predict correctly whether the beam will go left or right.

Both general rules involve retrieving an arbitrary chunk from declarative memory, either a property or a fact. Normally the retrieval of arbitrary chunks will not produce the right rules. The chunks retrieved are however not arbitrary, since ACT-R's activation mechanism ensures the chunk with the highest activation is retrieved. Since activation represents the odds that a chunks is needed, the chunk with the highest odds of being needed is retrieved. This activation can itself again be manipulated by explicit declarative memory strategies like rehearsal.

In the model this is reflected by the fact that both property-retrieval and find-fact-on-feedback can be influenced by prior knowledge. If there is an association strength between beam and weight, indicating knowledge that a beam has something to do with weight, property-retrieval will choose weight in favour of label. If there is an association strength between beam and "greater-than", a "greater-than" fact will be retrieved by find-fact-on-feedback.

Since the general rules are just production rules, they can be in direct competition with the task-specific rules they generate. So if property-retrieval generates a rule X to retrieve the label, X will compete with property-retrieval. So if X is doing a bad job, which it will if it retrieves the label that has no relevance at all to solving the problem, its evaluation will decrease, and it will eventually lose the competition, in which case property-retrieval will create an example of retrieving weight. However find-fact-on-feedback is only activated if feedback indicates an incorrect answer, so when an expectation-failure occurs, the rules it produces are in competition with each other. The rule with the highest success rate will eventually win.

Figure 5 summarises the property-retrieval rules, and figure 6 summarises the find-fact-on-feedback rules. Figure 6 shows the case in which a "Don't know" rule fires. If instead an incorrect answer is predicted, a dependency is created in the same manner. Apart from the general rules, the model contains lisp functions to generate random beams and production rules to give feedback. When the model produces an incorrect answer, it will try the same beam again until it can predict the right outcome.

Property-retrieval

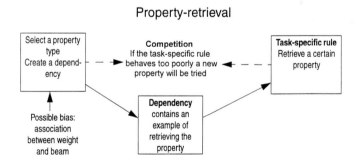

Figure 5: How property-retrieval works

Find-fact-on-feedback

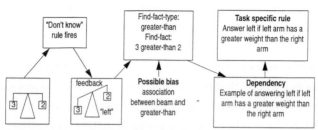

Figure 6: How find-fact-on-feedback works

Simulation results

The general rules turn out to be sufficient to learn the task. The following rules are examples of (correct) rules learned by the model. The rule generated by property-retrieval is a rule that retrieves the weight property for both arms of the beam and stores them in the goal:

```
(P GEN-GOAL-PRODUCTION10
     =OLDGOAL10-VARIABLE>
        ISA GEN-GOAL
        TYPE SOLVE-BEAM
        OB1 =O6-VARIABLE
        OB2 =O7-VARIABLE
        PROP1 NONE
        PROP2 NONE
     =P7-VARIABLE>
        ISA PROPERTY
        OF =O6-VARIABLE
        TYPE WEIGHT
        VALUE =ONE-VARIABLE
     =P8-VARIABLE>
        ISA PROPERTY
        OF =O7-VARIABLE
        TYPE WEIGHT
        VALUE =SIX-VARIABLE
  ==>
     =OLDGOAL10-VARIABLE>
        PROP1 =ONE-VARIABLE
        PROP2 =SIX-VARIABLE
        PROPTYPE WEIGHT)
```

Again note that all identifiers starting with an =-sign are variables. One of the rules generated by find-fact-on-feedback is a rule that predicts when the right arm of the beam will go down.

```
(P GEN-GOAL-PRODUCTION12
     =OGOAL11-VARIABLE>
        ISA GEN-GOAL
        TYPE SOLVE-BEAM
        OB1 =O6-VARIABLE
        OB2 =O7-VARIABLE
        PROP1 =ONE-VARIABLE
        PROP2 =SIX-VARIABLE
        ANSWER NONE
        PROPTYPE WEIGHT
     =F61-VARIABLE>
        ISA GEN-FACT
        TYPE GT-FACT
```

```
     SLOT1 =SIX-VARIABLE
     SLOT2 =ONE-VARIABLE
==>
   =OGOAL11-VARIABLE>
     ANSWER RIGHT)
```

The model was tested in several conditions, differing in the bias given for the properties and the fact-type. The following table summarises the conditions:

P+   Association between beam and weight

P-   Association between beam and label, so a bias for the wrong property

F+   Association between beam and greater-than

F-   Association between both beam and greater-than, and beam and number, so two possible fact-types were favoured.

F--   No associations between beam and fact-types, four fact-types are possible.

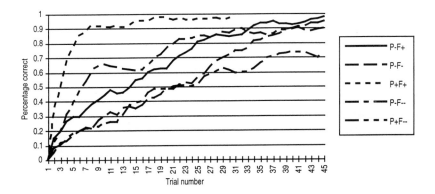

Figure 7: Results of the beam model

Each experiment has a P- and an F-condition. Each experiment has been run 30 times for 50 trials. Figure 7 shows the results. As can be seen in the graph, in the P+F+ condition ACT-R learns to solve the task quite rapidly, and the fact that the model doesn't reach a 100% score within a few trials is only due to the fact that beams are generated randomly, only occasionally producing a beam in which balance is the correct answer. Performance decreases if the model has less initial information. In the case of the P-F-- condition, the model often fails to find the correct rules for the task.

The results in the figure above suggest a gradual increase of performance. This is however not the case, but a result of averaging 30 runs. If individual runs are examined, each has a certain point where performance increases dramatically. To make this clear the following graph depicts the average number of incorrect tries for each trial in the P-F+ condition, averaged with respect to the point where the model switches from examining the label property to examining the weight property. So at x=0 the model creates a dependency that contains an example of retrieving weight.

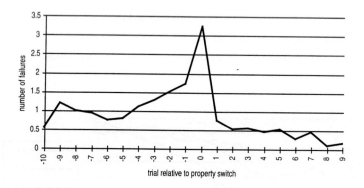

Figure 8: Average number of failures for trials relative to a property switch

The dependency is created at the moment that the model has failed several times to predict the right answer. As a result, the evaluation of the rule that retrieves the labels drops and the general rule can propose a new dependency. In a sense, this process resembles the impasse-insight state of insight problem solving.

The card task

General rules are of course only general if they can be used for several different tasks. So the same rules were used for a new task, a card-classification task. In this task, cards with pictures must be sorted into two categories. The pictures are either one or two squares or circles, which are either red or green and either large or small. The criterion to sort on is the colour (red=yes; green=no), which the subject has to discover. The same general rules can be used to learn this task. First, a property must be selected, so it can be either colour, shape, size or number. After that, the relevant aspect is tied to the answer. The following rules are examples of rules learned by the model:

```
(P GEN-GOAL-PRODUCTION167
     =OLDGOAL1167-VARIABLE>
         ISA GEN-GOAL
         TYPE SOLVE-CAT
         OB1 =O164-VARIABLE
         PROP1 NONE
     =P165-VARIABLE>
         ISA PROPERTY
         OF =O164-VARIABLE
         TYPE COLOUR
         VALUE =GREEN-VARIABLE
  ==>
     =OLDGOAL1167-VARIABLE>
         PROP1 =GREEN-VARIABLE
         PROPTYPE COLOUR)

(P GEN-GOAL-PRODUCTION169
     =OGOAL167-VARIABLE>
         ISA GEN-GOAL
         TYPE SOLVE-CAT
         OB1 =O164-VARIABLE
         PROP1 =GREEN-VARIABLE
         ANSWER NONE
         PROPTYPE COLOUR
     =GREEN-VARIABLE>
         ISA GEN-FACT
         TYPE COLOUR
         SLOT1 GREEN
  ==>
     =OGOAL167-VARIABLE>
         ANSWER NO)
```

Discrimination-shift learning

One of the advantages of explicit learning strategies compared to implicit learning is, that change can be handled more easily. If something in the environment is no longer valid, an explicit strategy may react by proposing new knowledge to replace the old. An example of a task in which the rules change is discrimination-shift learning (Kendler & Kendler, 1959). Figure 9 shows an example of this task. Subjects have to learn to discriminate the four stimuli in two reinforcement categories, for example white is positive and black is negative. In this sense it closely resembles the card task discussed previously.

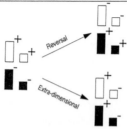

Figure 9: Example of a discrimination-shift task

After the subject has made 10 consecutive correct predictions, the reinforcement scheme is changed: either a reversal-shift, in which all stimuli that received previous positive reinforcement get negative reinforcement and vice-versa, or an extra-dimensional shift, in which the dimension is changed on which the reinforcement is given, in the example from white to large. It is apparent that adults and older children are faster at learning the reversal-shift condition, while young children and animals are faster at the extra-dimensional shift. Figure 10a shows the results of an experiment by Kendler and Kendler (1959). The ACT-R model of adult behaviour uses the same 8 production rules as used in the beam-task, implementing the property-retrieval and find-fact-on-feedback strategies. It learns rules that are quite similar to the rules for the card task. The small-child/animal model uses only 2 of the 8 production rules, implementing only limited find-fact-on-feedback strategy. So the latter model hardly uses any explicit reasoning at all, but rather stores regularities in the environment in dependency chunks. The results of these models are shown in figure 10b.

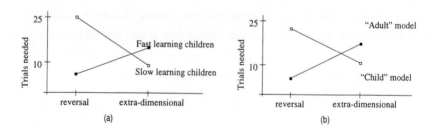

Figure 10: Trials needed to learn the discrimination-shift task, (a) from Kendler & Kendler Experiment, (b) by the ACT-R model

Despite the fact that the discrimination-shift task is generally not considered to be an insight problem, it nevertheless requires the subject to notice that something has changed, and to discover the new relations. So it can be seen, in a sense, as an elementary insight problem.

Conclusions

The goal of cognitive modelling is to create computer simulations of cognitive processes. A criterion for a good model is of course whether the results of the simulation match the empirical data. A second criterion, that becomes increasingly more important, is the question whether the model can learn the knowledge it needs. A model that uses a large set of specialised production rules is less convincing than a model that gathers its own knowledge. The learning mechanisms that are part of the architecture are often not capable of doing this job by themselves, so they need augmentation. In this chapter it is argued that the mechanisms of the architecture correspond to implicit learning. These mechanisms can be augmented by explicit learning, that is implemented by knowledge in memory that directs the implicit learning mechanisms. The following table summarises the memory systems and learning mechanisms and strategies in ACT-R.

	implicit mechanisms	explicit strategy
declarative memory	base-level learning	maintenance rehearsal
	association learning	elaborate rehearsal
procedural memory	parameter learning	practice
	production compilation	dependency-manipulating rules

Although implicit mechanisms are fixed, explicit strategies have to be learned. So individuals probably differ in their explicit strategies, although they may well have lots of them in common. Rehearsal, for example, is a strategy used by almost all adults, though it is clearly not something we were born with. An interesting question is, whether the same property is also true for the dependency-manipulating rules. Is there a sequence of rules that unfolds during development? The model of the discrimination-shift task at least hints in this direction. On the other hand we may well expect large individual differences. Experiments in which subjects have to solve difficult problems often show that every subject solves a problem in a different way.

An interesting question is how the issues discussed here can be related to other architectures. The emphasis on learning models is often attributed to the ascent of neural network models. A neural network model typically starts out with an untrained network that gains knowledge by experience. Neural networks are powerful in the sense that a three-layer network can learn any function if properly configured. This power is also a weakness, especially if you take the time taken to learn something into account. Neural networks usually do not have any goal-structures, so they lack the mechanisms to be able to focus learning. To summarise: neural networks do a very good job at implicit learning, but the step towards explicit learning is difficult to make because of the absence of any goals or intentional structures.

In the SOAR architecture on the other hand, goals and deliberate reasoning are even more important than in ACT-R (Newell, 1990; reference for an extensive comparison of ACT-R and SOAR Johnson, 1998). The ACT-R models presented in this chapter only deliberate if existing simple rules prove to be insufficient and, more importantly, if there is any knowledge present on how to deliberate. So if ACT-R has to choose between actions A and B, a cost benefit analysis between the rule "do A" and the rule "do B" will decide. Only if both rules prove to perform badly, explicit learning strategies will try to find a more sophisticated rule. A SOAR model on the other hand will always try to make a deliberate and rational choice between A and B, a process that may require a lot of processing and specific task knowledge. A SOAR model that has to choose between A and B, and has no particular additional knowledge, will get into a infinite sequence of impasses. SOAR's single learning mechanism is chunking, which summarises the processing done between an impasse and its resolution into a new production rule. Although chunking is a mechanism, it is only activated after an impasse has been resolved, therefore after a deliberate problem solving attempt. Since chunking is SOAR's only learning mechanism, this may cause trouble. For example, to learn simple facts, for which ACT-R has a separate declarative memory, SOAR needs the elaborate scheme of data-chunking. Data-chunking eventually produces rules like "IF bird THEN note it has wings". To be able to learn this, however, a lot of deliberating has to be done by production rules *that are not part of the architecture*. So in a sense SOAR walks the reverse way: instead of building explicit learning on top of implicit learning, it accomplishes typical implicit learning tasks by elaborate explicit schemes. The critical reader will be able to find more examples of SOAR's problems with simple satisfying behaviour in Johnson (1998).

Since many other architectures like EPIC (Meyer & Kieras, 1997) currently support no learning at all, ACT-R presently seems to be the best platform for supporting explicit learning strategies on a basis of implicit learning. To be able to fully sustain explicit learning though, some technical issues in ACT-R must be resolved. Most notably a mechanism must be included to create new chunk-types. The models discussed in this chapter circumvented this problem by using a generic goal type (GEN-GOAL) for all goals.

This chapter may be a starting point for several avenues of further research. A more thorough inventory of possible general rules has to be made. This leads to a further question: where do the general rules themselves originate? This question is best studied in a developmental setting. Is it possible to specify a sequence of general rules that are learned during development, that can account for the fact that older children can handle more abstract concepts? A good starting point would be to make a model of the complete balanced-beam task (Siegler, 1976) that can explain the stage-wise learning aspects of this task.

Norman (1993) distinguishes experiential and reflective cognition in a human-computer interaction setting. Experiential cognition corresponds to the search-process discussed in this chapter, and reflective cognition to reflection and explicit strategies. According to Norman, designers have to ask themselves the question whether their design is supposed to support experiential or reflective processes, and create it accordingly. Current methods for task analysis used in human-computer interaction typically do not support any learning. In this sense our research apparatus for human-computer interaction can only model experiential cognition. To be able to model the user as an active learner, however, a modelling environment is needed that supports explicit leaning. The SOAR architecture provides a deliberate learning environment, and is used as such already. The ACT-R architecture may well be a good alternative, since it provides a more flexible model of explicit learning that can account for individual differences, and can also model implicit learning phenomena.

References

Anderson, J.R. (1990). *The Adaptive Character of Thought*. Hillsdale, NJ: Lawrence Erlbaum.

Anderson, J.R. (1993). *Rules of the Mind*. Hillsdale, NJ: Lawrence Erlbaum.

Atkinson, R.C. & Shiffrin, R.M. (1968). Human memory: A proposed system and its control processes. In K.W. Spence & J.T. Spence (Eds.), *The Psychology of Learning and Motivation* New York: Academic Press.

Craik, F.I.M. & Lockhart, R.S. (1972). Levels of processing: a framework for memory research. *Journal of Verbal Learning and Verbal Behavior, 11*, 671-684.

Johnson, T. (1998). A comparison between ACT-R and SOAR. Chapter 1.1 of this book.

Johnson-Laird, P. (1983). *Mental Models*. Cambridge, MA: Harvard university press.

Kendler, T.S. & Kendler, H.H. (1959). Reversal and non-reversal shifts in kindergarten children. *Journal of Experimental Psychology, 58*, 56-60.

Knoblich, G. & Ohlsson, S. (1996). Can ACT-R have insights? In U. Schmid, J. Krems & Wysotzki (Eds.), *Proceedings of the First Europeen Workshop on Cognitive Modelling* (report no. 96-39, pp. 161-169). Berlin, Technische Universität Berlin, Fachbereich Informatik.

Meyer, D.E. & Kieras, D.E. (1997). A Computational Theory of Executive Cognitive Processes and Multiple-Task Performance: Part 1. Basic Mechanisms. *Psychological Review, 104*, 3-65.

Miller, G.A. (1956). The magical number seven plus or minus two: Some limits on our capacity for processing information. *Psychological Review, 63*, 81-97.

Newell, A. (1990). *Unified Theories of Cognition*. Cambridge, MA: Harvard University Press.

Newell, A. & Rosenbloom, P.S. (1981). Mechanisms of skill acquisition and the law of practice. In J.R. Anderson (Eds.), *Cognitive Skills and Their Acquisition* Hillsdale, NJ: Prentice-Hall.

Norman, D.A. (1993). *Things That Make Us Smart*. Reading, MA: Addison-Wesley.

Rumelhart, D.E. & McClelland, J.L. (1986). *Parallel Distributed Processing: Explorations in the Microstructure of Cognition.* Cambridge, MA: MIT Press.

Schank, R.C. (1986). *Explanation Patterns: Uunderstanding Mechanically and Creatively.* Hillsdale, NJ: Erlbaum.

Shanks, D.R. & John, M.F.S. (1994). Characteristics of dissociable human learning systems. *Behavioral and Brain Sciences, 17*(3), 367-447.

Siegler, R.S. (1976). Three aspects of cognitive development. *Cognitive Psychology, 8*, 481-520.

Taatgen, N.A. (1996). A model of free-recall using the ACT-R architecture and the phonological loop. In H.J.v.d. Herik & T. Weijters (Eds.), *Proceedings of Benelearn-96*, (pp. 169-178). Maastricht, the Netherlands: Universiteit Maastricht, MATRIKS.

Taatgen, N.A. (1997). A rational analysis of alternating search and reflection in problem solving. In Michael Shafto & Pat Langley (eds.) *Proceedings of the 19th Annual Conference of the Cognitive Science Society.* (pp. 727-732). Hillsdale, NJ: Erlbaum.

3.2 Skill Acquisition Can Be Regarded as Program Synthesis: An Integrative Approach to Learning by Doing and Learning by Analogy

Ute Schmid & Fritz Wysotzki

Abstract

In this paper we propose an approach to skill acquisition which is based on a technique for inductive program synthesis developed in the domain of automatic programming. This approach enables us to model skill acquisition as generalization on three levels: In a first step, learning by doing is performed by generalizing over problem states which were explored when solving a given problem. This process is similar to compilation or chunking of production rules. But in contrast to these approaches, we represent procedural knowledge as conditional programs. In a second step, descriptive generalization of the initial conditional program is performed. A recursive program scheme is constructed which generalizes over recursive enumerable problem spaces. In a third step, learning by analogy is performed by abstracting from the concrete semantic of the operation symbols contained in a recursive program scheme. The abstract scheme represents the class of structurally identical problems. By describing how problem schemes can be constructed as generalization over knowledge gained during solving concrete problems, our approach gives a unifying framework for describing learning by doing and learning by analogy. Additionally, we consider the acquisition of some types of motor and process control behavior as a special variant of the acquisition of problem solving skills, and demonstrate how acquisition of behavioral skills can be integrated in our framework.

Introduction

In artificial intelligence as well as in cognitive psychology acquisition of problem solving skills is usually described as construction of (production) rules. Disposal of such rules enables a (cognitive) system to solve succeeding problems "automatically", without the need to perform complex search and inference processes (Anderson 1983). A usual claim is that problem solving skills are acquired during problem solving processes, that is through **learning by doing** (Anderson, Conrad, & Corbett 1989). Anderson (1983) describes the automatisms on which problem solving is based as "procedural knowledge" (know how) in contrast to "declarative knowledge" (know that). In cognitive science procedural knowledge is usually represented by production rules. In approaches to problem solving, where not the problem solving skills but (declarative) knowledge about problem structures is the prominent aspect, usually problem schemes or frames are used as representation format (Novick & Holyoak 1991, Anderson & Thompson 1989).

Problem solving is generally modelled as heuristic search in a problem space (Newell & Simon 1972). There are standard procedures for forward search (as A*, Nilsson 1980) as well as goal driven production systems (ACT-R, Anderson 1993; SOAR, Newell 1991). In both frameworks the definition of problem operators together with conditions for their application - i.e. production rules - is central. Selection and application of production rules is performed by an interpreter: the interpreter selects and applies a production rule to data in working memory until the problem solving goal is reached or until no rule is applicable. Production rules can be regarded as conditioned programms without loops. All "knowledge" about cyclic processing of operations is contained in the interpreter. A usual claim in cognitive science is, that the strategy of the interpreter is part of a fixed general cognitive architecture and that only the knowledge represented in the production rules can be subject of changes due to skill acquisition (Klahr, Langley, & Neches 1987). This restriction of learning to chunking of production rules makes it difficult to model learning of processing strategies as for example the cyclic structure of operator application to solve the Tower of Hanoi problem (Shell & Carbonell 1989). But there is empirical evidence that people can acquire this kind of knowledge (Klix & Rautenstrauch-Goede 1967, Anzai & Simon 1979).

An alternative approach to the acquisition of problem solving skills trough learning by doing is **learning by analogy**. A new problem is solved by analogical reasoning (Gentner 1983), that is, the solution of a structural similar example problem is adapted to solve the new problem[22]. Learning is usually described as generalization over the common structure of example and goal problem (Novick & Holyoak 1991, Anderson & Thompson 1989). Anderson & Thompson (1989) demonstrate how analogical reasoning and learning can be incorporated into a production system architecture (see also ACT-R, Anderson 1993). Example problems and solutions are represented as "scheme-like structures". New problems are represented in the same way. Empty slots of a current problem (i.e. the new solution) are filled by structure mapping between example and new problem. Learning is done by compilation of the trace of the analogical process, thereby gaining production rules containing the information formerly represented in the problem schemes. An alternative approach is, as mentioned above, to model analogical learning by the construction of generalized problem schemes.

Anderson's proposal does not address the following aspects: (1) The schemes for representing the structure of problems and solutions are represented in the system from the beginning. Thereby Anderson supposes, that the (cognitive) system already has knowledge about the relevant structure of the problem domain. But the crucial deficit of novices is that they may have *no* knowledge about the relevant problem structures (Novick 1988, Schmid & Kaup 1995). (2) There is no statement about the kind of problem structures which can be handled by the proposed approach to analogical mapping and transfer. The examples in Anderson and Thompson (1989) are restricted to generalized problem isomorphs, i.e. identical structures where variable and operation symbols can be substituted. Empirical studies demonstrate, that people also can use non isomorphic examples to reason and learn by analogy (Pirolli & Anderson 1985, Reed & Bolstad 1991). Both aspects are generally seldom treated in cognitive science: There are very few proposals for modelling the acquisition of schemes (Rumelhart & Norman 1978, 1981; see also Cornuejlos 1997). While there are some empirical studies using non-isomorphic examples in analogical reasoning (see above) there is no systematic classification of types of structural similarities which can be used in analogical reasoning and learning. This is also true for most computational models on analogical problem solving[23] (Falkenhainer, Forbus, & Gentner 1989, Holyoak & Thagard 1989).

We propose a computational model for learning by doing and learning by analogy which covers all aspects discussed above. That is, our model describes:

- building behavioral programs from problem solving experience as an alternative approach to compiliation/chunking of production rules,

---

[22] so called "within domain analogies" in contrast to the "between domain analogies" as for example considered by Gentner (1983), see Vosniadou and Ortony (1989).

[23] A lot of work is being done on the influence of different degrees of surface similarity, that is semantic or pragmatic features of example and goal problem (Novick 1988, Holyoak & Thagard 1989).

- induction of problem schemes by generalization over behavioral programs, thereby giving a formal approach to model acquisition of schemes which represent knowledge about cyclic (recursive) structures of operator applications in problem solving,

- analogical problem solving and learning on the basis of program schemes, introducing first ideas on how to deal with non-isomorphic structures.

We do not propose that our approach is another unifying cognitive architecture (Anderson 1993, Newell 1991). We do not claim that the knowledge representation formats and inference techniques employed in our model are adequate descriptions of human cognitive processes. But we try to model certain aspects of human problem solving for the existence of which there is some empirical evidence in a uniform and formally sound way.

In the following sections we first give an overview of our computational model. Then we present its different aspects in some detail. That is, we describe how behavioral programs can be constructed from problem solving experience. Than we introduce a method of inductive synthesis of recursive program schemes and demonstrate the application of such schemes in analogical problem solving and learning. In the last section we show that our approach can also be applied to model some types of the acquisition of motor and process control behavior.

An integrative framework for skill acquisition

To give the general idea of our approach we present an example of a simple blocks world problem (see figure 1). There are three blocks A, B and C stacked as a tower. The problem solving goal is to unstack the tower, that is to clear the bottom block C. The system has one operator - *puttable(x)* - and its application condition (x must be free to be put on the table; *cleartop(x))* at disposal. The problem space consists of three states: the three-block tower, the tower where A is already on the table and the goal state (C is free and A and B are on the table). When decomposing the three-block-tower for the first time, the system has to check whether there is an operator at hand which is applicable to the initial state. Application of the operator transforms the state into a new state. If this state is not the goal state, the system has again to select an operator which is applicable and so on. If the system is confronted with a problem for the first time, it has to be solved by heuristic search. Problem solving gives the system experience with what operators can be applied to which state to transform it into the goal state. This experience can be represented as a conditional program with predicates characterizing states and corresponding operator sequences, where constants are replaced by variables (a more comprehensive description is given in the following section). This first kind of generalization over problem states is an alternative way to model skill acquisition by knowledge compilation or chunking in production systems (Rosenbloom & Newell 1986, Anderson 1986). If the system is confronted with the same or another initial state of an already solved problem, the constructed conditional program can be used to solve the problem in an effective way, omitting heuristic search.

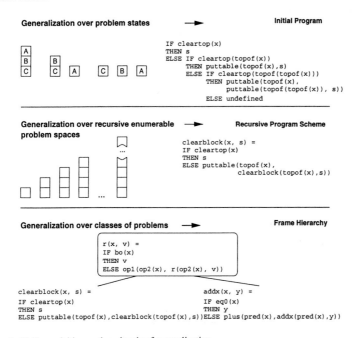

Figure 1: Skill acquisition as three levels of generalization

We believe that experience in solving a special problem not only results in the acquisition of automatisms for solving this problem, but that additionally a generalized knowledge structure is inferred. If a problem solver has gained experience in decomposing towers in a three-blocks world, this experience helps him also to decompose towers in an *n*-blocks world. That is, the problem solver generalizes over recursive enumerable problem spaces. This kind of descriptive generalization can be modelled by a method of inductive synthesis of recursive program schemes (RPSs; see Wysotzki 1983, Schmid & Wysotyki 1998 and section 4). This representation format corresponds to problem schemes (or frames) and has the characteristics, that it simultanuously catches the *structure* of a problem (considered as a scheme) and that it is executable (as a program after appropirate interpretation). The notion of schemes as programs was also employed by Rumelhart and Norman (1981).

RPSs can be considered mathematically to be elements of a term algebra, that is they are not restricted to a special programming language. Operation symbols contained in an RPS can be interpreted semantically by different operations. Thereby, an RPS represents not only a structure of how to solve a specific problem, but a structure for solving a class of structural isomorphic problems. These characteristics can be exploited for analogical transfer. If a behavioral program (RPS) with a certain recursive (cyclic) structure exists, a structural isomorphic (or structural similar) problem can be solved by analogical transfer omitting the effort of inducing an RPS from scratch (see section 5).

Our approach is incorporated into the architecture of the experimental system IPAL which is implemented as a first prototype in LISP (see figure 2). Input to the system is a set of problem states, a goal state and a set of operators and their conditions for application. For each problem state the optimal sequence of operators to transform it into the goal is constructed by a problem solving algorithm. Combining these sequences to an initial program realizes the first step of generalization. In the next step it is checked whether there is a sufficiently similar problem in the knowledge base. An RPS can be expanded to an initial program being able to handle a prescribed finite number of cases only. If an RPS in the knowledge base exists whose initial program has a structural similarity higher than S to the current initial program, the new RPS is constructed by analogical transfer. Otherwise the new RPS is inferred by descriptive generalization with an inductive program synthesis technique mentioned above. The new RPS is stored in memory. If the new RPS was gained by analogical transfer, additionally a generalized RPS is constructed which becomes the

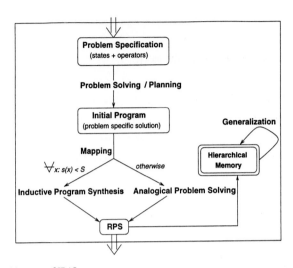

Figure 2: System Architecture of IPAL

parent of both the RPSs involved in the analogical process. Generalized schemes can be used in the same way as the example RPSs for (analogical or rather abstraction based) reasoning. Thereby the knowledge structure may become hierachically organized with learning experience.

Acquisition of problem solving skills

Here we describe the first step of generalization, i.e. the construction of initial programs from problem solving experience, in more detail. For illustration we use the "clearblock"-Problem (see figure 1). The three problem states are represented by conjunctions of predicates:

(1)   *cleartop(A), cleartop(B), cleartop(C)*

(2)   *on(B,C), cleartop(A), cleartop(B)*

(3)   *on(A,B), on(B,C), cleartop(A).*

The goal predicate is *cleartop(C)*. The operator puttable is represented as production rule:

on(x,y), cleartop(x) rightarrow puttable(x),

with the semantics ADD *cleartop(y)* DEL *on(x,y)*.

Additionally we use the selector function *topof(x) = y $\Leftrightarrow$ on(y,x)*.

The problem solver tries to construct a solution for each initial state. State (1) fulfills the goal already, no operator has to be applied. State (2) fulfills the condition part of the production rule. The rule is instantiated with {*x/B, y/C*} and *puttable(B)* is applied. Operator application transforms state (2) into state (1), the goal is fulfilled. In state (3) the operations *puttable(B)* and *puttable(C)* are executed.

The construction of an initial program is preformed by following steps:

- Constants are represented constructively, in dependence from the constants occuring in the goal predicate. In the clearblock problem we rewrite *B = topof(C)* and *A = topof(topof(C))*.

- We use situation calculus (Green, 1969) to represent operator sequences as terms. That is, we add an additional parameter *s* (a situation variable) to each operator. The operator *puttable(x)* in the clearblock problem is rewritten to *puttable(x,s)*.

- The remaining constants are variabilized[24]. Thereby a generalization over the given problem space (figure 1) is achieved. If *C* is replaced by a variable *x*, we regard all situations where a fixed but arbitraty block *x* is clear as goal states. This block *x* does not have to be placed on the table but can be on top of other blocks.

- A minimal conjunction of predicates is calculated, which discriminates all problem states associated with different operator sequences (see table 1). This is a typical concept acquisition

---

[24] Variablization can be considered as a by-product of learning: If production rules are applicable to constants *C* and expressions *topof(C)*, information about the data structure of the problem domain can be extrapolated.

problem and can be handled with decision tree techniques given in the machine learning literature. We use the decision tree algorithm CAL2 proposed by Unger and Wysotzki (1981). In the clearblock example we have to discriminate three states which can be achieved by the single predicate *clearblock*. In the goal state *clearblock(x)* is true, in the second state *clearblock(topof(x))* is true and in the third state *clearblock(topof(topof(x)))* is true.

Table 1: Problem states and associated operator sequences for the clearblock problem

(1)	cleartop(x)	s
(2)	cleartop(topof(x))	puttable(topof(x),s)
(3)	cleartop(topof(topof(x)))	puttable(topof(x),puttable(topof(topof(x)),s))

- The predicates are ordered by complexity of terms (which corresponds to a complete partial order over the data type) and are composed to a conditional expression. The resulting initial program for the clearblock problem is given in figure 1.

We are exploring an alternative approach for constructing initial programs which (1) enables us to deal with problems with higher complexity, especially with goal states which are composed of dependent sub-goals[25]; and (2) which provides a different representation format for initial programs which makes inductive program synthesis more simple for some problems (see section 4). Instead of the two-step procedure of heuristic search and decision tree construction, the initial program is built in one step by a goal-driven planning algorithm (see Wysotzki 1987, Schmid & Wysotzki 1996). The resulting plan is a binary tree with the goal as root node. Left branches represent cases where the top predicates are true, right branches apply the operators to achieve the top predicates. That is, the plan corresponds to a conditional program. We demonstrate this planning approach for the clearblock problem.

Operators are represented by basic programs instead of production rules. For each predicate regarded in the goal state a corresponding basic program is given which describes what to do, if the predicate is true or if the predicate is not true in a situation:

---

[25] For example to reach the goal *on(A,B) and on(B,C)* the sub-goal *on(B,C)* has to be achieved first.

$G_{\text{cleartop}(x)} = cleartop(x)(s|\ |,\ puttable(topof(x))(s|cleartop(topof(x))|)).$

The right hand side of the basic program is to be read as "if cleartop(x) is true than situation s has not to be changed, otherwise apply the operator *puttable(topof(x))* but first ensure that *cleartop(topof(x))* holds". The operators given in basic programs are annotated at the right branches of the plan. The conditions for operator application given in the basic programs are introduced as new goals. The initial program for the clearblock problem constructed by planning is given in figure 3.

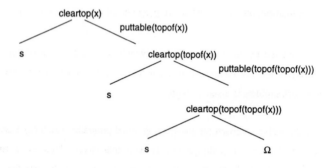

Figure 3: Initial program constructed by planning (Ω means "undefined")

Scheme induction

To model descriptive generalization over recursive enumerable problem spaces we use a method of inductive program synthesis introduced by Wysotzki (1983) and further developed and implemented by Schmid (Schmid & Wysotzki 1998). Alternative approaches to this problem were presented in the context of planning (iterative macro-operators: Shell & Carbonell 1989) and in explanation-based learning (n-generalization: Shavlik 1990).

To grasp the general idea of the method, consider numerical induction problems (see also Gold 1967) as used in intelligence tests, for example *1, 4, 9, 16, ...* . To give the next element of this sequence, one has to infer the rule by which the element at position i ($i = 1$ to 4) can be constructed. As more elements are taken into consideration the more the set of possible rules gets restricted. If restricted. If you only look at the first two elements for example the rule $e^{(i+1)} = e^{(i)} + 3$ and the rule $e^{(i)} = i \times i$ are covering the data. But the first rule does not hold for the next two elements. Of course the second rule, which covers all four elements of the sequence is also only hypothetical. If the next element would not be 25 a new rule has to be considered. But for the examples at hand, the observed regularity is best covered by our second rule. In the following we employ the idea of discovering regularities and perform an inductive generalization (Holland, Holyoak, Nisbett, & Thagard 1986) not for simple numerical expressions, but for terms. We demonstrate the method with the clearblock problem. The theoretical background and a formal description of the approach is given in Schmid and Wysotzki (1998).

First we take the initial program given in figure 3 as input to inductive program synthesis. We use the McCarthy conditional $g(x,y,z) =_{Def} IF\ x\ THEN\ y\ ELSE\ z$ to represent it as a term with prefix notation only:

$$G = g(cleartop(x),\ s,\ puttable(topof(x),$$
$$g(cleartop(topof(x)),\ s,\ puttable(topof(topof(x)),$$
$$g(cleartop(topof(topof(x))),\ s,\Omega))))).$$

The initial program represents the problem solving experience gained in a three block world263 when working on the clearblock problem. The symbol Ω (undefined) indicates that the system has gained no experience for the case that the second block on a block x is not clear. Descriptive generalization will now be performend by extrapolation over the structure of the initial program. The general idea is to identify a term tr corresponding to a sub-tree starting at the root in G which occures repeatedly with a subsitution Θ of variables v by terms t. To this aim we decompose G in a sequence of terms $G^{(i)}$ with $G^{(i+1)} = tr(G^{(i)}_{\Theta})$. In terms of (theoretical) computer science that is, we interprete G as an element of a Kleene sequence (linear expansion) belonging to some recursive program. By definition $G^{(0)} = \Omega$ holds. Now we can rewrite G as sequence

$$G^{(0)} = \Omega$$
$$G^{(1)} = g(cleartop(x),\ s,\ puttable(topof(x),\ \Omega))$$

$$G^{(2)} = g(cleartop(x), s, puttable(topof(x),$$

$$g(cleartop(topof(x)), s, puttable(topof(topof(x)), \Omega)))))$$

$$G^{(3)} = g(cleartop(x), s, puttable(topof(x),$$

$$g(cleartop(topof(x)), s, puttable(topof(topof(x)),$$

$$g(cleartop(topof(topof(x))), s, \Omega))))) = G$$

with $tr = g(cleartop(x), s, puttable(topof(x), m))$ and $\Theta = \{x/topof(x)\setminus\}$. Symbol m marks the place where a sub-term can be inserted into the structure. We can rewrite the sequence by

$$G^{(0)} = \Omega$$

$$G^{(1)} = g(cleartop(x), s, puttable(topof(x), G^{(0)}{}_\Theta))$$

$$G^{(2)} = g(cleartop(x), s, puttable(topof(x), G^{(1)}{}_\Theta))$$

$$G^{(3)} = g(cleartop(x), s, puttable(topof(x), G^{(3)}{}_\Theta))$$

and extrapolate

$$G^{(i+1)} = g(cleartop(x), s, puttable(topof(x), G^{(i)}{}_\Theta))$$

for all $i \in \mathbb{N}$, thereby getting in the limit the recursive program scheme

$$G(x,s) = g(cleartop(x), s, puttable(topof(x), G(topof(x),s))).$$

Taking the inital program given in figure 1 as input to program synthesis, the procedure gets more complicated (see figure 4a for a representation as decision tree). The problem is that each THEN-branch represents a complex operator sequence which has to be decomposed for extrapolating an recursive program scheme. This can be done by rewriting the operator sequences introducing new variables for counting operator applications and dealing with the THEN-branches as a seperate induction problem:

$$H^{(0)} = s$$
$$H^{(1)} = puttable(topof'(1,x))$$
$$H^{(2)} = puttable(topof'(1,x), puttable(topof'(2,x), s))$$

can be extrapolated to

$$H(i,n,x,s) = g(equal(i,n), s, puttable(topof'(i,x), H(succ(i), n, x, s)))$$

where i is a counting variable for the number of topof-applications and n is the number of puttable-operations which have to be performed. The clearblock-RPS is:

$$G(x,s) = G'(0,x,s)$$
$$G'(n,x,s) = g(cleartop(topof(n,x)), H(0,n,x,s), G'(succ(n),x,s)).$$

$G'(n,x,s)$ only calculates the number of blocks n lying on top of x. This number is input to the additional function H which handles the application of the *puttable* operations.

While descriptive generalization of the clearblock problem is simple when using plans as initial programs, it is complicated and results in a more complex solution for initial programs gained by forward application of production rules. The problem arises in all cases where the problem structure is not a simple tail-recursion[26]. In figure 4b an initial program for a simple tail-recursive problem is given. The problem solving goal is to put the uppermost block of a tower on the table. The initial program can be folded to the RPS $T(x) = g(cleartop(x),puttable(x), T(topof(x)))$.

---

[26] Tail-recursion has the structure $G(x) = g(boolop(x), op(x), G(minop(x)))$. If recursion terminates the result can directly be given. In more complex cases, as for example the clearblock problem, recursion depends on a stack. When recursion terminates, the result has to be used to calculate the expression obtained by each recursive call.

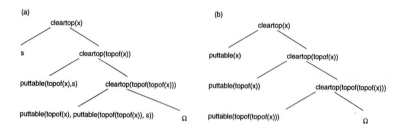

Figure 4: Initial programs constructed from forward application of production rules (Ω means "undefined")

That the representation of a problem has effects on problem solving success is well known from psychological studies (c.f. Simon 1970). Our approach suggests, additionally, that the problem solving strategy used by a (cognitive) system influences the ease of generalization.

Analogical problem solving

Analogical problem solving can be described by four processes (see Novick & Holyoak 1991):

- *Retrieval*: Search for an example problem already solved which is structurally similar to the current (goal) problem.

- *Mapping*: Compare the structures of example and goal problem. (If retrieval is guided by a similarity measure regarding problem structures rather than attributes, mapping is performed simultaneously with retrieval).

- *Adaptation:* Adapt the example solution to the goal problem. (We will show that this process can be performed purely syntactically for isomorphic problem structures. For non-isomorphic problems additionally semantic information of the problem domain has to be regarded.)

- *Learning*: Construct a scheme which generalizes over the structure of example and goal problem.

In our approach we use analogical problem solving for the construction of RPSs from initial programs. We regard a current initial program as goal problem and search for a recursive generalization of this initial program. Already inferred RPSs are stored in a (partial) hierachical memory structure. How this structure is constructed is described below. To compare the goal problem with the RPSs stored in memory, these RPSs (example solutions) have to be expanded to initial programs again (example problems). This "unfolding" (Burstall & Darlington 1977) is performed until the depth corresponds to that of the current initial tree. Similarity between goal problem and example problem is calculated by a measure for tree distance proposed by Lu (1979). This measure is a purely syntactical approach to compare structures and is extremely suitable for our purpose: initial programs are terms which can be represented by trees. Similarity between trees is calculated as sum of all operations which have to be performed to transform one tree into another tree. Three operations are defined: Substituting one node label by another (s), deletion of a node (d) and insertion of a node (i). The three types of operations can be associated with different weights. Similarity between two trees x and y is:

$$ds(x,y) = s * n_1 + d * n_2 + i * n_3$$

where n_i represents the frequency of performing one operation.[27]

If a tree can be transformed into another by unique substitutions only, the problems are isomorph. This is for example the case for the problems *factorial* and *sum* given in figure 5a,b below. The substitutions are *{1/0, mult/plus}*.

Calculation of structural similarity between two initial programs provides simultaneously the mapping between both problems. Adaptation is easily achieved for isomorphic problems: The substitutions gained by the tree transformation can be applied to the RPS corresponding to the selected example problem. If the RPS for calculating *factorial* is already known

---

[27] Currently we are exploring an extension of this similarity measure where information about types and arity of function symbols (nodes) are taken into acount.

$$fac(x) = g(equal0(x), \ 1, \ mult(x, fac(pred(x))))$$

the RPS for calculating the *sum* of x can be generated by substituting *1* by *0* and *mult* by *plus*.

The new RPS is stored in memory. Example and goal RPS are generalized by variabilization of all symbols which occur at identical positions in both structures but are differently named. The generalized RPS is stored as parent node to example and goal RPS. This strategy causes the memory to become more and more hierarchically organized with experience. The hierarchical organization additionally prevents retrieval from becoming inefficient when the number of RPSs in the memory increases: Search for a suitable example problem starts with the roots of the RPSs hierarchies. Only the RPS structure where the root RPS has the highest similarity to the goal problem is further explored. In the next step, all children of the selected root RPS are explored. Afterwards, only the branch with the highest similarity to the example RPS is regarded and so on. Note that similarity can reduce when proceeding to the more special RPSs lower in the hierarchical structure. In this case a generalized RPS is used for analogical problem solving. That is, the new problem is not solved by analogy, but by application of an abstract problem scheme.

Finally we will give an example of analogical problem solving with non-isomorphic structures. We will demonstrate how a RPS for calculating the factorial function (see figure 5a) can be constructed from the RPS of the clearblock problem (see figure 5c) by analogical transfer. That is, we show analogical transfer from a visually concrete to a mathematically abstract problem domain. Figure 5 gives the initial programs represented as trees. Note that the tree in figure 5c corresponds to the tree of the clearblock problem given in figure 3. We use the more complex term representation here because this kind of representation is input to structure mapping with the tree distance. Table 2 gives the transformation which has to be performed. Additionally to substitution of node labels, two deletions of *topof* nodes have to be performed. The two trees are not only non-isomorphical, but there is even a lack of unique mapping from clearblock to factorial. For analogical transfer it has to be determinded, at which position in the clearblock-RPS *topof* has to be replaced by *pred* and at which position *topof* has to be deleted (i.e. replaced by the identity function). This can be done by regarding the context of the trees when calculating the transformation: *topof* is deleted in the first argument of *puttable* only, therefore it will deleted in the first argument of *mult*. Both of the non-isomorphic RPSs are:

$$G(x,s) = g(cleartop(x), \quad s, \ puttable(topof(x), \quad\quad G(topof(x),s)))$$

$F(x) = g(equal0(x), \quad 1, mult(x, \qquad F(pred(x))))$.

Table 2: Mapping of the clearblock and the factorial problem (mapping *topof* to the identity function *id(x) = x* corresponds to deletion of a node)

Clearblock	Faculty
x	x
s	1
cleartop	equal0
puttable	mult
topof	pred
topof	id

$\rightarrow$ non unique mapping

$\leftarrow$ surjective mapping

An alternative strategy to "direct" adaptation is to try to generate an isomorphic relation between problems by transforming the example problem with the help of background knowledge (O'Hara 1992). We represent term rewrite rules to represent background knowledge. If we use

cleartop(x) $\rightarrow$ notexists(topof(x))

that is, if we look at the problem in a new way, we can gain at least a partial isomorphism to the factorial problem (see figure 5a and 5d).

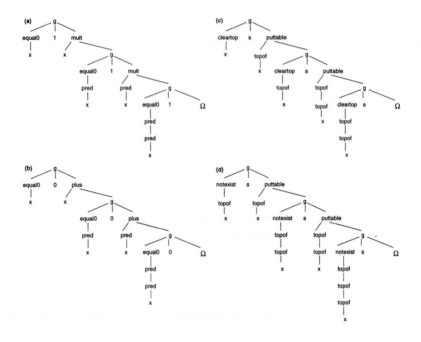

Figure 5: Initial programs represented as term trees for factorial (a), sum (b), clearblock (c) and transformed clearblock (c)

If we omit the special case of $x=0$ (calculating only the factorial of $x-1$) and allow for a constant as parameter, the problems are isomorphic:

$G(x,s) =$ g(notexists(topof(x)), s,   puttable(topof(x),   G(topof(x),s)))

$F(x,1) =$ g(equal0(pred(x)),   1,   mult(pred(x),   F(pred(x),1))).

This solution can be repaired further on by rewriting the RPS for the factorial problem:

F(x)   = F'(x,x)

F'(x,y) = g(equal0(pred(x)), y,   mult(pred(x), F'(pred(x),y))).

The RPS $F'(x,y)$ calculates the factorial by multiplying y (instantiated with x) with the recursively calculated factorial of $x-1$. Thereby an isomorphical relation between the clearblock problem and the factorial problem has been constructed.

While our first strategy of "direct" adaptation remains purely syntactical, the second strategy of problem transformation relies heavily on knowledge about the problem domain. While there is evidence that people can use structurally similar but not isomorph structures for analogical transfer (see Pirolli & Anderson 1985, Schmid & Kaup 1995) there is little knowledge about the strategies people employ to adapt solutions in such cases. We believe that both strategies are possible. But this is clearly a point for further investigation.

Acquisition of motor and process control skills

In this section we describe how the acquisition of motor and process control skills can be integrated in our framework. In artificial intelligence as well as in cognitive psychology, the acquisition of problem solving skills and the acquisition of motor or process control behavior is usually explored within different approaches. Problem solving skills ("cognitive skills") are typically described by production rules or similar approaches as described in the sections above. Control behavior on the other hand is typically described by neural or cybernetic circuits ("control programs"). Acquisition of control skills is often modelled by reinforcement learning (Dean, Basye, & Shewchuk 1993), sometimes by artificial neural nets, for example with back propagation as learning procedure (Nguyen & Widrow 1989). Well known approaches to this domain in artificial intelligence are BOXES (Michie & Chambers 1968), CART (Connell & Utgoff 1987) and ASE/ACE (Barto, Sutton, & Anderson 1983), mainly concerned with maintaining a stable system state. We do not argue that this kind of "low level" skill learning (in most cases leading to the "credit assignment" problem) is not important for modelling human skill acquisition. However we are interested in this paper in control behavior as analogous to problem solving, employing problem solving together with machine learning techniques.

If we look at motor/control behavior skills from the perspective of problem solving, we identify the following similarities and differences: In problem solving, an intelligent system manipulates problem states to reach a pre-defined goal in an otherwise static environment. In motor or process control behavior a system interacts with another system to reach or maintain a goal state. States and operations might describe aspects of the controlling system itself and of its environment (in behavior control tasks as for example riding a bicycle) or of another system (in process control as for example performing a chemical synthesis task). Problem states are in general real valued parameters describing the current characteristics of the system which is to be controlled (as values for heat and pressure) or the controlling system itself (as position and speed). The controlling system is provided with a set of operators which can be continuous (as move for n meters, raise temperature to n degrees). But the conditions for operator applications may be not known, that is, there may be no or only an incomplete domain model. Additionally, operator applications are not the only way to change system states; the controlling system might have to deal with additional influcence factors from the environment (as wind), i.e. so called open systems. Problem solving is done by operator applications whereby the system is moving along trajectories in some (in most cases continuous) state space in or into a goal area. Whereas in classical problem solving the complete problem space could be explored, this is in general not possible in the continuous problem spaces we deal with in motor/process control.

Acquisition of motor/control behavior skill can be regarded as similar to the construction of initial programs from problem solving experience (see section 3). In a first step, a representative set of input states ("training data") has to be generated. Then a problem solving algorithm determines the optimal control action for each state by means of an empirical evaluation function. Other than in discrete problem spaces, here the goal state usually is not a point, but an area in the parameter space (i. e. continuous problem space). Müller and Wysotzki (1995) employ a decision tree technique to split the state space automatically into sub-areas with unique control actions (CAL 5, see Appendix). The resulting decision tree represents a control program: It can be read as a nested conditional expression, where a state is tested in which area of the parameter space it falls and the appropriate control action is executed, giving the next state and so on, i.e., this program can be applied recursively, where the i-th input is the result of the application of a control operation to the input $i - 1$.

In the following we will describe this kind of generalization (over problem states) in more detail. As a real world example we use the roll axis stabilization (as a reaction to disturbances) of a communication satellite in orbit with respect to its position to the earth's axis (Müller & Wysotzki 1995)[28]. The position manoeuvers of the satellite are carried out by thruster torques delivering a set of discrete control actions, the application of which consumes fuel. The control task is to bring the satellite axis back into a certain small acceptable target interval of its attitude angle consuming as little fuel as possible (i.e. performing a small number of control actions) after distortions.

The state space of the process is defined by the attitude angle φ of the satellite and its rate $\dot{\varphi}$. The target area of control is some region around $\varphi = 0$ and $\dot{\varphi} = 0$ (some maximal value of $|\varphi|$ is given which must not be exceeded). There are additional variables describing oscillations of the two solar generators of the satellite, which influence the process states considered as noise.

In a first step a training set of n randomly selected points in the two dimensional state space X is constructed, which are interpreted as distorted states when compared with the goal state. Each input is a tuple $m_j = (\varphi, \dot{\varphi}) \in X$. Additionally there is a set of control actions $P_f = \{f_1, \dots f_q\}$ and an evaluation function $F: X \rightarrow R$, which maps the state space into the set of real numbers. Part of F is the minimal distance to the target area. For each input (i.e. distorted state) the local optimal control action is calculated, using gradient descent (hill climbing) on F: All available control actions are applied to a given input state and thereby a set of following states is constructed (the next state is computed using a simulation program since of course it is not possible to experiment with the satellite. For detaills see Müller & Wysotzki 1995). The (unique) action f_{opt} which leads to a following state with minimal value of F is associated with the input state. For the satellite problem local optimal actions result in global optimal trajectories (see below).

---

[28] This is an application conducted by Wolfgang Müller and Fritz Wysotzki of the Fraunhofer Institute for Information and Data Processing, Branch Lab for Process Optimization (EPO), Berlin, as part of the project WISCON, supported by the German Ministry of Science and Technology.

The pairs (m_j, f_{opt}) are now used to construct a control program. Here the classification algorithm CAL5 (Unger & Wysotzki 1981, Müller & Wysotzki 1994) is used, which constructs decision trees by automatic calculation of optimal discretizations of continuous parameter values (see figure 6).

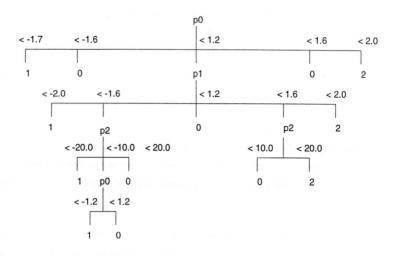

Figure 6: Program for controlling the behavior of a satellite represented as a decision tree $(p_0 = \varphi,$ $p_1 = \dot{\varphi}, p_2 =$ oscillation of one solar generator; $0 =$ no control action, $1 = + T_c, 2 = T_c)$

The decision tree classifies system states m_j with respect to the control action f which should be applied to each state. It can be read as a conditional program ("IF φ is less than -1.7 THEN use thruster torque T_c ..."). This program generalizes over the presented input states from which it was constructed, segmenting the whole state space in regions with associated optimal control actions. Since we assume that there are no "obstacles" (e.g. instability regions) in the state space to be avoided by the control mechanism, the tree contains implicitly almost optimal control trajectories from a given input state to the goal area. This is due to the fact that our problem solving algorithm is greedy, that is we have a local criterion which guarantees global optimality (there are no "obstacles" causing back-tracking in the problem space). It has been shown that the generalization error during tree learning does not greatly influence the optimality of the created control trajectories. While the initial steps - problem solving and construction of the control program - are to be time consuming processes, the resulting program can be used for efficient real time process control (see figure 7).

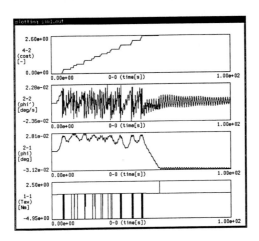

Figure 7: Plot of real time control for the satellite

Discussion

We have proposed to looking at skill acquisition from the viewpoint of program synthesis. Thereby we gain *(1)* a unifying view for acquisition of cognitive as well as motor/ process behavior and *(2)* have a sound theoretical background in theoretical computer science. Induction and analogical inference of recursive program schemes can be viewed as a general approach to the acquisition of problem solving skills as proposed in section 1. If we take a more restricted view on recursive program schemes as functional programs, our approach can be seen as a contribution to research on the acquisition of programming skills: In a first step it describes how straightforward programs are constructed by problem solving on desired inputs to a functional program. Problem solving operators can be restricted to represent builtin functions of a given programming language. The initial program for factorial (see figure 5a) can be constructed by exploring what to do for calculating the factorial of $n = 3$ in a straight forward way using the basic definitions for the built-in function *mult* as operator and the boolean function *equal0* as predicate to describe inputs (i.e. problem states). Inductive program synthesis can be viewed as an "all purpose inference strategy" to construct recursive programs. Our approach to analogical problem solving and learning describes how recursive programs can be constructed by analogical transfer and how a programming novice gains experience of problem structures in the domain of recursive programming by generalizing over example problems.

Taking this more restricted perspective, our approach is not only a contribution to cognitive modelling but also to automatic programming and knowledge-based software engineering (Lowry & McCarthy 1991). Enriching classical approaches to inductive program synthesis by problem solving and analogical reasoning and learning can result in more powerful systems. Usually, input in inductive synthesis systems is a set of input/output examples which have to be reformulated by background knowledge about data structures and built-in operations to construct initial programs (Summers 1977). We propose an alternative strategy where initial programs can be constructed from example inputs alone, constructing corresponding outputs by problem solving. Introducing a memory for RPSs for programming by analogy has for a long time been considered as means for increasing effectivity and power of inductive program synthesis systems (Manna & Waldinger 1975), buht has rarely been realized (Sadohara & Haraguchi 1995). In the domain of automatic theorem proving there is already some evidence that analogical reasoning can increase system performance (Melis 1995). Furthermore, enriching built-in functions by the set of already synthesized RPSs opens the way to constructing more complex programs.

Acknowledgements

Implementation of the system was done by Mark Müller, incorporating work which was done in two student projects at the Berlin University of Technology.

References

Anderson, J. (1993). *Rules of the Mind*. Hillsdale, NJ: Lawrence Erlbaum

Anderson, J., & Thompson, R. (1989). Use of analogy in a production system architecture. In S. Vosniadou & A. Ortony (Eds.), *Similarity and Analogical Reasoning* (p. 267-297). Cambridge University Press

Anderson, J. R. (1983). *The Architecture of Cognition*. Cambridge, MA: Havard University Press

Anderson, J. R. (1986). *Knowledge Compilation: A General Learning Mechanism*. In R. S. Michalski, J. G. Carbonell, & T. M. Mitchell Eds.), *Machine Learning - An Artificial Intelligence Approach* (VOL 2, p. 289-310). Tioga

Anderson, J. R., Conrad, F. G., & Corbett, A. T. (1989). Skill acquisition and the LISP tutor. *Cognitive Science, 13*, 467-505

Anzai, Y., & Simon, H. (1979). The theory of learning by doing. *Psychological Review, 86*, 124-140

Barto, A. B., Sutton, R. S., & Anderson, C. W. (1983). Neuronlike adaptive elements that can solve difficult learning control problems. *IEEE Transactions on Systems, Man and Cybernetics, 13*(5)

Burstall, R., & Darlington, J. (1977). *A Transformation System for Developing Recursive Programs*. JACM, *24*(1), 44-67

Connell, M. E., & Utgoff, P. E. (1987). Learning to control a dynamic physical system. In Proc. AAAI-87 (p. 456-460). Seattle

Cornuejlos, A. (1997). Analogy as minimization of description length. In N. Nakhaeizadeh & C. Taylor (Eds.), *Machine Learning and Statistics. The Interface* (p. 321-335). New York: Wiley

Dean, T., Basye, K., & Shewchuk, J. (1993). Reinforcement learning for planning and control. In S. Minton (Ed.), *Machine Learning Methods for Planning* (p. 67-92). Morgan Kaufmann

Falkenhainer, B., Forbus, K., & Gentner, D. (1989). The structure mapping engine: Algorithm and example. *Artificial Intelligence, 41*, 1-63

Gentner, D. (1983). Structure-mapping: a theoretical framework for analogy. *Cognitive Science, 7*, 155-170

Gold, E. (1967). Language identification in the limit. *Information and Control, 10*, 447-474

Green, C. (1969). *Application of Theorem Proving to Problem Solving* (Tech. Rep.). IJCAI 1.

Holland, J., Holyoak, K., Nisbett, R., & Thagard, P. (1986). *Induction - Processes of Inference, Learning, and Discovery*. Cambridge, MA: MIT Press

Holyoak, K. J., & Thagard, P. (1989). Analogical mapping by constraint satisfaction. *Cognitive Science, 13*, 295-355

Klahr, D., Langley, P., & Neches, R. (1987). *Production System Models of Learning and Development*. Cambridge, MA: MIT Press

Klix, F., & Rautenstrauch-Goede, K. (1967). Struktur- und Komponentenanalyse von Problemlöseprozessen. *Zeitschrift für Psychologie, 174*, 167-193

Lowry, M. L., & McCarthy, R. D. (1991). *Automatic Software Design*. Cambridge, Mass.: MIT Press

Lu, S. (1979). A tree-to-tree distance and its application to cluster analysis. *IEEE Transactions on Pattern Analysis and Machine Intelligence, PAMI-1*(2), 219-224

Manna, Z., & Waldinger, R. (1975). Knowledge and reasoning in program synthesis. *Artificial Intelligence, 6*, 175-208

Melis, E. (1995). A model of analogy-driven proof-plan construction. In C. S. Mellish (Ed.), *Proceedings of the Fourteenth International Joint Conference on Artificial Intelligence* (pp. 182 -189). San Mateo: Morgan Kaufmann

Michie, D., & Chambers, R. A. (1968). Boxes: An experiment in adaptive control. In E. Dale & D. Michie (Eds.), *Machine Intelligence* (Vol. 2, p. 137-152). Edinburgh: Oliver and Boyd

Müller, W., & Wysotzki, F. (1994). Automatic construction of decision trees for classification. In K. Moser & K. M. Schader (Eds.), *Annals of Operation Research* (Vol. 92, p. 231-247). Wijdenes, The Netherlands: J. C. Baltzer AG Science Pub.

Müller, W., & Wysotzki, F. (1995). Automatic synthesis of control programs by combination of learning and problem solving methods. In N. Lavrač & S. Wrobel (Eds.) *Machine Learning: ECML-95* (pp. 323 - 326). Berlin,: Springer

Newell, A. (1991). *Unified Theories of Cognition*. Cambridge, MA: Cambridge University Press

Newell, A., & Simon, H. A. (1972). *Human Problem Solving*. Englewood Cliffs, NJ: Prentice Hall

Nguyen, D., & Widrow, B. (1989). The truck backer upper: an example of self-learning in neural networks. In *Proc. IJCNN* (Vol 2, p. 357-363).

Nilsson, N. J. (1980). *Principles of Artificial Intelligence*. New York: Springer

Novick, L. R. (1988). Analogical transfer, problem similarity, and expertise. *Journal of Experimental Psychology: Learning, Memory, and Cognition, 14* (510-520)

Novick, L. R., & Holyoak, K. J. (1991). Mathematical problem solving by analogy. *Journal of Experimental Psychology: Learning, Memory, and Cognition, 14*, 510-520

O'Hara, S. (1992). A model of the redescription process in the context of geometric proportional analogy problems. In *Analogical and Inductive Inference, int. Workshop aii '92, Dagstuhl Castle, Germany* (Vol. LNAI 642, p. 268-293). Heidelberg: Springer

Pirolli, P., & Anderson, J. (1985). The role of learning from examples in the acquisition of recursive programming skills. *Canadian Journal of Psychology, 39*, 240-272

Reed, S. K., & Bolstad, C. (1991). Use of examples and procedures in problem solving. *Journal of Experimental Psychology: Learning, Memory, and Cognition, 17*(4), 753-766

Rosenbloom, P. S., & Newell, A. (1986). The chunking of goal hierarchies: A generalized model of practice. In R. S. Michalski, J. G. Carbonell, & T. M. Mitchell (Eds.), *Machine Learning - An Artificial Intelligence Approach* (Vol. 2, p. 247-288). Morgan Kaufmann

Rumelhart, D., & Norman, D. (1978). Accretion, tuning and restructuring: Three modes of learning. In J. Cotton & R. Klatzky (Eds.), *Semantic Factors in Cognition* (pp. 37-53). Hillsdale, NJ: Erlbaum

Rumelhart, D. E., & Norman, D. A. (1981). Analogical processes in learning.In J. R. Anderson (Ed.), *Cognitive Skills and Their Acquisition* (p. 335-360). Hillsdale, NJ: Lawrence Erlbaum

Sadohara, K., & Haraguchi, M. (1995). Analogical logic program synthesis from examples. In N. Lavrac & S. Wrobel (Eds.), *Proceedings of the Eighth European Conference in Machine Learning (ECML-95)* (Vol. 912, p. 232-244). Springer

Schmid, U., & Kaup, B. (1995). Analoges Lernen beim rekursiven Programmieren (Analogical learning in recursive programming). *Kognitionswissenschaft, 5*, 31-41

Schmid, U., & Wysotzki, F. (1996). Fertigkeitserwerb durch induktive Programmsynthese und generalisiertes Planen. In W. Dilger, M. Schlosser, J. Zeidel, & A. Ittner (Eds.), *Proceedings of FGML-96 (19.-21.8.96, TU Chemnitz)* (p. 106-111). Chemnitz

Schmid, U., & Wysotyki, F. (1998). Induction of recursive program schemes. In C. Nedellec & C. Rouveirol (Eds.), Machine Learning: ECML-98 (p. 214-225). LNAI, 1398, Springer

Shavlik, J. W. (1990). Acquiring recursive and iterative concepts with explanation-based learning. *Machine Learning, 5*, 39-70

Shell, P., & Carbonell, J. (1989). Towards a general framework for composing disjunctive and iterative macro-operators. In *11th ijcai-89*. Detroit, MI

Simon, R.J. (1970). Encoding effects on complex problem solving. *Journal of Experimental Psychology, 83*, 227-231

Summers, P. D. (1977). A methodology for LISP program construction from examples. *Journal ACM, 24*(1), 162-175

Unger, S., & Wysotzki, F. (1981). *Lernfähige Klassifizierungssysteme*. Berlin: Akademie-Verlag

Vosniadou, S., & Ortony, A. (1989). Similarity and analogical reasoning: A synthesis. In S. Vosniadou & A. Ortony (Eds.), *Similarity and Analogical Reasoning* (p. 1-17). Cambridge: Cambridge University Press

Wysotzki, F. (1983). Representation and induction of infinite concepts and recursive action sequences. In *Proceedings of the 8th IJCAI, Karlsruhe*

Wysotzki, F. (1987). Program synthesis by hierarchical planning. In P. Jorrand & V. Sgurev (Eds.), *Artificial Intelligence: Methodology, Systems, Applications* (p. 3-11). Amsterdam: Elsevier Science

Appendix

The decision tree algorithm CAL 5

See Unger and Wysotzki (1981, pp. 42 ff.) and Müller and Wysotzki (1994) for more details.

Given:

- A list of training examples M. Each example is represented by an attribute (feature) vector $(x_1, \ldots x_n)$ associated with a class (optimal operator) k.

  A new attribute x to be introduced into the decision tree can be selected either by a pre-defined order (from x_1 to x_n) or by using an entropy measure method (selecting that attribute which dis-criminates best between classes).

- A decision threshold $S \leq 1$.

1. Introduction of the next attribute x_i.

2. Automatic construction of optimal intervals (discretization).

   (a) Take all values a_j of the attribute x_i which occur in the training examples. Order the values by the $\leq$ relation with minimal and maximal values of the range of the parameter x_i as lower and upper bound ($-\infty$ and $+\infty$ if no special restriction is known): $min < a_1 < a_2 \ldots < a_m < max$.

   (b) Construct intervals for each attribute value: $I = (a_j, a_{j+1})$.
   Each interval is associated with the classes k_l which are associated with the examples where $x_i = a_j$. Each class is annotated by the frequency n_{kj} with which it occurs (see figure below).

   (c) Recursion: To form intervals on the x_i axis, collect samples from left to right, until a class decision can be made on a given level of confidence $1 - \alpha$.

Let I be a current interval containing n samples of different classes k and let n_{kl} be the number of samples belonging to class k_l. Then $q_{kj} = n_{kj}/n$ is an estimate of the conditional probability $p(k_l|x)$ in I, where x is the current node (sample at interval I).

- The hypothesis:

  H1: There exists a class k_l in I with $p(k_l|x) \geq S$

- is tested against the hypothesis:

  H2: For all classes k_l in i the inequation $p(k_l|x) < S$ holds on the given level of confidence $1 - \alpha$.

An estimation at level $1 - \alpha$ yields a confidence interval $[d_1, d_2]$ for $p(k_l|x)$. That means, that in a sequence of samples the true value of the probability lies in $[d_1, d_2]$ with probability $1 - \alpha$.

The hypotheses are tested in the following way:

- **H1:** $d_1(k_l) > S$ (if the complete confidence interval lies above the pre-defined threshold S, then H1 is true)

- **H2:** $d_2(k_l) < S$ for all k_l occuring in interval I (if for each class k_l in I the confidence interval lies below S, then H2 is true).

Decision on the dominance of a class in I:

i. If a class k_l exists, where H1 is true, then k_l dominates in I. The interval is closed. The corresponding path in the decision tree is terminated.

ii. If for all classes in I H2 is true, then no class dominates in I. The interval is closed. A new attribute has to be introduced (Step 1).

iii. Otherwise the interval I has to be extended by collecting the next sample (merging the current interval $I=(a_j, a_{j+1}$ with the succeeding interval $I' =(a_{j+1}, a_{j+2})$. This corresponds to an increase of the statistics to obtain a decision for H1 or H2 at confidence level 1 − α.

If there are no more samples for extending I, a majority decision is performed.

3. Merging of intervals.

Adjacent intervals with the same class label are merged.

4. The algorithm terminates when all intermediate nodes have disappeared, that is, each leaf of the current decision tree represents a dominant class or a majority decision for a class.

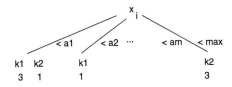

3.3 EPAM-like simulations of the recall of random chess positions

Fernand Gobet

Abstract

It is a classic result in cognitive science that chess masters can recall briefly presented positions better than weaker players when these positions are meaningful, but that their superiority disappears with random positions. However, Gobet and Simon (1996a) have recently shown that there is a skill effect in the recall of random chess positions as well. The impact of this result for theories of expert memory is discussed, and it is shown that chunk-based theories predict such a skill difference. CHREST, a computational, chunk-based model of chess expertise based on the EPAM theory of cognition, accounts for the skill differences well. The model's performance is also compared with human data where the role of presentation time for random positions is systematically varied from 1 s to 60 s. Preliminary results show that the model captures the main features of the human data, but also point to additional work for estimating the value of a few parameters with more precision.

Introduction

EPAM (Elementary Perceiver and Memorizer) is a cognitive architecture first developed by Feigenbaum and Simon in the early sixties. At its core lie mechanisms for storing chunks into long-term memory (LTM) through the construction of a discrimination net and mechanisms for handling information in short-term memory (STM). EPAM was originally built for offering a unifying theory of verbal behavior (Feigenbaum & Simon, 1962, 1984), was later used for simulating chess memory (Simon & Gilmartin 1973), and was recently applied to letter perception and expert digit-span memory (Richman & Simon, 1989; Richman, Staszewski & Simon 1995). Although not yet as influential as Soar (see the chapters of Ritter & Baxter and Krems & Johnson in this volume) or ACT-R (see the chapters of Knoblich & Ohlsson and Taatgen in this volume), EPAM keeps attracting researchers as a parsimonious, chunk-based explanation for perceptual and memory phenomena. As added value, EPAM addresses phenomena that are not yet accounted for by Soar and ACT-R and may offer a useful extension of these theories.

In this chapter, I focus on chess memory and present CHREST (for Chunk Hierarchy and REtrieval STructure), an expansion of Simon and Gilmartin's (1973) MAPP program, itself a program inspired by EPAM. After discussing the advantages of chess as a research domain, I present some data from chess memory experiments, with a special emphasis on the recall of random positions. These data are used to compare some leading theories in the field of expertise. I then describe in some detail CHREST and compare its behavior with that of humans in experiments where random positions are presented for durations between one and sixty seconds. Finally, I discuss the strengths and weaknesses of the current version of CHREST.

Chess as a research domain

Historically, chess has been an important domain in cognitive science. Several widespread concepts and techniques in the field come directly from this domain, such as progressive deepening, protocol analysis as a tool for studying problem solving behavior, and De Groot's recall paradigm, which consists of a brief presentation of domain-specific material. As a matter of fact, chess is often described as a key domain in research on expertise, an increasingly influential subfield of cognitive science (Charness, 1992; Ericsson & Lehmann, 1996).

How can we explain this popularity? As argued elsewhere (Gobet, 1993b), several factors speak in favor of chess. To begin with, chess is a complex and challenging domain, while, at the same time, allowing a clean formal description that makes it relatively easy to develop mathematical and computational models. In addition, chess has a good ecological validity (Neisser, 1976), allowing one to study experts in their habitual environment. As a consequence, many experimental manipulations are possible which are still close enough to the "real thing" to insure that chess players are highly motivated. Moreover, the Elo rating[29] (Elo, 1978) offers a quantitative scale of measurement widely used in the chess community which provides the researcher with a fine-grained classification. This makes it possible both to use statistical techniques like regression analysis and to meaningfully compare samples

---

[29]The ELO rating scale is an interval scale ranking competitive chess players, with a standard deviation of 200. Skill levels have standard names, which are used consistently in this paper (in parentheses, the corresponding range in Elo points): grandmaster (above 2500), international master (2400-2500), master (2200-2400), expert (2000-2200), class A players (1800-2000), class B players (1600-1800), and so on.

from different studies. Just think of domains such as medical or physics expertise, where participants are typically classified into three groups (novices, intermediates, and experts) which are hard to compare from one study to another, and you will readily realize the advantage offered by chess and its rating system. Finally, chess is a natural domain to consider for developing a computational model of cognition, because there already exists a number of empirical data on chess expertise (see Holding, 1985, or Gobet, 1993b, for reviews).

It is barely an exaggeration to say that De Groot's (1946/1978) seminal findings have shaped the field of expertise research. His two main empirical results have been vindicated, with some minor qualifications. First, there are no large differences in the statistics on search between experts and top-level grandmasters (see, however, Charness, 1981; Holding, 1985; and Gobet, 1998, for some differences between masters and players below expert level). Second, there are clear differences in a memory task consisting in the brief presentation of a position taken from a tournament game. Typically, players at and above master level recall the entire position correctly, save for one or two errors, while weaker players are overwhelmed by the task (see Figure 2 below). De Groot's theoretical insights have also been supported: masters' superiority, which is made possible in part by a highly differentiated mode of perception, is due more to the knowledge they have acquired through experience and study than through sheer talent.

A short history of random positions

A natural extension of De Groot's work was to ask chessplayers to recall meaningless positions (see Figure 1 for examples of game and random positions). This was first carried out in 1964 in Amsterdam by De Groot, Jongman, and Lemmens, who found that players of all skill levels were identically poor at recalling meaningless positions. Interestingly, they estimated that this result was so obvious and trivial that it did not deserve publication.

It is only in 1973 that a replication was carried out (and published) by Chase and Simon, who extended the Amsterdam work both with experimental complications (e.g., a copy task was added to the memory task) and theoretical considerations, commonly known as the "chunking theory" (Chase & Simon, 1973a, 1973b; Simon & Chase, 1973).[30]

Figure 1: Illustration of the types of positions typically used in chess research on memory. On the left, a *game position* taken from a tournament game. On the right, a *random position* obtained by shuffling the piece locations of a game position.

The use of meaningless material met two goals. First, it served as a control condition for ruling out the possibility that chess masters were performing better just because of superior mental abilities. Second, it addressed one of the challenges of cognitive psychology, which is, to put it simply, to tease apart structural components (the "hardware") from knowledge components (the "software"). The idea is that, because knowledge structures are of little use in the case of random positions, this type of material offers a baseline condition with which knowledge-rich stimuli may be compared. As is clear from research in neuropsychology and in developmental psychology, this approach countains many pitfalls, including the fact that the dichotomy hardware/software may represent quite a simplification and may collapse several levels of processing.

Like the unpublished data by De Groot and his colleagues, the data obtained by Chase and Simon with random positions were reassuring: there was no difference in recall between their three subjects, a master, a class A player, and a novice. Taken together with grandmasters' and masters' massive recall superiority with game positions over weaker players, the uniform poor recall with random positions was such a vivid illustration of the principle that knowledge

---

[30] The reader is referred to Vicente and De Groot, 1990, for a detailed history of this experimental paradigm.

is the key to expertise that it has become a classic, widely cited in textbooks of cognitive psychology and in papers on expertise. There is no doubt that the random position experiment contributed a lot to making Chase and Simon's papers "classics" in the field (Charness, 1992).

As usual, things are more complicated than the textbook account. When Herb Simon and I were working on CHREST, a re-implementation and extension of MAPP (Simon & Gilmartin 1973), a program aimed at simulating chess memory, it occurred to us that the model was making predictions about the recall of random positions that were at variance with the classical no-skill-difference result. As will be described later in more detail, CHREST constructs a discrimination net of chunks by scanning positions from a database of master games and identifying patterns of pieces in these positions. As the number and the average size of its chunks increased in these early simulations, the model was getting better and better at remembering game positions. But the model was also predicting a small, but robust increase in recall with random positions. This was a matter of serious concern, for it was clear that the simulations were correct and that the skill differences in recall were due to a simple mechanism: just by chance, it is more likely for a large discrimination net than for a small one that chunks could be found in random positions. At the same time, we were collecting data on chess memory which included random positions. Sure enough, the results with random positions were compatible with the model's predictions. As our puzzlement grew, we decided to do a systematic review of experiments using random positions (Gobet and Simon, 1996a, 1996c). Altogether, we found 13 studies. In 12 of them, masters did maintain some advantage, even if it was less impressive than with game positions. The only exception was Chase and Simon's (1973) study, where the master did actually worse than the novice! While the skill differences were not significant in most studies because of lack of statistical power, it became clear that the effect was genuine when the various studies were pooled together (see Figure 2).

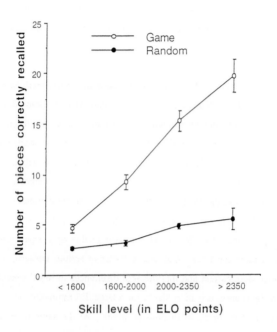

Figure 2. Mean number of pieces placed correctly as a function of type of positions (game or random) and skill level. Positions contained 25 pieces on average. Error bars indicate standard errors of the means. After Gobet and Simon, 1996a.

Random positions as a litmus test for theories of expert memory

Our first reaction was to conclude that random positions do not offer the kind of control stimuli hoped for. This is certainly an annoyance for the field, but not as bad as could be feared, as independent evidence shows that there is no correlation between chess skill and general cognitive abilities, including visual memory for non-domain-specific material (Gobet & Simon, 1996a; Holding, 1985). Our second reaction was to realize that random positions offer a powerful way of teasing apart current theories of chess expertise. In a comparison of four theories of chess skill (Gobet, 1996), I show that two of them, the chunking theory (Chase & Simon, 1973), and the template theory (Gobet & Simon, 1996b), an extension of the chunking theory, predict masters' superiority with random positions.

I also show that two other approaches, the long-term working memory theory (Ericsson & Kintsch, 1995) and Holding's (1985) SEEK's theory, which emphasizes the role of high-level, conceptual knowledge, do not account for the result, the former because it predicts too good a recall with random positions, and the latter because it predicts too low a performance. As mentioned above, the chunking theory proposes that expertise in a domain develops by the creation of a discrimination net, through which stimuli can be rapidly recognized. With learning, individual features or parts of stimuli are chunked, which allows a more efficient storage of the information in short-term memory (STM). Now and then, masters adventitiously recognize chunks in random positions, which explains their superiority with this type of material. The template theory adds to this view the idea that chunks that recur often in the domain of expertise develop into larger and more complex structures (templates), which have slots that allow values of variables to be stored rapidly. Note that a similar idea is present in the skilled memory theory (Chase & Ericsson, 1982) and in the long-term working memory theory (Ericsson & Kintsch, 1995). The difference is that the latter theories propose a general, multi-purpose retrieval structure, while the template theory proposes several, specific structures that may be used only after they have been accessed by recognition processes. Since templates contain large chunks, their access conditions are unlikely to be met with random positions. On the other hand, the retrieval structure proposed by Ericsson and Kintsch can be used even with random positions; hence their incorrect predictions that masters can store information from random positions rapidly.

The skill difference in recalling random positions indicates that this material does not tap hardware variables only. However, because the amount of knowledge used is low, this material still offers a reasonable solution for reaching tentative conclusions about the hardware of the cognitive system and, therefore, for testing some of the system constants proposed in the EPAM theory (Feigenbaum & Simon, 1984), from which both the chunking and template theories stem.

A computer program (CHREST) has been developed in the last five years to implement the template theory. Simulations show that templates are very rarely accessed with random positions, because the conditions of their evocation are not met in this environment. Without templates, the current implementation is close enough to the specifications of the chunking theory to allow us to study the template and chunking theories together.

Description of CHREST

Earlier accounts of CHREST have been given in De Groot and Gobet (1996) and in Gobet (1993a, b). The model consists of the following components: recognition LTM, semantic LTM, and STM. STM is made of 2-5 visual chunks (simulations presented later will explore the effect of varying STM size). STM is a queue, with the exception of the largest chunk met at any point in time (the *"hypothesis"*), which is kept in STM until a larger chunk is met. Figure 3 presents an overview of the model.

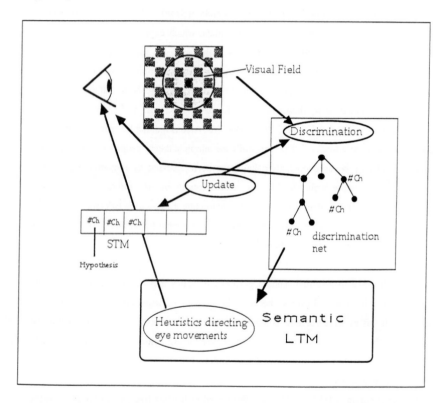

Figure 3: Overview of CHREST.

Attention is modeled by eye movements (see Chapter 8 of De Groot & Gobet, 1996, for more about mechanisms directing eye movements). For each new fixation, the model sorts the pieces found in the visual space through the discrimination net. (The visual space is defined as the squares located at most two squares away from the fixation point.) Learning new chunks essentially occurs in the same way as in the EPAM model, with the qualification that only one type of (implicit) test is carried out in CHREST: "What is the next item in the visual space?", while EPAM allows for testing various features of objects. The uniformity of tests has been adopted in order to grow large nets; it is assumed that other tests in addition to the location of pieces are carried out by human players, such as tests dealing with threats, plans, and other concepts.

The net is grown by two learning mechanisms, *familiarization* and *discrimination*. When a new object is presented to the model, it is sorted through the discrimination net. When a node is reached, the object is compared with the *image* of the node, which is the internal representation of the object. If the image under-represents the object, new features are added to the image (familiarization). If the information in the image and the object differ on some feature or some sub-element, a new node is created (discrimination).

Two other learning mechanisms (one for creating templates and the other for creating semantic links) will not be described here, since these features of the program are almost never relevant with random positions and were not used in the simulations.

Role of presentation time: Human data

In order to test the plausibility of the parameters used in CHREST, Gobet and Simon (1995) collected data from random and game positions where the presentation time was systematically varied from 1 s to 60 s. Data are based on 20 subjects: 5 (international) masters (mean Elo=2498), 8 experts (mean Elo=2121) and 7 class A players (mean Elo=1879). Positions for the random condition were created by randomly placing pieces from a game position on the chessboard, and were presented to subjects on a computer screen. For the random condition, in which we are interested here, one position was presented for each of the following presentation times: 1, 2, 3, 4, 5, 10, 20, 30, and 60 s. The results are given in Figures 4 to 6 (thick lines).

Simulations

Learning phase

Three nets, having 1,000, 10,000, and 80,000 nodes (referred to below as, respectively, 1k, 10k and 80k nets) were created by letting the program scan a database of several thousand positions. The size of the three nets was chosen in order to have nets of roughly three different orders of magnitude. The matching between the three nets and levels of expertise (respectively class A players, experts, and masters) was rather loose and based on earlier simulations. For ease of exposition, I will directly compare these 1k, 10k, and 80k programs with class A, experts, and masters, respectively. The reader should, however, keep in mind that this is only an approximation.

Performance phase

Twenty random positions were presented for each of the presentation times. For each position, CHREST moved its simulated eyes around the board, storing recognized chunks into STM, and, when applicable, using the following learning mechanisms. First, as described before, CHREST chunks two chunks together (that is, adds a chunk as a test to another chunk). It takes 10 seconds to carry out this operation, like in the EPAM theory (see Simon, 1976, for a discussion of this parameter). Typically, a new test is added to the hypothesis. Second, chunks that have been in STM for at least 4 seconds are "flagged," which means that episodic cues permit the access to this node. Flagging is a type of familiarization. Little is said in the EPAM theory about the time needed to familiarize a node, except that this operation is faster than discrimination. This value has arbitrarily been set to 4 s in CHREST. Flagged nodes can be recalled during the reconstruction phase even if they are not any more in STM.

The following parameters were used during the simulations (see De Groot & Gobet, 1996, for the parameters related to eye movements):

* time to create a chunk in LTM	10 s
* time to flag a node	4 s
* time to place a symbol into STM	50 ms
* time to compare two symbols	50 ms
* time to carry out a test in the net	10 ms

The three versions of the program were used with 4 different STM capacity parameters (from 2 to 5 slots).

Recall of random positions as a function of skill

When we pool presentation times equal or less than 10 s, Gobet and Simon's (1995) recall percentages (Class A: 11.7%, experts: 17.0%, masters: 23.7%) show the same pattern illustrated by Figure 2. Run on the positions used by Gobet and Simon (1995), CHREST simulates the skill effect with random positions, though the percentage of recall is somewhat less than with humans, in particular with the 80k net. With a STM span of 5 slots, the 1k, 10k and 80k nets obtained a performance of 10.5%, 15.6%, and 17.1%, respectively.

Role of presentation time

Percentage correct.

The results on percentage correct are illustrated in Figure 4. In general, a larger span allows a better recall, though the effect is not large. This is due to the fact that chunks stored in STM or LTM overlap, and, as a consequence, additional chunks bring less and less new information. The fit is rather good for the class A and expert programs, but the master program does not reach the level of humans. In all cases, the program is below human performance with one and two seconds. It is possible that humans perceive configurations according to Gestalt rules that are not captured by the way chunks are stored in the program. Additional time allows more chunks to be found and compensates for this.

Number of chunks.

Obviously, the number of chunks stored increases with STM span. The program with a small STM span obtains a number of chunks similar to that of human players (see Figure 5). Note that the number of chunks with humans may be underestimated, because pieces placed individually (on average, one piece per position reconstructed) were not counted as chunks.

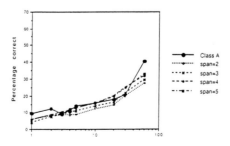

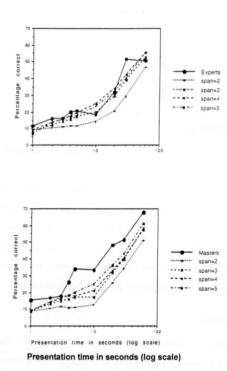

Figure 4: Percentage correct as a function of the presentation time. Thick lines represent the data from Gobet and Simon (1995). Dotted lines represent CHREST simulations with 1k nodes (upper panel), 10k nodes (middle panel), and 80k nodes (lower panel) with STM spans ranging from 2 to 5.

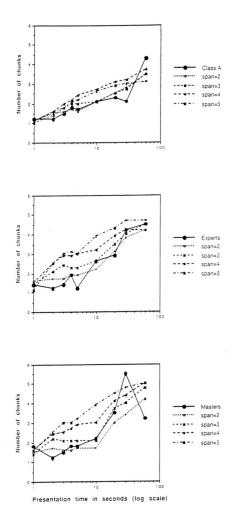

Figure 5: Number of chunks as a function of the presentation time. Thick lines represent the data from Gobet and Simon (1995). Dotted lines represent CHREST simulations with 1k nodes (upper panel), 10k nodes (middle panel), and 80k nodes (lower panel) with STM spans ranging from 2 to 5.

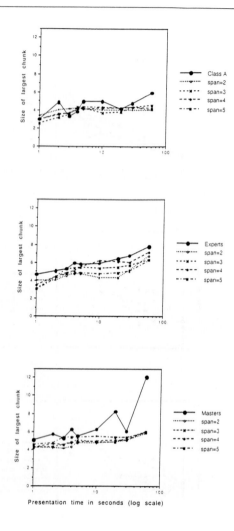

Figure 6: Average size of the largest chunk as a function of the presentation time. Thick lines represent the data from Gobet and Simon (1995). Dotted lines represent CHREST simulations with 1k nodes (upper panel), 10k nodes (middle panel), and 80k nodes (lower panel) with STM spans ranging from 2 to 5.

Size of the largest chunk.

In general, the largest chunk output by the program is smaller than human players' (See Figure 6). This discrepancy is particularly clear with the master version. The correlation between number of STM slots and size of the largest chunk is rather low (0.20, 0.27, 0.39, for the 1k, 10k, and 80k versions of the program).

Conclusions

In general, the simulations show that CHREST, using several parameters from the EPAM theory, successfully accounts for the role of presentation time in the recall of random chess positions. Given that most of the EPAM applications were done with verbal material (see Feigenbaum & Simon, 1984), it was important to show that EPAM parameters are plausible with visuo-spatial material as well. Three sets of mechanisms were crucial for the success of the simulations: (a) mechanisms allowing chunks to be rapidly recognized and sorted by the discrimination net; (b) mechanisms allowing chunks to be created or tagged when the presentation time is sufficiently long; and (c) mechanisms directing the attention of the program. Further work will have to analyze why the program does not reach the recall level of masters and why it tends to underestimate the size of the largest chunk.

In spite of its checkered history, the technique of using random chess positions has provided a powerful tool for testing theories of chess memory. It remains to be seen if similar techniques can show such a discriminative power in other domains of expertise as well.

References

Charness, N. (1981). Search in chess: Age and skill differences. *Journal of Experimental Psychology: Human Perception and Performance, 2,* 467-476.

Charness, N. (1992). The impact of chess research on cognitive science. *Psychological Research, 54,* 4-9.

Chase, W. G., & Ericsson, K. A. (1982). Skill and working memory. In G. H. Bower (Ed.), *The psychology of learning and motivation* (Vol. 16). New York: Academic Press.

Chase, W. G., & Simon, H. A. (1973a). Perception in chess. *Cognitive Psychology, 4,* 55-81.

Chase, W.G., & Simon, H.A. (1973a). Perception in chess. *Cognitive Psychology, 4,* 55-81.

Chase, W. G., & Simon, H. A. (1973b). The mind's eye in chess. In W. G. Chase (Ed.), *Visual information processing.* New York: Academic Press.

De Groot, A. D. (1946). *Het denken van den schaker.* Amsterdam: Noord Hollandsche.

De Groot, A. D. (1978). *Thought and choice in chess.* (Revised translation of De Groot, 1946; 2nd ed.). The Hague: Mouton Publishers.

De Groot, A. & Gobet, F. (1996). *Perception and memory in chess. Heuristics of the professional eye.* Assen: Van Gorcum.

Elo, A. (1978). *The rating of chess players, past and present.* New York: Arco.

Ericsson, K. A., & Kintsch, W. (1995). Long-term working memory. *Psychological Review, 102,* 211-245.

Ericsson, K.A., & Lehmann, A. C. (1996). Expert and exceptional performance: Evidence of maximal adaptation to task constraints. *Annual Review of Psychology, 47,* 273-305.

Feigenbaum, E.A., & Simon, H.A. (1962). A theory of the serial position effect. *British Journal of Psychology, 53,* 307-320.

Feigenbaum, E.A., & Simon, H.A. (1984). EPAM-like models of recognition and learning. *Cognitive Science, 8,* 305-336.

Gobet, F. (1993a). A computer model of chess memory. *Proceedings of 15th Annual Meeting of the Cognitive Science Society,* (pp. 463-468).

Gobet, F. (1993b). *Les mémoires d'un joueur d'échecs* [Chess players' memories]. Fribourg (Switzerland): Editions universitaires.

Gobet, F. (1998). Chess players' thinking revisited. *Swiss Journal of Psychology, 57,*18-32.

Gobet, F. (in press). Expert memory: A comparison of four theories. *Cognition*

Gobet, F. & Simon, H. A. (1995). *Role of Presentation Time in Recall of Game and Random Chess Positions.* Complex Information Processing Paper #524 Carnegie Mellon University, Pittsburgh, PA 15213.

Gobet, F. & Simon, H. A. (1996a). Recall of rapidly presented random chess positions is a function of skill. *Psychonomic Bulletin & Review, 3,* 159-163.

Gobet, F. & Simon, H. A. (1996b). Templates in Chess Memory: A Mechanism for Recalling Several Boards. *Cognitive Psychology, 31,* 1-40.

Gobet, F. & Simon, H. A. (1996c). Recall of Random and Distorted Positions: Implications for the theory of expertise. *Memory & Cognition, 24,* 493-503.

Holding, D. H. (1985). *The psychology of chess skill.* Hillsdale, NJ: Erlbaum.

Neisser, U. (1976). *Cognition and reality. Principles and implications of cognitive psychology.* San Francisco: Freeman & Company.

Richman, H. B., & Simon, H. A. (1989). Context effects in letter perception: Comparison of two theories. *Psychological Review, 3,* 417-432.

Richman, H. B., Staszewski, J., & Simon, H. A. (1995). Simulation of expert memory with EPAM IV. *Psychological Review, 102,* 305-330.

Simon, H. A. (1976). The information storage system called "Human memory". In M. R. Rosenzweig & E. L. Bennett (Eds.), *Neural mechanisms of learning and memory,* . Cambridge: MA: MIT Press.

Simon, H. A., & Chase, W. G. (1973). Skill in chess. *American Scientist, 61,* 393-403.

Simon, H. A., & Gilmartin, K. J. (1973). A simulation of memory for chess positions. *Cognitive Psychology, 5,* 29-46.

Vicente, K. J. & de Groot, A. D. (1990). The Memory recall paradigm: Straightening out the historical record, *American Psychologist,* February, 285-287.

3.4 The effect of previous problems in the Tower of London: Reminding or general learning imitating reminding?

Gareth E. Miles & Stephen J. Payne

This chapter reports a model of human performance on a problem solving task (the Tower of London) that has not previously been computationally modelled The purpose of the model is to explore, in the context of experimental data, the use of reminding and exemplar use in a well-structured problem solving task (see Miles, in preparation). The exploration of reminding and exemplar use in structured tasks offers new perspectives on phenomena normally associated with ill-structured domains. In particular, strong accounts of general problem solving in structured knowledge lean domains, such as the Tower of Hanoi (e.g. Anzai & Simon, 1979), may allow reminding/exemplar use to be integrated with, and understood in the context of, other problem solving behaviour. This approach is consistent with doubts expressed by case-based reasoning researchers (Hammond, Seifert & Gray, 1991; Kolodner, 1993) about the generality of findings from psychological studies looking at problem solving by analogy to previous examples.

The Tower of London is a variant of the Tower of Hanoi that has commonly been used in the neuro-psychological assessment of frontal lobe disorders. The first section of this chapter details our TOL-PS model of human performance at this task and its implementation in Anderson's (1993) ACT-R, comparing it with a recent model of the task (Ward & Allport's, 1997, Move Selection Framework). Following this, one of the experiments from Miles (in preparation) is briefly described, supporting the conclusion that solving particular previous problems affects participants' problem solving. The most immediate explanation of this effect is that participants retrieve and use their old solutions - a "reminding" effect. However, the TOL-PS model suggests how the same effects might instead be explained by adaptive adjustment of preferences among competing general heuristic strategies (termed 'heuristic switching' by us). Previously, a similar explanation was found by Lovett & Anderson (1996), to fit transfer data from a water-jug isomorph better than a competing exemplar model. We then demonstrate how such a 'heuristic switching' explanation is implicit in our ACT-R implementation of TOL-PS.

Fortunately the methodology used by the experimental study enables the effect of 'heuristic switching' to be assessed independently of exemplar-based effects. A post-hoc analysis of the experiment provides evidence that 'heuristic switching' is almost certainly not an adequate explanation of the results. This analysis is discussed in terms of the TOL-PS model (which presumably needs extension to treat the reminding effects) and in terms of the assumptions behind ACT-R's rational analysis mechanisms (as described in Anderson, 1990, 1993).

The TOL-PS model of problem solving in the Tower of London

The Tower of London (TOL) was developed to assess spatial planning ability in brain damaged patients (Shallice, 1982). The TOL is a variant of the Tower of Hanoi (TOH), removing the constraint that disks can only be placed on larger disks.   TOL can also be described as a constrained version of Blocks World, (Ward & Allport, 1997), a domain classically used to examine planning in AI (e.g. Sacerdoti, 1974; Schmid & Wysotzki, this volume). Example problems are given in fig 1.

Problem type A: Problem type A':

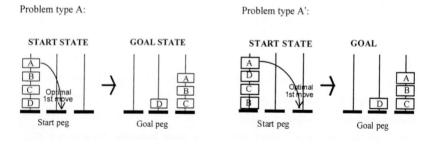

Figure 1: Two example 4-disk Tower of London problems (with optimal first moves indicated)

The closeness of TOL to TOH, makes it reasonable to assume that models of the latter will apply to the former with minimal adaption. The analysis of a single participant completing the TOH conducted by Anzai & Simon (1979) and extended by VanLehn (1991) covers a wide spectrum of the strategies for solving the TOH and it is likely that these strategies are also applicable to the Tower of London. Table 1 outlines the strategies identified by Anzai & Simon (1979).

Strategy	Description
Selective search	Only immediate moves are considered with some restrictions (e.g. don't move the same disk consecutively)
Goal-peg	A transition between selective search and disk sub-goaling
Disk subgoaling	Participant focuses on largest disk not in place, then sub-goals the removal of the disk immediately blocking this disk; if this disk is blocked then this disk is sub-goaled to a non-blocking location. The sub-goaling of blocking disks is recursed till a blocking disk can be removed.
Pyramid subgoaling	Very similar to disk subgoaling; a recursive strategy that focuses on removing blocking pyramids rather than disks. This allows the participant to take advantage of regularities in the Tower of Hanoi problem space and chunk moves together. It more economic cognitively than the disk-subgoaling strategy

Table 1: Strategies evident in the protocol of Anzai & Simon's single participant protocol (adapted from Anzai & Simon, 1979, and VanLehn, 1991)

We argue that two of these strategies can be disregarded in the case of the TOL. Firstly, VanLehn (1991) notes that the original description of the transitional goal-peg strategy is 'rather terse and hence open to varying interpretations.' (VanLehn, 1991, pg 8). VanLehn ignores the strategy in his analysis and we will do the same, by making the assumption that this strategy represents a period of mixed use of selective search and disk-subgoaling strategies.

Secondly, the pyramid sub-goaling strategy is a more abstract version of the disk-subgoaling strategy. The predicted moves of the two strategies are equivalent and the predicted pattern of move latencies is also similar; the main measurable difference between the strategies is the type of verbal utterance that is associated with each. In the context of the TOL the concept of moving pyramids is minimally useful and the removal of two or three blocking disks is relatively easy. The pyramid sub-goaling strategy hence seems an unnecessary elaboration.

The two strategies that remain, selective search and disk-subgoaling, are both instantiations of classic problem solving algorithms. Selective search, concentrated on the immediate area of the problem space, is classic forward search with hill-climbing; and disk sub-goaling is strong means-ends analysis leading to operator sub-goaling. This latter method seeks to identify and then remove the 'biggest' difference between the current state and the goal state. See Newell & Simon (1972) for more detail on these weak methods. The TOL-PS model given in table 2 is based upon these two main problem solving algorithms (these rules appear in the bottom panel).

In somewhat more detail, then, these are the two main general problem solving algorithms embodied in the TOL-PS model:

1. FOR - Forward search. The FOR strategy has two possible instantiations; with and without look-ahead (FOR2 and FOR1 respectively). FOR1 only considers the next move, whilst FOR2 plans up to three moves ahead. FOR1 is very limited, often guessing moves, and is assumed to be superseded by FOR2 after participants have completed two or three TOL problems.

2. MEA - Means ends analysis. The MEA strategy is an implementation of Newell & Simon's (1972) means-ends analysis; all disks are considered and the one deemed to represent the most important difference between the goal and start states is sub-goaled. Usually the most important disk to get in place will be underneath other disks in the goal state and/or the start state.

TOL-PS's choice of strategy depends on which of three production rules matches the goal of solving a TOL problem; either choose_mea, choose_for2 or choose_for1. This is decided by ACT-R's conflict resolution scheme, with the most 'rational' production being the favourite (it is assumed to be choose_mea prior to the experiment, but tends toward choose_for2 as the experiment continues). Some additional rules are used to manage impasses and constrain moves (e.g. not moving a disk twice in a row). Most of these are adapted from VanLehn's (1991) model of TOH.

A general overview of TOL-PS is given in table 2, with an example production expanded in fig 2. Each method is described as a cluster of similar production rules; for instance *mea_two_equal_height* in fig 2 is very closely related to the rules in *mea_two_equal_height_one_goaled* and slightly less so to *mea_tallest*[31]. It is conceived that each cluster share similar origins (e.g. were specialised from the same 'parent' production).

Meta cognitive productions	FOR2 strategy productions
choose_mea_strategy	FOR2_swap
choose_for2_strategy	FOR2_2nd_disk
choose_for1_strategy	FOR2_remove_indirect_block_and_complete
problem_completed	FOR_specific
make_old_moves_illegal	FOR2_fail
	FOR2_fail_after_start
MEA strategy productions	**FOR1 strategy productions**
mea_tallest	FOR_goalpeg_only [nc]
mea_two_equal_height	FOR_guess_move_alternate_pegs
mea_two_equal_height_one_goaled	FOR_guess_move
mea_fail	FOR_guess_move_disregard_goal
mea_fail_after_start	FOR_guess_move_disregard_last
	FOR_guess_move_last_resort

Table 2: Productions in TOL-PS

---

[31] All these productions cover different scenarios within the MEA strategy. They all look at the goal state and work out which disk is the hardest to get in place; *mea_tallest* simply picks the disk below the most disks in the goal state; *mea_two_equal_height* deals with the case when two disks are equally 'blocked' in the goal state, by selecting the one that is more blocked in the current state; lastly

Production: mea_two_equal_height

Left Hand Side

If the goal is to solve the problem and the strategy used is means-ends analysis
and there is a disk X, not in its goal location, and directly on a peg Y in the goal state, but
currently not above peg Y, and its movement is blocked by n1 other disk

> and peg Y has n2 disks on it in the goal state
>
> and another peg, Z, also has n2 disks on it in the goal state
>
> and a final peg, W, has n3 disks on it in the goal state
>
> and n3 is less than n2
>
> and disk V that is directly on peg Z in the goal state, and is not above peg Z, has n4 disks blocking its movement
>
> and n3 is greater than n4

Right Hand Side

> Then create a subgoal to get disk X to its goal location on peg Y

Figure 2: An example production from TOL-PS

TOL-PS was matched to human performance on novel base problems in the experiment reported here, and in three subsequent close variations of the design (Miles, in preparation). A problem solution was considered to be matched if the model was capable of generating that behaviour without guessing a move; only move choice data was used. A total of 888 first attempts at a problem were matched, taken from 198 different participants; on eighteen different problems (6x 3-disk, 6x 4-disk and 6x 5-disk). An initial version of TOL-PS was capable of generating (without guessing) 90% of the observed behaviour, with the addition of three minor productions to the model this increased to 95%. No significant pattern of behaviour generated by the model was absent in the human data; indeed the initial model was found to be too constrained. The model fits were achieved by manipulating the rationality of different problem solving productions, as assessed by ACT-R's rational conflict resolution scheme; this reflected changes in perceived worth that were assumed to occur naturally in a problem solving episode.

---

mea_two_equal_height_one_goaled is a specialisation of this that copes with situations where one of the considered disks is already in its goal location.

moves that help toward a subgoal (getting an identified disk to its goal location), but will still consider moves that satisfy other, simultaneously active, subgoals. Up to three subgoals can be active, the subgoals being ordered in terms of perceived difficulty; the lower a disk is in the goal state the more difficult the subgoaling of the disk is considered (TOL-PS MEA strategy often uses a similar principle).

The consideration of more than one subgoal, prior to all moves, allows the planner to react to opportunities, an important element in human problem solving (Hayes-Roth & Hayes-Roth, 1979); however this feature does violate some of the assumptions of more general models of cognition, which are constrained to a single goal stack (e.g. ACT-R, Anderson, 1993; & SOAR, Newell, 1990). Although single active goal models may be unable to capture the occasional opportunism and reactivity of humans they do provide a simple and powerful account of core human performance on the TOH (Anzai & Simon, 1979; Karat, 1982; Anderson, 1993), and have been argued to reflect the most important control principles of human problem solving (Anderson, 1983). In the light of this, we believe considerable experimental support would be needed to prefer a multiple-goal model of TOL.

In the 888 novel problem solutions fitted to TOL-PS, there is no discernible evidence of multiple goals nor opportunistic behaviour - indeed some apparent opportunities to fulfil subgoals that would be assumed active by MSF are missed[32]. Additionally, MSF may get into trouble when two active goals interact; Ward & Allport provide some provisos to stop erratic behaviour, but we argue that these lack parsimony.

TOL-PS is more highly specified than the MSF; it identifies three distinct general methods that can be applied to the TOL (FOR1, FOR2 and MEA), implementing them in an ACT-R computer simulation and providing evidence for the adequacy of this model. The general methods identified are derived from existing accounts of problem solving in related tasks and appear to cover the full space of approaches to solving TOL problems.

---

[32] Though note Ward & Allport (1997) did examine a wider range of TOL problems (eg flat start state problems).

An experimental investigation of reminding in a simple domain [33]

An analogical reasoning framework

The TOL-PS model was developed to help model a series of experiments investigating exemplar use in a knowledge lean domain (reported in full in Miles, in preparation). The TOL was selected because a) it allowed **structural** correspondences of a problem to be manipulated with little change in it's **superficial** appearance, b) models and data from the TOH domain could be easily adapted to provide a baseline domain theory, and c) it is a structured spatial domain with markedly different characteristics to standard analogy domains. This work was conducted within an analogical reasoning framework (See Reeves & Weisberg, 1994, for a recent review) and was motivated as a study of exemplar use in a structured domain (contrasting with the ill-structured domains typically used; see VanLehn, 1989).

Recent work in skill acquisition has suggested that the use of examples of previously attempted problems is critical during the early stages of skill learning and is still common after a skill has been acquired (Pirolli & Anderson, 1985; Ross & Kennedy 1990; Allen & Brooks, 1991). Much of the data on the effects of specific prior problems has been published in the cross-domain analogy literature where baseline performance, without the retrieval and use of a prior problem, is poor (e.g. Gick & Holyoak, 1980). The most complete models of cross domain analogy; ARCS-ACME (Thagard, Holyoak, Nelson & Gochfield, 1990; Holyoak & Thagard, 1989) and MAC/FAC-SME (Gentner & Forbus, 1991; Falkenheimer, Forbus & Gentner, 1986) separate the mechanism underlying the use of prior problems into discrete retrieval and mapping stages. A similar mechanism is thought to govern the use of within-domain analogy (Reeves & Weisberg, 1994) and work by Brian Ross, John Anderson and others has helped to advance this notion (Ross, 1984, 1987, 1989; Singley & Anderson, 1989; Anderson & Fincham, 1994).

---

[33] The data reported here is taken from experiments 1a and 1b in Miles (in preparation); these were run concurrently and analysed together.

The experiment, summarised in the next section, uses a design common in the analogical reasoning literature. An example of a similarly designed within-domain analogy study is Ross' (1987) attempt to eliminate the cueing of the relevant solution principle as an explanation for an observed reminding effect on applied probability problems (presented as stories). Ross used four conditions; a "novel" condition in which the example (or base problem) was not at all similar to the target problem (superficial similarity/structural similarity = 0/0); the other three conditions all used **superficially** similar examples, with the example either having corresponding (+/+), neutral (+/0) or reverse corresponding (+/-) **structural** relations to the target problem. Solution-principle cueing could not explain why reversed correspondences (+/-) caused a significant drop in performance compared to the novel condition (0/0) or why **superficial** aspects of the example affected the assignment of objects to roles in the problem solution, leading to false assignments when the example (base problem) and the target problem were opposed (i.e. +/-). Other similar designs include Ross (1984), Gentner & Toupin (1986), Gentner et. al. (1993) and Holyoak & Koh (1987).

A competition based version of the common **training problem - pause - test problem** design used by Ross (1987) was used[34]; with two training problems and two test problems, each training problem corresponding to one of the test problems. Three classes of training to test relationship were compared: repeated problems (+/+); false analogies (+/-); and novel/no relationship (0/0)[35]. These correspond to three of the four conditions used by Ross, the fourth condition (+/0) is not possible in our paradigm.

The experiment

Two TOL problems, A and A', are shown in fig 1; they are an example of superficially similar problems that are structurally dissimilar (The optimal solution to A starts with a move to peg 2, whilst for A' for first move is to peg 3). Additional, similarly related, pairs of problems were created.

---

[34] Only optimal solutions were acceptable in the training problems, forcing all participants to exhibit a common successful solution.

[35] In this experiment novel data was taken from the final training problem (asymptotic performance having been reached). In subsequent experiments (Miles, in preparation) the pattern of results reported here was supported.

The three conditions in the experiment (i.e. +/+, 0/0, +/-) were realised by either: a) testing with one, training with the other (false analogies, +/-); b) testing and training with the same problem (repetition, +/+); or c) testing and training with unrelated problems from different pairs (novel, 0/0).

	First move accuracy	Mean first move latency (log10 secs)	SD of first move latency (log10 secs)
Repetition (+/+)	29/52	.854	.260
Novel (0/0)	48/52	.818	.199
False analogy (+/-)	51/52	.741	.196

Table 3: Results of experiment (taken from Miles, in preperation)

Fifty two participants took part in the experiment[36]. Data taken from the 4-disk section of our experiment exhibited the greatest clarity (the earlier 3-disk section did not allow all the desired comparisons to be made). The main measures used were of first move accuracy and latency, and the results are shown in table 3. Clearly showing a +/+ > 0/0 > +/- effect, analogous to Ross (1987). All differences are significant at the $p < .05$ level (n = 52; paired t-test for latency; sign test for errors), with the exception of the 0/0 vs +/+ comparison on errors (due to a ceiling effect) and +/- vs 0/0 on latency when there is no hint (possibly because of high variance in the no-hint +/- latencies).

We suggest that unlike other simple (within-domain) transfer effects (e.g. Thomas, 1974; Reed, Ernst & Banerji, 1974; Greeno, 1974), this effect could be attributed to the influence of retrieved exemplars; ie. the retrieval and then use of old solutions, in a way often seen in analogical reasoning (e.g. Ross, 1984, 1987) and case-based reasoning (e.g. Hammond, 1990; see Kolodner, 1993). However, before accepting this reminding hypothesis, a new idea about method-choice must be fully considered: Heuristic switching.

---

[36] Just over half the participants (n = 28) were in an experimental group that received a hint that previous solutions would be useful prior to each test problem.

Could general learning alone account for these data?

In Lovett & Anderson (1996) an Einstellung effect in a water-jug isomorph was attributed to variation in the preference for two opposed operators. This preference was acquired over 8 training problems that favoured one operator (overshoot) and persisted over three test problems solvable using the opposed operator (undershoot). Lovett & Anderson found that a preference-based explanation of how history of success effected problem solving fitted their data better than an exemplar retrieval account (based on Nosofsky's, 1984, instance model of categorisation).

Our treatment of a preference-based explanation differs from Lovett & Anderson's in that: a). in this case we are concerned that a single episode might be causing a preference effect, and b) we examine preference amongst hypothetical methods, inferred from modelling human performance in our domain, that have no exact simple one-to-one behavioural consequences (unlike preference amongst singular operators). In this context we refer to the possible preference-based explanation of our results as 'heuristic switching'. In what remains of this chapter, the TOL-PS (Tower Of London - Problem Solver) is used as a basis for deciding empirically between the heuristic switching and reminding accounts; the model proves critical to our assessment of heuristic switching as a viable explanation for the apparent reminding effect reported above.

Heuristic switching: A non-retrieval account of exemplar-specific effects

Heuristic switching is different from reminding in that it is an entirely general explanation of effects attributable to an earlier example problem; it does not require any problem-specific information to be retrieved when the target problem is presented. Heuristic switching by our definition is the favouring of one general problem solving method over another because the former method has proved useful in the past.

Whilst, Lovett & Anderson (1996) describe the same idea, the 'heuristic switching' effect hypothesised here is resultant from a single previous problem; implying a much greater swing in preference than found by Lovett & Anderson, possibly mediated by awareness and a deliberate choice between methods.

Consider a problem solver with equally preferred general heuristics X and Y, both applicable to all problems in domain P. If s/he completes a single problem where heuristic X will provide an optimum solution, s/he will begin to favour heuristic X and will thus perform better on subsequent P problems where X provides an optimum solution and worse than normal on P problems in which Y provides the optimum solution.

This idea is consonant with Anderson's (1990; 1993) rational scheme for managing conflict resolution in the ACT-R production system. The ACT-R cognitive architecture acquires a preference for productions that have been successful in the past (Anderson, 1993). A typical case might see two applicable rules competing to determine behaviour; whilst both might be instantiated (i.e. their pre-conditions were matched), ACT-R will tend to use the previously most successful one.

Our critical assumption is that structurally similar problems (i.e. +/+) are likely to favour the same general heuristics; novel problems (i.e. 0/0) are likely to show no bias; and structurally dissimilar problems (i.e. +/-) are likely to favour opposing general heuristics. This assumption would allow us to explain a +/+ > 0/0 > +/- 'reminding' effect (e.g. Ross, 1987) as switching between general problem solving heuristics (though in the case of Ross, 1987, the re-use of object correspondences is much harder to dismiss). To predict the findings of the TOL study above, we assume that accuracy and latency are traded-off and both broadly relate to a common index of performance.

Heuristic switching in TOL-PS

How heuristic switching, between the two general problem solving methods FOR2 and MEA, could potentially account for our 'reminding effect' can be demonstrated by considering problems A and A'. The TOL-PS model can be forced to use each method on each problem (yielding a 2x2 comparison), the resulting traces are summarised below. TOL-PS' performance clearly shows that these two inversely related problems, used in all Miles' TOL experiments, favour different general problem solving heuristics (MEA on A, FOR2 on A').

The two strategies will be considered one at a time. Prior to the consideration of each strategy, the ACT-R conflict resolution parameter values set for the production choosing that strategy are given. These are notional pre-experiment values, reflecting the hypothesis that to start with participants will favour means-ends analysis (i.e. MEA). For our purposes the important ones are r and b; the former estimates the proportion of eventual successes given a production is fired (0-1), whilst b estimates how much more effort (expressed as seconds) it will take to succeed[37]. The r and b values given after each trace reflect the values TOL-PS would eventually learn for the strategy choice production if that problem was repeatedly attempted using that strategy. In ACT-R (Anderson, 1993) parameters r and b have their effect on competition among production rules by affecting the computation of expected gain: PG - C. Parameter r affects P the probability of the gain, whilst b effects C the cost of that gain (G is the value of the gain). Assuming a set of productions have matched (i.e. *choose_mea*, *choose_for1*, *choose_for2* in TOL-PS at every impasse), the production with the highest PG - C value will be chosen (see Anderson, 1993).

MEA: (choose_mea starting parameter values: q = 1, r = .65, a = 2, b = 9)[38]

MEA on A: The MEA method on both problems follows a similar course, producing an optimal series of moves in the first case, Problem A.

Pre-condition matching:		**Action:**
MATCH: choose_mea	>	MEA strategy chosen
MATCH: mea_tallest	>	Subgoal Disk C
MATCH: 1blk	>	Move A to peg 2
MATCH: 1blk	>	Move B to peg 2
MATCH: move	>	Move C to peg 3
eventually..		

---

[37] In TOL-PS success is associated with completing a problem, whilst failure is associated with either exceeding a move limit or pointless actions (ie trying to plan a move, ie FOR2, but not finding a suitable move, as happens with problem A).
[38] The b parameter values given in these examples are realistic estimates of the time taken (in seconds) to eventually complete a problem, i.e. the eventual cost of the goal. If a strategy choice leads to an error or to a dead-end then the estimate for b will be higher than if it facilitates an optimal move.

MATCH: problem_completed   >   Success!

Learning: choose_mea parameters tend to: $r = 1, b = 7$

MEA on A': A non-optimal set of moves

Pre-condition matching: **Action:**

MATCH: choose_mea   >   MEA strategy chosen

MATCH: mea_tallest   >   Subgoal Disk C

MATCH: 1blk   >   Move A to peg 2

MATCH: 1blk   >   Move D to peg 2

MATCH: move   >   Move C to peg 3

eventually..

MATCH: too_many_moves   >   Failure!

Learning: choose_mea parameters tend to: $r = 0, b = 22$

FOR2: (choose_for2 starting parameters: $q = 1, r = .45, a = 2, b = 14$)

FOR2 on A: The FOR2 method applied to these problems shows the opposite relationship; On problem A:

Pre-condition matching: **Action:**

MATCH: choose_for2   >   FOR2 strategy chosen

MATCH: for2_fail   >   Failure!

Learning: choose_for2 parameters tend to: $r = 0, b = 14$

FOR2 on A': But on problem A' the method is successful:

Pre-condition matching: **Action:**

MATCH: choose_for2   >   FOR2 strategy chosen

MATCH: 2nd_disk_subgoal   >   Move A to 3

                                           >   Move D to 2

eventually..

MATCH: problem completed   >   Success!

Learning: choose_for2 parameters tend to: r = 1, b = 8

These four traces have demonstrated that certain structurally dissimilar problems do favour different general heuristics in our domain. Further it is suggested how this might impact on participants preference for a general method (i.e. during evaluation of productions, when ACT-R's rational analysis parameters are used).

An Empirical Evaluation of the Heuristic Switching Hypothesis

To appreciate how heuristic switching was assessed it is necessary to consider the design of our experiment in more detail; fig 3 provides an overview. Any given base problem - target problem pair will tend to produce a method preference, but the target problem is preceded by another irrelevant base problem and sometimes (50%) an irrelevant target problem.

This means that, depending on this varying context, the same base problem/target problem pair might be relatively more- or less-favoured by heuristic switching. The experiment thus allows a post-hoc comparison between pairs of problems. The derived comparisons are indicated by arrows in fig 3, with the problem favoured by heuristic switching coded Fav, and it's not favoured partner coded Not Fav. These pairs utilise one of two regularities in the design that allow the heuristic switching hypothesis to be assessed:

Cell	Training problems (both orders used)		Test 1	Test 2
1	A & B	Pause	$A^{(+/+,\ Fav)}$	$B'^{(+/-,\ Not\ Fav)}$
2	A & B	"	$B'^{(+/-,\ Fav)}$	$A^{(+/+,\ Not\ Fav)}$
3	A' & B'		$A^{(+/-,\ Fav)}$	$B'^{(+/+,\ Not\ Fav)}$
4	A' & B'		$B'^{(+/+,\ Fav)}$	$A^{(+/-,\ Not\ Fav)}$
5	A & B		$B^{(+/+,\ Not\ Fav)}$	$A'^{(+/-,\ Fav)}$
6	A & B		$A'^{(+/-,\ Not\ Fav)}$	$B^{(+/+,\ Fav)}$
7	A' & B'		$B^{(+/-,\ Not\ Fav)}$	$A'^{(+/+,\ Fav)}$
8	A' & B'	"	$A'^{(+/+,\ Not\ Fav)}$	$B^{(+/-,\ Fav)}$

Figure 3: Design of experiment 1(a & b) reported by Miles (in preparation). Problems linked by arrows were paired for the post-hoc heuristic switching analysis found in this chapter.

Firstly, of the four problems in the study only A favours MEA; the rest favour FOR2. If A is the irrelevant problem then worse test performance would be expected than if A did not precede the test. In our design this allows cell 1- test 2 vs. cell 2 - test 1; and cell 3 - test 2 vs. cell 4 - test 1 (see fig 3).

Secondly, because of the above, it is assumed that participants gradually develop a preference for FOR2 throughout the experiment. The more problems that favour FOR2 a participant does the more positive their evaluation of this method should be.

Hence it is predicted that if the test problem is problem A then better performance will be found on test 1 than on test 2 (due to one less preceding FOR2 problem). The counter prediction is made for test problems of type B, A' and B' (better performance on test 2).

The TOL-PS model ran each of these schedules confirming the predicted preferences found in fig 3. It was noted that TOL-PS's preference for a strategy was strongly effected by the nature of the preceding problem. TOL-PS predicts both a latency and accuracy advantage for 'favoured' problems. In the case of problem A the advantage is latency only (accordingly participants were accurate on problem A), whilst for problems B, A' and B' only an accuracy advantage is directly predicted. The latter should translate into a latency advantage; Miles (in preparation) presents evidence that participants solving the TOL often catch errors prior to making a move and as a result are slower. It is assumed caught errors are positively correlated with errors made, thus a latency advantage is expected on these problems.

Results and Analysis

In our design, the eight cells in fig 3 were repeated six times (three with hint, three without), giving 48 sets of data (one per participant)[39]. To implement the comparison outlined above, each problem was paired with another; the test conditions of each pair are identical except for the order of the test problems and critically the Favoured/Not-favoured status of the problem.. As previously stated, the comparisons made are indicated by arrows in fig 3. First move accuracy and latency measures were used; the results from these measures is summarised in table 4.

	First move accuracy	Mean first move latency (log10 secs)	SD of first move latency (log10 secs)
Favoured group	38/48	.770	.253
Not-favoured group	36/48	.817	.228

Table 4: Results of heuristic switching analysis

The accuracy comparison contrasted performance on favoured problems with their paired 'not favoured' counterparts. On Favoured problems participants made 38 of 48 correct first moves, versus 36 of 48 on Not-favoured problems; this predicted difference was not significant. First move latency was the dependent variable in a five way by-items ANOVA. The data analysed were performance on given test problems, the items were paired according to the scheme indicated by fig 3 (arrows indicating a pair).

Note that, items are paired in order to minimise the effect of secondary variables (e.g. reminding condition), and that the preference level prediction is relative (so a favoured item

---

[39] The last four participants, from the hint group, were excluded as the comparisons outlined in fig 3 are not possible (the participants are from cells 1, 3, 6 and 8).

might be in the lower half of a median split by absolute preference level, but its not-favoured partner will always be ordered below it).

The factors included in the ANOVA were preference level (favoured, not favoured), hint condition (present, none), reminding condition (+/+, +/-), and problem type (A, A', B, B'); all these factors were between item except the preference level that was within item.

The main effect of preference level, whilst in the predicted direction (i.e. first moves on favoured problems were faster), is weak, $F(1,32) = 1.288$, MSe = .041, p > .25. However there is an interaction between task type and preference level, $F(3,32) = 3.320$, MSe = .041, p = .032; this is graphed in fig 4. The simple effect of preference on task type A is significant, $F(1, 32) = 7.518$, p = .01; though not so on other task types. This appears to indicate that any heuristic switching effect is localised to this task type (the only one where MEA leads to an optimum solution); though the low n of this comparison makes it suspect. The other finding from the ANOVA was an expected main effect of condition, $F(1,32) = 4.182$, MSe = .062, p < .05.

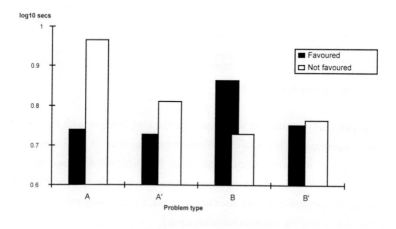

Figure 4: First move latency (log10 seconds) - Interaction of predicted preference from heuristic switching with problem type

Discussion

Although some effect of heuristic switching was found, this was isolated to problem type A. Note only task type A is **directly** predicted to exhibit a latency effect in TOL-PS, the latency predictions for the other problem types emerge from the assumption that errors and long latencies will be correlated - this assumption may be invalid. However, generally the latency and accuracy data both responded to preference level in the expected way, but at a weak level. This indicates that although heuristic switching is meaningful in the TOL, supporting our TOL-PS model with its separate FOR2 and MEA strategies, it does not occur with sufficient magnitude and universality to explain the hypothesised reminding effects described in our study.

The null effect of predicted preference might occur because special reminding based strategies are dominating MEA and FOR2; hence few opportunities for heuristic switching will be present. Though this interpretation supports our original account of the 'reminding effect', it seems unsatisfactory given the interaction of task type and preference level; opportunities for heuristic switching must be occurring on at least some task types, and the frequency of opportunities should be similar on the other task types. Given isolated effects of heuristic switching and the assumption of sufficient opportunity, how might the TOL-PS model be altered to accommodate the null main effect of predicted preference? Two possibilities can be suggested. First, the productions in the model might be somehow made more general. If we assume that it is the general strategies of forward search and means-ends analysis that gain credit for successes, rather than their specific applications to TOL, then one would predict negligible effects of within-experiment success or failure. After all, means ends analysis and forward search have presumably been used huge numbers of times by our participants which will result in a great deal of inertia in their r-parameters .

Second, the productions in the model might be altered, so that first moves are no longer so special and the top-level problem solving productions are more specific. We have explored an alternative version of the model: TOL-PS-F, where the F stands for flat. In this variant all the meta-cognitive productions that choose a strategy are removed. Instead the top goal matches directly to the productions that deal with specialist situations (e.g. mea_two_equal height). Of course the rules in this model will still adapt preferences, and heuristic switching will therefore occur. However, the predicted heuristic switching effect is reduced because there are no longer rules that only apply before the first move. This has the effect of distributing the implications of success and failure, because there is sometimes mixed use of strategies, and the first-move productions are necessarily more specific, and thus not implicated in all successes or failures. These alterations only marginally change the behaviour of the model, but do imply that strategy choice is implicit (unlike in Anzai & Simon, 1979).

Summary

There have been a number of ideas examined in this chapter; the main contributions made are as follows:

- The TOL-PS model of problem solving in the Tower of London has been presented and compared favourably with a recently published model.

- The Tower of London can be used to demonstrate an 'exemplar effect' in a simple domain

- Reminding /Exemplar effects may be explained by radical shifts in preference for problem solving methods - referred to here as heuristic switching

- Heuristic switching is not an adequate explanation of the exemplar effect found in the Tower of London

- Finally, by making TOL-PS's rules more specific or less specific a weak heuristic switching effect can be simulated.

References

Allen, S. W. & Brooks, L. R. (1991). Specializing the operation of an explicit rule. *Journal of Experimental Psychology: General*, 120, 3-19.

Anderson, J. R. (1990). *The adaptive character of thought*. Hillsdale, NJ: Erlbaum.

Anderson, J. R. (1993). *Rules of the mind. Hillsdale,* NJ: Erlbaum.

Anderson, J. R., & Fincham, J. M. (1994). Acquisition of procedural skills from examples. *Journal of Experimental Psychology: Learning, Memory, and Cognition, 20*, 1322-1340.

Anzai, Y., & Simon, H. A. (1979). The theory of learning by doing. *Psychological Review,* *86*, 124-140.

Falkenhainer, B., Forbus, K. D., & Gentner, D. (1986). The structure-mapping engine. In *Proceedings of the American Association of Artificial Intelligence* (pp. 272-277). Philadelphia: American Association for Artificial Intelligence

Gentner, D., & Forbus, K. D. (1991). MAC/FAC: A model of similarity-based retrieval. In *Proceedings of the Thirteenth Annual Conference of the Cognitive Science Society* (pp. 504-509). Hillsdale, NJ: Erlbaum.

Gentner, D., Ratterman, M .J., & Forbus, K. D. (1993). The roles of similarity in transfer: Seperating retrievability from inferential soundness. *Cognitive Psychology, 25*, 524-575.

Gentner, D., & Toupin, C. (1986). Systematicity and surface similarity in the development of analogy. *Cognitive Science, 10*, 277-300.

Gick, M. L., & Holyoak, K. J. (1980). Analogical Problem Solving. *Cognitive Psychology, 12*, 306-355.

Greeno, J. G. (1974). Hobbits and orcs: Acquisition of a sequential concept. *Cognitive Psychology, 6*, 270-292.

Greeno, J. G., Magone, M. E., & Chaiklin, S. (1979). Theory of constructions and set in problem solving. *Memory & Cognition, 7*, 445-461.

Hammond, K. J. (1990). Case-based planning: A framework for planning from experience. *Cognitive Science, 14*, 383-443.

Hammond, K. J. (1991). Functionality in analogical transfer: A hard match is good to find. *Journal of the Learning Sciences, 1*, 111-152.

Hayes-Roth, B., & Hayes-Roth, F. (1979). A cognitive model of planning. *Cognitive Science, 3*, 275-310.

Holyoak, K. J., & Thagard, P. (1989). Analogical mapping by constraint satisfaction. *Cognitive Science, 13*, 295-355.

Holyoak, K. J. & Koh, K. (1987). Surface and structural similarity in analogical transfer. *Memory & Cognition, 15*, 332-340.

Karat, J. (1982). A model of problem solving with incomplete constraint knowledge. *Cognitive Psychology, 14*, 538-559.

Kolodner, J. L. (1993). *Case-based reasoning.* San Mateo, CA: Morgan Kaufmann Publishers.

Larkin, J. (1989). Display-based problem solving. In D. Klahr & K. Kotovsky (Eds.), *Complex information processing: The impact of Herbert A. Simon.* Hillsdale, NJ: Erlbaum.

Logan, G. D. (1988). Toward an instance theory of automatization. *Psychological Review, 95,* 492-527.

Lovett, M. & Anderson, J. R. (1996). History of success and current context in problem solving: Combined influences on operator selection. *Cognitive Psychology, 31,* 168-217.

Miles, G. E. Understanding reminding in a knowledge lean domain. *PhD Thesis,* in preparation.

Newell, A. (1990). *Unified theories of cognition.* Cambridge, MA: Cambridge University Press.

Newell, A., & Simon, H. A. (1972). *Human problem solving.* Englewood Cliffs, NJ: Prentice-Hall.

Norofsky, R. (1984). Choice, similarity, and the context theory of classification. *Journal of Experimental Psychology: Learning, Memory, and Cognition, 10,* 104-114.

Pirolli, P. L., & Anderson, J. R. (1985). The role of learning from examples in the acquisition of recursive programming skills. *Canadian Journal of Psychology, 39,* 240-272.

Reder, L. M. (1987). Strategy selection in question answering. *Cognitive Psychology, 19,* 90-137.

Reed, S. K., Ernst, G. W., & Banerji, R. (1974). The role of analogy in transfer between similar problem states. *Cognitive Psychology, 6,* 436-450.

Reeves, L. M., & Weisberg, R. W. (1994). The role of content and abstract information in analogical transfer. *Psychological Bulletin, 115,* 381-400.

Ross, B. H. (1984). Remindings and their effects in learning a cognitive skill. *Cognitive Psychology, 16,* 371-416.

Ross, B. H. (1987). This is like that: The use of earlier problems and the separation of similarity effects. *Journal of Experimental Psychology: Learning, Memory, and Cognition, 13,* 629-639.

Ross, B. H. (1989). Distinguishing types of superficial similarities: Different effects on the access and use of earlier problems. *Journal of Experimental Psychology: Learning, Memory, and Cognition, 15,* 456-468.

Ross, B. H., & Kennedy, P. T. (1990). Generalizing from the use of earlier examples in problem solving, *Journal of Experimental Psychology: Learning, Memory, and Cognition, 16,* 42-55.

Sacerdoti, E. D. (1974). Planning is a hierarchy of abstraction spaces. *Artificial Intelligence, 5*, 115-135.

Schmid, U. & Wysotzki, F. (this volume).

Shallice, T. (1982). Specific impairments of planning. *Philosophical Transactions of the Royal Society London, B298*, 199-209.

Singley, K., & Anderson, J. R. (1989). *The transfer of cognitive skill.* Cambridge, MA: Harvard Press.

Thagard, P., Holyoak, K. J., Nelson, G., & Gochfield, D. (1990). Analog retrieval by constraint satisfaction. *Artificial Intelligence, 46*, 259-310.

Thomas, J. C. (1974). An analysis of behaviour in the Hobbit-Orcs problem. *Cognitive Psychology, 6*, 257-269.

Vanlehn, K. (1991). Rule acquisition events in the discovery of problem-solving strategies. *Cognitive Science, 15*, 1-47.

Ward, G. & Allport, A. (1997). Planning and problem-solving using the five-disc Tower of London task. *The Quarterly Journal of Experimental Psychology, 50A*, 49-78.

Wolfgang Battmann, Stephan Dutke (Eds.)

Processes of the Molar Regulation of Behavior

Contemporary research in experimental and general psychology either tends to "micro-deterministic" models focusing on isolated molecular phenomena or emphasizes global conceptions lacking empirical corroboration. This edition presents a series of articles trying to join the advantages of both approaches: They analyze the emergence of molar structures of human behavior on the basis of general psychological theories of emotion, memory, and action, which are strong in their domain with regard to their empirical evaluation, but, in addition, have high explanatory potential beyond it. Part I addresses memory and representation, Part II emotion, action, and thinking, and Part III focuses on resources and coping with stress. The fourth part discusses methodological aspects and examples of contemporary history of psychology related to the molar regulation of behavior. The chapters take a programmatic and integrative perspective in explaining emergence, structure, and functioning of molar behavior against the background of reliable domain-specific theories and, hence, bridge a gap in contemporary psychology.

ISBN 3-931660-11-7

Price: 50,- DM

PABST SCIENCE PUBLISHERS
Eichengrund 28, D-49525 Lengerich, Tel. ++ 49 (0) 5484-308,
Fax ++ 49 (0) 5484-550, E-mail: pabst@pabst-publishers.de
Internet: http://www.hsp.de/pabst/

Roland W. Scholz, Alf C. Zimmer (Eds.)

QUALITATIVE ASPECTS OF
DECISION MAKING

The volume *Qualitative Aspects of Decision Making* deals with three issues that may widen research on judgement and decision making. Firstly, the concepts and their formal or semantic relations in normative and cognitive modelling are addressed. Particularly *alternative representations of uncertainty* are treated which reflect different qualities of knowledge. Secondly, the *meaning* of the decision to the subject's world and its environment are treated. Thus *contextualizations* of the task and a theory of the subject task relation are discussed. Thirdly, the *complexity* of a decision task is conceived as a specific quality which, for example, requires multiple representations and strategies of knowledge integration.

All contributions are focusing on psychological models and theories. Empirical methods ranging from experiments through surveys to case studies are used. Theoretical and applied issues are dealt with. Applications and qualitative aspects are introduced from *economy, medical, legal* and *environmental sciences.*

ISBN 3-931660-57-5

60,- DM/SFr, 420,- ÖS

PABST SCIENCE PUBLISHERS
Eichengrund 28, D-49525 Lengerich, Tel. ++ 49 (0) 5484-308, Fax ++ 49 (0) 5484-550,
E-mail: pabst@pabst-publishers.de, Internet: http://www.pabst-publishers.de

Jetzt

Die psychologischen Fachzeitschriften bei PABST:

❶ PSYCHOLOGISCHE BEITRÄGE
International, traditionell progressiv: Publikationen mit der Relevanz für alle Teilgebiete der Psychologie

**❷ MPR-online
METHODS OF PSYCHOLOGICAL RESEARCH**
International, interdisziplinäre Methodenzeitschrift: das erste psychologisch-wissenschaftliche Online-Journal aus Deutschland

❸ VERHALTENSTHERAPIE & VERHALTENSMEDIZIN
Wissenschaftlich fundiert, praxisorientiert: Übersichten und aktuelle Informationen für Therapeut(inn)en

**❹ FORENSISCHE PSYCHIATRIE UND
PSYCHOTHERAPIE**
Innovativ, praxisorientiert: Übersichten und aktuelle Informationen (nicht nur) für forensische Therapeut(inn)en

❺ ABO AKTUELL
Arbeits-, Betriebs- und Organisationspsychologie für die Wirtschaft

PABST SCIENCE PUBLISHERS
Eichengrund 28, D-49525 Lengerich, Tel. ++ 49 (0) 5484-308, Fax ++ 49 (0) 5484-550,
E-mail: pabst@pabst-publishers.de, Internet: http://www.pabst-publishers.de